641.3

Official Publisher Partnership

OCR
Home Economics for A2

Food, nutrition and health today

Alexis Rickus
Bev Saunder

AN HACHETTE UK COMPANY

Orders: please contact Bookpoint Ltd, 130 Milton Park, Abingdon, Oxon OX14 4SB.
Telephone: (44) 01235 827720.
Fax: (44) 01235 400454.
Lines are open from 9.00–5.00, Monday to Saturday, with a 24-hour message answering service. You can also order through our website www.hoddereducation.co.uk

If you have any comments to make about this, or any of our other titles, please send them to educationenquiries@hodder.co.uk

British Library Cataloguing in Publication Data

A catalogue record for this title is available from the British Library

ISBN: 978 0 340 97366 0

First edition published 2009

This edition published 2009

Impression number 10 9 8 7 6 5 4 3 2 1

Year   2012 2011 2010 2009

Hachette UK's policy is to use papers that are natural, renewable and recyclable products and made from wood grown in sustainable forests. The logging and manufacturing processes are expected to conform to the environmental regulations of the country of origin.

Cover photo © Jacobs Stock Photography/Digital Vision/Photolibrary Group.

Typeset by Dorchester Typesetting Group Ltd

Illustrations by Oxford Designers and Illustrators

Printed in Great Britain for Hodder Education, an Hachette UK Company, 338 Euston Road, London NW1 3BH

Contents

Introduction

This book has been written to meet the specification OCR GCE Home Economics: Food, Nutrition and Health. The book covers all areas of the specification and will help prepare you for the written examination and the investigative study.

How to use this book

The book is divided into two sections covering both A2 units:

Unit G003 Home Economics: (Food, Nutrition and Health) Investigative Study

Unit G004 Home Economics: (Food, Nutrition and Health) Nutrition and Food Production

The specification divides the content into discrete subsections. To help organise your learning we have used the same structure for the chapters in this book.

The **Nutrition and Food Production** unit is divided into six topics, which deal with knowledge and understanding of the following topics:

● Introduction to nutrition

● Nutrients and energy

● Groups with special dietary needs

● Properties of food

● Design, development and production of food

● Developments in the food industry.

The final unit in the book focuses on the **Investigative study.** You will find there a logical explanation of the four assessment criteria and guidance on the use and application of research methods.

Assessment and revision: A full explanation of how the A2 specification is examined is explored in a final chapter. Techniques to improve examination performance and revision are covered. Candidates' responses, with written feedback from examiners, are included to help you improve your exam skills.

The learning features

Each chapter begins with clear learning objectives followed by a general introduction, which gives a broad outline of the topic to be studied. The chapter is punctuated by different learning activities. The learning activities are linked to the content and could be:

Practical opportunities: These are opportunities to apply the theory in the chapter to food practical situations. The development of food practical skills is a very important aspect of the A2 course. Practical opportunities may involve food tasting or making a meal for a specific context or individual.

Research opportunities: These activities provide the opportunity for independent research on the topic studied. Research may involve using the internet, or carrying out some primary research by a visit or completing a survey.

The use of data: Developing the skill of extracting and selecting information from data is important. On occasion the opportunity to demonstrate these skills will be required in the formal examination. By practising these skills now you will feel confident in dealing with this style of question and drawing relevant conclusions.

Discussion: There are many opportunities to discuss the topics studied during each chapter. The discussion points may be situated during a chapter, with one or two thought-provoking questions on the topic. Discussion will help clarify issues, check your understanding and allow you to consider the points of views of others.

Review: The review will help you check your understanding of the topic studied. There is a variety of review activities and, to ensure you understand each topic, they are best completed individually.

Review by case study: A real-life situation is described in a case study providing the opportunity for you to extract information and draw relevant conclusions. There may be questions linked to the case study to help draw important issues to your attention.

The purpose of all these activities is to help you understand and apply the subject knowledge to situations and to develop the skills of analysis required to achieve success in the subject. The activities can be used for independent study or as group exercises.

Look out for definitions of key terms and trigger words in **assessment hints** boxes throughout the chapters.

Check your understanding: At the end of each chapter you can check your understanding with an activity based on the subject-specific terminology used in the chapter. The subject-specific terms have been explained in the chapter, and these activities are a valuable tool in reinforcing learning and identifying gaps in your knowledge and understanding.

Examination-style questions appear at the end of each chapter. The questions have been written in the style you should expect in the external examination. The purpose of the questions is to test whether you have acquired the underpinning subject knowledge and whether you are able to write in the manner required during the A2 examination. Mark-schemes for these questions can be found at the back of the book.

Food, nutrition and health are dynamic and exciting areas to study. To ensure you have a good understanding of the latest issues in food, nutrition and health we suggest that you follow their development in the media and discuss them in class.

We have made some suggestions on where to find further information in the book; the internet is a valuable tool for accessing government reports and information from charitable organisations. It is important to read about the findings of current social research and be aware of contemporary issues in the news. However, to understand the subject properly you will be expected to talk to people about their experiences and views on important issues. We hope that this textbook will help support your studies and develop your interest in the issues explored even further.

Acknowledgements

Bev and Alexis would like to thank their husbands Simon and Scott, and their children William, Sophie and Tom for their patience and understanding during the writing process.

A special thanks to Rick Jackman, Janet Dodson, Megan Reilly, and Barbara DiNicoli for their technical advice.

Every effort has been made to trace the copyright holders of material reproduced here. The authors and publishers would like to thank the following for permission to reproduce copyright illustrations:

Fig. 1.02 © Eyewire; fig. 1.04 © Photodisc/Getty Images; fig. 2.01 © Photolibrary.com; fig. 2.02 © Donald Erickson/iStockphoto.com; figs 2.04, 2.07 © Ingram Publishing Limited; fig. 2.09 © Grigoriy Lukyanov – Fotolia.com; fig. 2.11 © Floortje/iStockphoto.com; fig. 2.13 © Paul Cowan/iStockphoto.com; fig. 2.15 www.PurestockX.com; fig. 2.17 © ranplett/iStockphoto.com; fig. 2.18 © Klaudia Steiner/iStockphoto.com; fig. 2.19 © Viktor Kitaykin/iStockphoto.com; fig. 2.22 © Tomas Bercic/iStockphoto.com; fig. 2.23 © eyewave – Fotolia.com; fig. 2.24 © Heino Pattschull – Fotolia.com; fig. 2.25 Medical-on-Line/Alamy; fig. 2.26 © Krzysiek z Poczty – Fotolia.com; fig. 2.27 © Ingram Publishing Limited; fig. 2.28 © Stockbyte/Getty Images; fig. 2.29 Image Source/Getty Images; fig. 2.30 © Morgan Lane Photography/iStockphoto.com; fig. 2.31 © Photodisc/Getty Images; fig. 2.32 Sam Bailey/Hodder Education; fig. 2.33 ©iStockphoto.com/Michael Valdez; fig. 2.34 © javier fontanella/iStockphoto.com; fig. 2.35 www.PurestockX.com; fig. 2.36 © Sean Locke/iStockphoto.com; fig. 2.37 Nikreates/Alamy; fig. 2.38 © Pål Espen Olsen/iStockphoto.com; fig. 2.40 Healthy Start; fig. 2.41 © David Marchal/iStockphoto.com; fig. 2.42 © Stockbyte/Getty Images; fig. 2.43 © Olga Lyubkina/iStockphoto.com; fig. 2.44 Andrew Callaghan/Hodder Education; fig. 2.45 © Photodisc/Getty Images; fig. 2.46 Sam Bailey/Hodder Education; fig. 2.47 © YinYang/iStockphoto.com; fig. 2.48 © Stockbyte/Getty Images; fig. 2.49 © James Ferrie/iStockphoto.com; fig. 2.50 © Floortje/iStockphoto.com; fig. 2.51 Chris Pancewicz/Alamy; figs 2.52, 2.54 © Stockbyte/Getty Images; fig. 2.58 © Photodisc/Getty Images; fig. 2.59 © Tom Marvin/iStockphoto.com; fig. 2.60 mediablitzimages (uk) Limited/Alamy; fig. 2.61 © Amy Myers/iStockphoto.com; figs 3.02, 3.03, 3.04 ©Photodisc/Getty Images; fig. 3.05 © Purestock; fig. 3.06 © www.pointofocus.com/iStockphoto.com; fig. 3.07 © zhang bo/iStockphoto.com; fig. 3.10 © Igor Dutina/iStockphoto.com; fig. 3.11 © digitalskillet/iStockphoto.com; fig. 3.12 © Nuno Silva/iStockphoto.com; fig. 4.01 © Photodisc/Getty Images; fig. 4.03 www.PurestockX.com; fig. 4.05 © Photodisc/Getty Images;

fig. 4.07 British Egg Industry Council; fig. 4.08 Sam Bailey/Hodder Education; fig. 4.09 © Ingram Publishing Limited; fig. 4.10 © jerryhat/iStockphoto.com; fig. 4.11 mediablitzimages (uk) Limited/Alamy; figs 4.12, 4.13 © Ingram Publishing Limited; fig. 4.14 Helene Rogers/Alamy; fig. 4.18 Martin Lee/Rex Features; figs 4.20, 4.21 © iStockphoto.com; fig. 4.22 © Dušan Zidar – Fotolia.com; figs 4.24, 4.25 mediablitzimages (uk) Limited/Alamy; fig. 4.26 www.PurestockX.com; fig. 4.28 © Photodisc/Getty Images; fig. 4.29 © Linda & Colin McKie/iStockphoto.com; fig. 4.30 © Emrah Turudu/iStockphoto.com; fig. 4.31 Andrew Callaghan/Hodder Education; fig. 4.32 Sam Bailey/Hodder Education; fig. 4.33 © Suzannah Skelton/iStockphoto.com; fig. 4.37 © Chris Hepburn/iStockphoto.com; fig. 4.38 © Owen Price/iStockphoto.com; fig. 4.39 Andrew Callaghan/Hodder Education; fig. 4.40 Sam Bailey/Hodder Education; fig. 4.41 ©Siede Preis/Photodisc/Getty Images; fig. 4.42 © MARIA TOUTOUDAKI/iStockphoto.com; fig. 4.43 © Jan Tyler/iStockphoto.com; fig. 5.01 Keith Leighton/Alamy; fig. 5.02 © Dr. Heinz Linke/iStockphoto.com; figs 5.03, 5.05 © Photodisc/Getty Images; fig. 5.07 © iStockphoto.com; figs 5.12, 5.13 © Stockbyte/Photolibrary Group Ltd; fig. 5.15 © Jan Rihak/iStockphoto.com; fig. 5.16 © sumnersgraphicsinc – Fotolia.com; fig. 5.17 © Kelly Cline/iStockphoto.com; fig. 5.18 © Cornel Stefan Achirei/iStockphoto.com; fig. 5.20 © 2008 kamel ADJENEF/iStockphoto.com; fig. 6.01 Helene Rogers/Alamy; fig. 6.03 © Don Bayley/iStockphoto.com; fig. 6.04 © Paco Ayala – Fotolia.com; fig. 6.05 TransparencyData Limited; fig. 6.07 © Photodisc/Getty Images; fig. 6.08 Marine Stewardship Council, www.msc.org; fig. 6.11 © Iain Sarjeant/iStockphoto.com; fig. 6.12 Fairtrade Foundation, www.fairtrade.org.uk; fig. 6.14 © Andrejs Pidjass/iStockphoto.com; fig. 6.15 © Dr. Heinz Linke/iStockphoto.com; fig. 6.16 © Photodisc/Getty Images; fig. 6.17 BILL BARKSDALE/AGSTOCKUSA/SCIENCE PHOTO LIBRARY; fig. 6.18 © ron sumners/iStockphoto.com; fig. 6.21 © Kelly Cline/iStockphoto.com; fig. 6.22 © European Communities; fig. 6.23 © Photodisc/Getty Images; fig. 6.24 © Stockbyte/Photolibrary Group Ltd; fig. 7.01 © Royalty-Free/Corbis; fig. 7.03 Image Source/Alamy; fig. 7.04 © Photodisc/Getty Images; fig. 7.05 © Don Bayley/iStockphoto.com; fig. 7.07 © Photodisc/Getty Images; fig. 7.08 Eye-Stock/Alamy; figs 7.11, 7.12 © Photodisc/Getty Images.

Crown copyright material is reproduced with the permission of the Controller of HMSO and the Queen's Printer for Scotland. Scores on the Doors is a registered trademark of TransparencyData Limited. The authors and publishers would also like to thank the British Nutrition Foundation for permission to use material from www.nutrition.org.uk.

INTRODUCTION TO NUTRITION

Learning objectives

By the end of this chapter you will be able to:

- explain what is meant by the concepts of nutrition, a balanced diet and malnutrition in the UK
- list the different groups of nutrients
- explain the significance of studying nutrition
- list the different terms used to describe nutrient requirements
- describe the Dietary Reference Values for food energy and nutrients developed by the Committee on Medical Aspects of Food and Nutrition Policy (COMA)
- assess the groups at risk of malnutrition and the treatment of malnutrition.

Introduction

Food is essential for life. The human body needs energy to carry out the essential processes of growth and maintenance. Food provides energy and many other vital components to ensure we stay healthy. These vital components in food are referred to as **nutrients**. All food contains nutrients, which are chemicals that have important roles in the body – for example, the growth of bones. Nutrients are needed to build and repair cells and body tissues. They maintain organs and bones and provide the body with energy and warmth. You should be familiar with the names of the five main nutrients:

1 Protein is required for growth, repair and general maintenance of the body.

2 Carbohydrates are the main energy source for the body.

3 Fats are an important source of energy, and components of all cell membranes. Fats insulate the body.

4 Vitamins are responsible for controlling many chemical reactions in the body.

5 Minerals control many chemical processes and maintain fluid balances in the body.

Nutrients can be divided into two groups:

1 **Macronutrients** are required by the body in large amounts and include proteins, fats and carbohydrates.

2 **Micronutrients** are needed by the body in much smaller amounts and include vitamins and the mineral elements calcium, potassium and phosphorus, essential fatty acids and the trace minerals iron, zinc and iodine.

Strictly speaking, neither water nor dietary fibre are nutrients. Water is sometimes referred to as a nutrient because it is essential for life. Dietary fibre or starch polysaccharide (NSP) has an important role in the diet but is not a nutrient as it is not digested and absorbed into the body. Nutrients have clear functions in the diet. The specific dietary functions of each nutrient will be explored in detail in Topic 2.

A lack, or poor absorption, of a nutrient can cause a **deficiency disease**. Vitamins and minerals are usually associated with deficiency diseases. Generally, deficiency diseases have clearly identifiable symptoms. For instance, anaemia is a deficiency disease associated with a lack of iron and the symptoms include abnormal paleness of the skin, lack of energy or tiring easily.

Figure 1.01 shows how nutrients can be divided into two groups: the macronutrients and the micronutrients. Macronutrients are required in relatively large amounts by the body. Micronutrients are required in much smaller quantities by the body, and only very small amounts are needed daily.

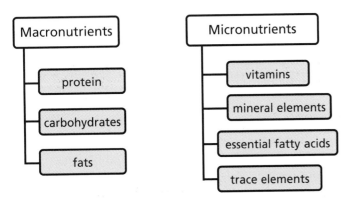

Figure 1.01 *The nutrients*

Activity 1.1

Research opportunity
Copy the diagram above and add examples of food sources for each nutrient.

Concept of nutrition

When defining **nutrition** we can focus on the role of nutrients in the body. The definition offered by the British Nutrition Foundation states 'nutrition is the study of the nutrients in food, how the body uses nutrients and the relationship between diet, health and disease'. This definition places emphasis on the effect of food on the body. However, the study of nutrition should also include references to wider social issues and their impact on food consumption. Today emphasis is placed on a healthy diet and lifestyle to prevent disease.

Activity 1.2

Research
Some food products are marketed with clearly stated health benefits.
Collect some magazine articles and examples of food packaging and examine the health and nutritional claims presented.
Which health and nutritional concerns are the products targeting?

The significance of studying nutrition

During the early part of the twentieth century the study of nutrition was concerned with research into the amount of each nutrient that should be consumed and the diseases associated with a nutrient deficiency.

Activity 1.3

Discussion

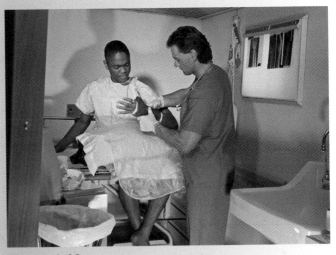

Figure 1.02

There are many people who need nutritional knowledge and understanding in their work.
Discuss the benefit of nutritional knowledge to the following people:

Midwife

Doctor

Food product developer

Pharmacist

School kitchen manager

Hospital dietician

Care home manager

Health visitor

Sports trainer

More recently the emphasis has changed, as it was recognised that many people living in developing countries actually consume too much of certain nutrients and this is more likely to be associated with disease. For example, a high intake of saturated fat has been associated with the increased incidence of coronary heart disease in developing countries.

The study of nutrition is becoming more significant in our society. In many countries the range and selection of food available is greater than ever before. The public are more interested in food-related issues and want to know about the food they eat. Governments are also interested in nutrition, as diseases related to diet can be a financial burden on the management of health care. Treating people with diet-related illnesses can be very expensive.

Balanced diet

No single food contains all the essential nutrients the body needs to function efficiently. The term **diet** is used to describe the actual food and drink a person consumes every day. A variety or mixture of foods should be consumed over a period of time to ensure an adequate intake of all the nutrients is achieved and a healthy body weight is maintained.

A **balanced diet** should provide the correct amounts of each nutrient that an individual needs. A balanced diet can be achieved by eating the correct amount of food from the different food groups. There are five main food groups, and combining all the groups gives the nutrients that are essential for growth, energy and body maintenance.

The eatwell plate

Use the eatwell plate to help you get the balance right. It shows how much of what you eat should come from each food group.

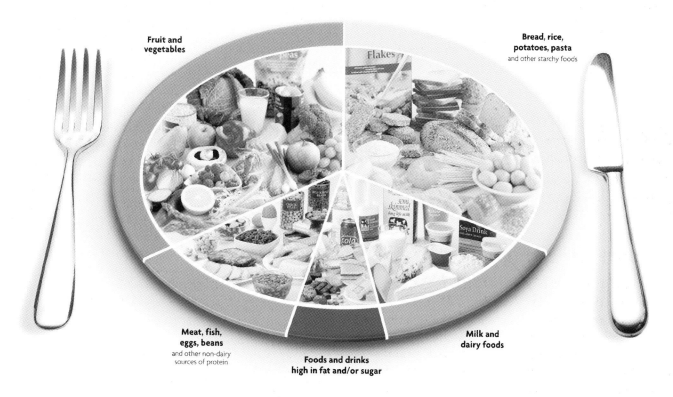

Figure 1.03 *The Eatwell plate*

Source: Food Standards Agency

These are:

- bread, cereals, and potatoes

- fruit and vegetables

- meat and fish

- milk and dairy foods

- fat and sugar.

To help the public understand the need for a balanced diet and eat the correct proportions of food from each food group, the 'Eatwell plate' has been devised by the Food Standards Agency. This is an updated version of the Balance of Good Health healthy eating plate.

The aim of the plate is to give practical advice by showing the types of food to be consumed. A picture image also gives a clear indication of the proportion of food that should be consumed from each group.

The plate is divided into five segments to represent the five food groups, as follows:

- Bread, rice, potatoes, pasta and other starchy foods 33%

- Fruit and vegetables 33%

- Milk and dairy foods 15%

- Meat, fish, eggs, beans and other non-dairy sources of protein 12%

- Foods and drinks high in fat and/or sugar 8%.

With the exception of fruit, vegetables and fish, the Eatwell plate does not include references to frequency of serving and 'recommended' portion sizes. At least five portions of a variety of fruit and vegetables should be consumed each day and two portions a week of fish, one of which should be oily.

Nutrient requirements

There is no international consensus on the healthiest or safest amount of each nutrient to consume. There are variations in nutrient requirements between different countries. The UK government currently suggests a Reference Nutrient Intake (RNI) for calcium in adults aged between 19 and 50 years of 700 mg per day. On the other hand, in the United States, the recommended daily intake is much higher at 1000 mg per day.

The UK government has a responsibility to try to ensure the nation is healthy. They set up guidelines for food and energy requirements for the population. The guidance on energy and nutrient requirements is used by health professionals, caterers and food manufacturers to allow informed decision making about meal planning, the development of new food products and to provide clearer food labelling to consumers. Meal planners in institutions such as schools, care homes, prisons and hospitals use the guidance on energy and nutrient requirements issued by the government.

Dietary Reference Values (DRVs)

In the early 1990s the Committee on Medical Aspects of Food and Nutrition Policy (COMA) established dietary reference values for different groups in the population based upon scientific dietary advice. COMA no longer exists, and the **Scientific Advisory Committee on Nutrition** (SACN) advises the Department of Health and the Food Standards Agency (FSA) on issues related to nutrition and nutrient intake. SACN recommends a range of intake levels for all nutrients and energy for males and females throughout life; these are called the **Dietary Reference Values (DRVs)**. Dietary Reference Values (DRVs) are estimates of the amount of energy and nutrients needed by different groups of healthy people in the UK population.

The amount of protein, fat, carbohydrates, vitamins and minerals that should be consumed varies between men and women and changes over the course of a person's life. DRVs have been established because different people have different nutrient requirements.

Activity 1.4

Discussion

Can you identify any groups in the population that may have specific nutritional requirements?

Can you suggest what these nutritional requirements might be?

The Dietary Reference Values can be used for guidance but should not be seen as exact recommendations. They are given as a daily intake but individuals often eat different foods each day and so the intake of energy and nutrients needs to be averaged over several days.

The main aim of the DRVs is to ensure that everyone gets enough of each nutrient at different ages and stages during their life to remain healthy.

Note that DRVs apply to healthy people only; those with illnesses or medical conditions may have different requirements.

Dietary Reference Value is a general term used to cover four types of intake:

1 **Estimated Average Requirement (EAR)** is the estimated average requirement of energy or a nutrient needed by a group of people. Generally EAR is used for recommendations for energy.

2 **Reference Nutrient Intake (RNI)** indicates the amount of a nutrient required to meet the dietary needs of about 97.5 per cent of a specified group of people.

3 **Lower Reference Nutrient Intake (LRNI)** is the amount of a nutrient that is sufficient for only a few individuals – about 2.5 per cent – and is likely to be inadequate for most individuals. Regular intake below this is likely to result in a deficiency.

4 **Safe intake** is used when there is not enough information to set an EAR, RNI or LRNI. A safe intake indicates an amount which is sufficient for almost all individual needs but below a level that could have undesirable effects.

Nutritional and energy requirements

The DRVs for all nutrients are detailed in the COMA report, 'Dietary Reference Values for Food Energy and Nutrients for the United Kingdom', published by the Department of Health in 1991. We will now explore the nutrient requirements (DRVs) for energy, fat and carbohydrate, protein, vitamins and minerals.

Estimated Average Requirement for Energy (EAR)

Individuals vary in their energy requirements. Energy requirement can depend on a range of factors, including gender, age, lifestyle and occupation. Estimates of energy requirements for different groups are termed EARs. They are an estimate of the energy required to meet the average requirements of specific groups. About half the people in the group will usually need more energy than the EAR and half the people in the group will usually need less. Some individuals require more energy than others do and as a result, an estimated average requirement is given for different age groups and during pregnancy and lactation. A detailed explanation of the factors affecting energy requirements will be explored in Topic 2.

The table below shows the estimated average requirements (EAR) for energy for specific groups based on COMA data published in 1991. The table shows how energy requirements vary considerably between different groups.

Age	EAR/kcal per day	
	Males	**Females**
0–3 months	545	515
4–6 months	690	645
7–9 months	825	765
10–12 months	920	865
1–3 years	1230	1165
4–6 years	1715	1545
7–10 years	1970	1740
11–14 years	2220	1845
15–18 years	2755	2110
19–50 years	2550	1940
51–59 years	2550	1900
60–64 years	2380	1900
65–74 years	2330	1900
over 75 years	2100	1810
pregnancy		+ 200*
lactation (breast feeding)		+ 450–480*

*extra amounts of energy required during pregnancy and lactation

Source: COMA, Dietary Reference Values for Food Energy and Nutrients for the United Kingdom (Department of Health, 1991)

Activity 1.5

Using the data

1 At what age do men require the most energy?

2 At what age do energy requirements fall in men?

3 Describe the difference between the energy requirements of a 7–10-year-old boy and a woman aged 19–50 years?

4 Can you give two reasons why men may require more energy than women?

5 How much energy does a pregnant woman aged 30 years require?

6 Give one reason why more energy is required during pregnancy and lactation.

Dietary Reference Values for fat

Fats are important for good health. However, eating too much of the 'wrong' type of fat can increase the risk of developing coronary heart disease. Different types of fat have an effect on blood cholesterol levels and in Topic 2, we will explore the possible role of fat in the development of heart disease.

It is not possible to set Dietary Reference Values (DRVs) for fat consumption as removing them from the diet is not usually associated with a deficiency disease.

However, guidance on the consumption of fat is useful to avoid over eating that could result in weight gain. The values expressed for fat are shown as a percentage of daily food energy intake. DRVs are given as population average, individual minimum and individual maximum. However, for the essential fatty acids a daily requirement is given.

The table below shows the DRVs for fat for adults as a percentage of daily total food-energy intake.

The contribution of saturated fatty acids (which may raise blood-cholesterol levels) is quite a significant amount at 11 per cent of total daily energy intake.

Contribution of nutrients to energy intake

The source of energy is very important in ensuring a balanced diet is achieved. COMA made suggestions on the four sources of energy and the contribution each should make to the diet. The first table on the next page shows the Dietary Reference Values for fats, carbohydrates, protein and alcohol as a percentage of daily total energy intake. (Some people do not consume alcohol so two sets of figures are provided.)

	Individual minimum	Population average (%)	Individual maximum (%)
Saturated fatty acids		11.0	
Cis-polyunsaturated fatty acids	n-3 0.2g/d n-6 1.0g/d	6.5	10.0
Cis-monounsaturated fatty acids		13.0	
Trans fatty acids		2.0	
Total fatty acids		32.5	
Total fat		35.0	

1 decigram = 0.1 gram (g/d). There are 10 decigrams in one gram.

Source: COMA, 1991

Source of energy	% Daily energy intake	
	Excluding alcohol	Including alcohol
Carbohydrates		
Non-milk extrinsic sugars NMES*	11	10
Intrinsic sugars/milk, sugar and starches**	39	37
Fat	35	33
Protein	15	15
Alcohol	0	5
Total	100	100

* NMES is free sugar not bound in foods. NMES are added to products or refined into products such as biscuits, cakes, table sugar and honey, but excluding milk sugar.
** Intrinsic sugars are a natural part of the food, e.g. sugars in fruits and vegetables.

Source: COMA, 1991

It is recommended that 50 per cent of our total energy intake is from carbohydrates. This figure is divided into Non-milk extrinsic sugars (NMES) and intrinsic sugars/milk sugar and starches. It is recommended that 39 per cent of energy intake should come from intrinsic sugars and starches. Non-milk extrinsic sugars or 'free sugar' should only contribute 11 per cent energy intake. Recent concerns about sugar consumption and tooth decay have suggested that the NMES figure should be set at a maximum of 10 per cent.

The contribution of protein in providing daily energy is set at 15 per cent. The primary function of protein is cell growth and repair and not to provide energy to the body.

Reference nutrient intakes for protein

According to research evidence, the average daily intake of protein in the UK is 88 g for men and 64 g for women, and this exceeds the reference nutrient intakes (RNI) for protein. (There is a significant requirement for protein in children, and for pregnant and breast feeding women.)

The table shows the reference nutrient intakes for protein for specific groups each day.

Age	Protein intake g/d
0–3 months	12.5
4–6 months	12.7
7–9 months	13.7
10–12 months	14.9
1–3 years	14.5
4–6 years	19.7
7–10 years	28.3
Males	
11–14 years	42.1
15–18 years	55.2
19–50 years	55.5
50+ years	53.3
Females	
11–14 years	41.2
15–18 years	45.0
19–50 years	45.0
50+ years	46.5
Pregnancy	+6*
Lactation: 0–4 months	+11*
4+ months	+8*

1 decigram = 0.1 gram (g/d). There are 10 decigrams in one gram.

* To be added to the adult requirement during pregnancy and lactation

Source: COMA, 1991

Reference nutrient intakes for vitamins

The figures devised for the micronutrients are regarded as a 'safe intake' and should prevent a deficiency disease and be sufficient to fulfil nutritional needs. Two terms are used to describe the amount of the vitamin or mineral required:

1 **Milligram** (mg): a unit of measurement of mass equal to a thousandth of a gram.

2 **Microgram** (µg or mcg): a unit of measurement of mass equal to a millionth of a gram.

This table shows the daily requirement for the key vitamins.

Age	Thiamin B1 mg/d	Riboflavin B2 mg/d	Niacin B3 mg/d	Vitamin B6† mg/d	Vitamin B12 µg/d	Folic acid µg/d	Vitamin C mg/d	Vitamin A µg/d	Vitamin D µg/d
0–3 months	0.2	0.4	3	0.2	0.3	50	25	350	8.5
4–6 months	0.2	0.4	3	0.2	0.3	50	25	350	8.5
7–9 months	0.2	0.4	4	0.3	0.4	50	25	350	7
10–12 months	0.3	0.4	5	0.4	0.4	50	25	350	7
1–3 years	0.5	0.6	8	0.7	0.5	70	30	400	7
4–6 years	0.7	0.8	11	0.9	0.8	100	30	400	–
7–10 years	0.7	1.0	12	1.0	1.0	150	30	500	–
Males									
11–14 years	0.9	1.2	15	1.2	1.2	200	35	600	–
15–18 years	1.1	1.3	18	1.5	1.5	200	40	700	–
19–50 years	1.0	1.3	17	1.4	1.5	200	40	700	–
50+ years	0.9	1.3	16	1.4	1.5	200	40	700	**
Females									
11–14 years	0.7	1.1	12	1.0	1.2	200	35	600	–
15–18 years	0.8	1.1	14	1.2	1.5	200	40	600	–
19–50 years	0.8	1.1	13	1.2	1.5	200	40	600	–
50+ years	0.8	1.1	12	1.2	1.5	200	40	600	**
Pregnancy	+0.1***	+0.3	*	*	*	+100	+10	+100	10
Lactation:									
0–4 months	+0.2	+0.5	2	*	+0.5	+60	+30	+350	10
4+ months	+0.2	+0.5	2	*	+0.5	+60	+30	+350	10

* No increase
** After the age of 65 years the RNI is 10 µg/d
*** From the last 28 weeks of pregnancy
† based on protein providing 14.7 per cent of the EAR for energy

Requirements for Vitamin D are not stated from 4 years as it assumed this will be met from exposure to sunlight.

Source: COMA, 1991

Reference nutrient intakes for minerals

The table shows the daily requirement for the key minerals.

Age	Calcium mg/d	Phosphorus mg/d	Sodium mg/d	Potassium mg/d	Iron mg/d	Iodine μg/d	Zinc mg/d	Magnesium mg/d
0–3 months	525	400	210	800	1.7	50	4.0	55
4–6 months	525	400	280	850	4.3	60	4.0	60
7–9 months	525	400	320	700	7.8	60	5.0	75
10–12 months	525	400	350	700	7.8	60	5.0	80
1–3 years	350	270	500	800	6.9	70	5.0	85
4–6 years	450	350	700	1,100	6.1	100	6.5	120
7–10 years	550	450	1,200	2,000	8.7	110	7.0	200
Males								
11–14 years	1,000	775	1,600	3,100	11.3	130	9.0	280
15–18 years	1,000	775	1,600	3,500	11.3	140	9.5	300
19–50 years	700	550	1,600	3,500	8.7	140	9.5	300
50+ years	700	550	1,600	3,500	8.7	140	9.5	300
Females								
11–14 years	800	625	1,600	3,100	14.8**	130	9.0	280
15–18 years	800	625	1,600	3,500	14.8**	140	7.0	300
19–50 years	700	550	1,600	3,500	14.8**	140	7.0	270
50+ years	700	550	1,600	3,500	8.7	140	7.0	270
Pregnancy	*	*	*	*	*	*	*	*
Lactation:								
0–4 months	+550	+440	+50	*	*	*	+6.0	+50
4+ months	+550	+440	+50	*	*	*	+2.5	+50

* No increase
** Insufficient for women with high menstrual losses

Source: COMA, 1991

Activity 1.6

Review extracting data from a table

Using the RNI tables for both vitamins and minerals shown above, answer the following questions. Use the correct units when appropriate.

1 How much vitamin C is required each day by adults aged 19–50 years?
2 During the last 28 weeks of pregnancy, how much thiamin in total, should a woman aged 19–40 years consume each day?
3 How much vitamin A do males aged 11–14 years require?
4 Why is there no recommendation for vitamin D from 4 years to 65 years?
5 Which group requires 0.8 μg of vitamin B12?
6 Which age groups require the most calcium?
7 How much potassium does a lactating woman aged 30 years require each day?
8 How much iron does a female aged 11–14 years require each day?
9 How much magnesium do people over 50 years require each day?
10 Which group requires 210 mg of sodium each day?

Alternative ways to measure nutrient intake

When the DRVs were published in 1991 it was hoped that the RNI values would replace the older **Recommended Daily Allowance (RDA)** values. Recommended Daily Allowance (RDA) are estimates of the average amount of a nutrient needed to meet the needs of groups of adults rather than individuals. The RDAs were wrongly used to assess individual diets and therefore were not accurate. DRV, as we have discussed, is an umbrella term which gives a range of intakes based on an evaluation of individual requirements for each nutrient. DRVs are a move away from the RDA 'one-size-fits-all' position to a system in which the needs of individuals can be accommodated.

However, RDA values are part of European food law. The EU has continued to use RDA on food labels to inform consumers about nutrients intake. RDAs are given as one figure for each nutrient. They are based on the needs of typical adults and do not vary with age, sex and physiological status, such as pregnancy. By contrast, the Reference Nutrient Intakes (see www.nutrition.org.uk) used in the UK offer more detail to meet an individual's needs.

Guideline Daily Amounts (GDAs)

Guideline Daily Amounts have been introduced by the food industry on some food packaging. The GDA is different from the Dietary Reference Values. GDAs are based on the estimated average requirement for energy for a healthy man (2500 kcal) and woman (2000 kcal) aged between 19 and 50 years. The fat GDAs are based on the Department of Health guidance issued in 1991. The maximum recommended intake of 6 g of salt per day is from the 1994 COMA recommendations. A more detailed discussion of the role of GDAs and different approaches to nutritional labelling can be found in Topic 5 on the Design, development and production of new food products.

We believe that where possible you should use the UK's RNI to draw conclusions about nutritional value of a food product or dish for an individual. However, because the numerical difference between the terms can be relatively small, it can be assumed that RNI and RDA are the same, if necessary.

Malnutrition

Figure 1.04

Malnutrition literally means 'bad' nutrition. Malnutrition can include undernutrition (or wasting) and overnutrition (or obesity). A suggested definition of malnutrition is a deficiency, excess or imbalance of nutrients that causes adverse effects on health and wellbeing. Malnutrition can also be more scientifically defined as having a **Body Mass Index (BMI)** of less than 18.5. Body Mass Index (BMI) is a statistical measurement which compares a person's weight and height. Unintentional weight loss greater than 10 per cent in the last three to six months or a combination of a BMI of less than 20 coupled with unintentional weight loss greater than 5 per cent within the last three to six months can also be used as an indicator of malnutrition.

Normally, the term malnutrition is used to refer to undernutrition rather than overnutrition. Most research regards malnutrition as a deficiency or insufficiency of nutrients.

Malnutrition in the UK

Malnutrition can affect anyone in society. A report published by the British Association for Parenteral and Enteral Nutrition (BAPEN) stated that malnutrition costs the UK more than £7.3 billion each year. This is more than double the cost for obesity, yet obesity has a much higher media profile. Public health policy increasingly tries to encourage people to eat less, and people that are underweight often go unnoticed.

The author of the BAPEN report, Professor Elia, estimated about 30 per cent of patients in hospitals and nursing homes have been found to be clinically malnourished. Further research evidence suggests that many will lose more weight while in hospital or care homes. A 2005 report by the European Nutrition for Health Alliance entitled 'Malnutrition within an Ageing Population: A Call to Action' found up to 10 per cent of nursing home residents lose 5 per cent of their body weight within one month and 10 per cent of their body weight within six months of admission to a nursing home.

Symptoms of malnutrition

The symptoms of malnutrition may include tiredness, slow growth in children, brittle nails, dry and scaly skin, slow wound healing and increased susceptibility to infections. Malnourished people are more likely to develop infections, visit their GP more frequently, and require longer hospital stays. Malnutrition can prevent people recovering from illness and make individuals more prone to developing health problems. Individuals can suffer reduced muscle strength and are more susceptible to hypothermia, apathy, depression and self-neglect.

Groups at risk of malnutrition

It is thought that more than three million people are malnourished in the UK. The most vulnerable groups to suffer malnutrition are described below.

Babies and children

Children can lack iron, calories, vitamins and protein in their diet. Poor nutrition in childhood can result in poor growth. Semi solid food should be introduced into a baby's diet from around the age of six months. This process is called **weaning** and is important at this age as it meets the increased nutritional needs of the growing child. A delay in weaning can contribute to children not receiving adequate iron and protein in their diet.

The elderly and older adults

Up to 14 per cent of people aged over 65 years in the UK are malnourished according to the European Nutrition for Health Alliance 2005 report, 'Malnutrition within an Ageing Population: A Call to Action'. Mobility problems can prevent some people from travelling to food shops, or preparing food for themselves. They may have problems reading food labels and opening food packaging. Loneliness, bereavement and depression can result in apathy towards food and individuals may not feel like eating. Sometimes elderly people can just simply forget to eat. An elderly person may eat poorly due to dental problems; they may find it difficult to chew food due to ill-fitting dentures and have difficulty swallowing food. Certain medication can affect appetite, reducing the desire to eat. Concerns about spending money can decrease the motivation to go shopping. Poor transport links can make accessing food shops more challenging in some areas.

People who abuse drugs or alcohol

Malnutrition can occur in people who abuse drugs and alcohol. Alcohol contains enough calories to suppress feelings of hunger, but it offers no other nutrients required to stay healthy. Drug addiction can also curb appetite, resulting in malnutrition.

People with eating disorders

Eating disorders such as anorexia nervosa can lead to malnutrition, as the amount of food eaten is often very limited.

People with certain illnesses and disease

Certain diseases have a higher risk of malnutrition, including cystic fibrosis, coeliac disease, liver disease, kidney disease and cancer. Disease can affect how the body absorbs and uses the nutrients that we eat or drink.

People may eat poorly because they are ill. People who are very ill or in pain may not eat enough to keep themselves healthy. Eating or swallowing can be difficult if an individual is unwell. Some illnesses can result in a lack of appetite and medication may decrease appetite or affect the digestion and absorption of nutrients. If food is not digested properly, the body cannot absorb the nutrients.

People on a low income

Poverty is probably the greatest social cause of malnutrition according to the European Nutrition for Health Alliance (2005). Those on a low income often find it difficult to buy enough food, or food of a sufficient variety, which can result in malnutrition. As the price of basic food products increases, more evidence of malnutrition and poverty could emerge in the UK.

Treatment of malnutrition

The National Institute for Health and Clinical Excellence (NICE) has created guidelines to help hospitals identify those who are malnourished or at risk of malnutrition. NICE sets out the nutritional support that these people should receive. The NICE guidelines recommend that the weight of a patient at risk of malnutrition is monitored closely during their stay in hospital. All hospital trusts should employ at least one nurse specialising in nutrition support.

The treatment of malnutrition may include making nutrient-rich foods available in small regular portions. Using energy-dense food and drink in meal preparation and snacks to restore missing nutrients is also helpful.

The consumption of supplements for specific deficiencies may help to address malnutrition, for example, iron tablets for the treatment of iron deficiency anaemia. The regular monitoring of an individual who is at risk should also be implemented.

Tackling the social, psychological or financial issues which are contributing to malnutrition may help to resolve the problem. For example, social services may become involved in the case of an elderly person who is unable to shop or prepare meals. Agencies that offer readymade meals delivered to the home can remove the pressure of shopping and preparing meals. Attending a local day centre that serves meals can help an elderly person increase their food intake and may help to reduce loneliness.

CHECK YOUR UNDERSTANDING

Check that you understand the meaning of the following key terms by defining each in a sentence.

Recommended Daily Allowance (RDA)

Dietary Reference Values (DRVs)

Guideline Daily Amounts (GDA)

malnutrition

micronutrients

Reference Nutrient Intake (RNI)

microgram

Body Mass Index (BMI)

Scientific Advisory Committee on Nutrition (SACN)

Estimated Average Requirement (EAR)

deficiency disease

diet

macronutrients

nutrients

balanced diet

milligram

Exam-style questions

1 Describe the concept of a balanced diet.

(2 marks)

2 Describe the concept of malnutrition in the UK.

(2 marks)

3 Explain why the elderly have a greater risk of malnutrition.

(6 marks)

(Total of 10 marks)

NUTRIENTS AND ENERGY

Learning objectives

By the end of this chapter you will be able to:

- describe the sources and dietary functions of protein, fats, carbohydrates, vitamins and minerals
- explain the effects of deficiencies and excesses of protein, fats, carbohydrates, vitamins and minerals
- identify the sources of novel proteins
- describe the effect of storage, preparation and cooking on vitamin C
- explain the value of vitamin supplements
- explain the relationship between vitamin C and iron, and calcium and vitamin D.
- identify good sources of energy in the UK diet
- outline the concept of energy balance.

Introduction

The macronutrients – protein, fat, and carbohydrate – and the micronutrients – vitamins and minerals – were introduced in Topic 1. This chapter is divided into sections that focus in depth on the macronutrients and the micronutrients, looking particularly at the sources, functions, structure, deficiencies and excesses of each type of nutrient.

Section 1   Protein

Introduction

About 17 per cent of the body is made up of protein. Protein comes from a Greek word meaning 'I am first'. All proteins are made up of carbon, hydrogen, oxygen and nitrogen, and most proteins also contain sulphur and some phosphorus. These elements are arranged into

Figure 2.01 *Protein foods*

units called **amino acids**, which form the building blocks of protein. Amino acids are joined together in chains by peptide links and these chains form the protein.

Protein is an essential constituent of all cells and must be included in the diet to enable the growth and repair of the body. Any excess protein consumed is used to provide energy. The reference nutrient intake (RNI) for protein can be found in Topic 1.

Biological value of protein

Amino acids are the building blocks of protein and there are about twenty different types commonly found in plant and animal proteins. **Indispensable (essential) amino acids** cannot be made by the human body in sufficient amounts for health. The body is able to make some amino acids for itself and these are called **dispensable (non essential) amino acids**.

For adults, there are eight indispensable amino acids:

- leucine
- isoleucine
- valine
- threonine
- methionine
- phenylalanine
- tryptophan
- lysine.

In children, histidine is also considered an indispensable amino acid, since they are unable to make enough to meet their needs.

The remaining, dispensable amino acids are:

- alanine
- glutamine
- arginine
- glycine
- aspartic acid
- proline
- asparagine
- serine
- cysteine
- tyrosine
- glutamic acid.

The quality of protein (i.e. its biological value) depends upon whether it can supply all of the indispensable amino acids in the quantities needed. If a protein contains the indispensable amino acids in the approximate amount needed, it is said to have a **high biological value**. If it is low in one or more of the indispensable amino acids, it is said to have a **low biological value**. The amino acid that is in shortest supply in relation to need is called the **limiting amino acid**.

Sources of protein

Figure 2.02 *Plant sources of protein*

Protein can be obtained from animal or plant sources. Animal sources of protein are meat, fish, cheese, eggs and milk. Plant sources of protein include pulses (peas,

Activity 2.1

Review

The table below shows the amount of protein per 100 g of food (*source: www.nutrition.org.uk*).

Rearrange the food in descending order, with the highest amount of protein per 100 g of food first. What can you conclude from this table?

Food	Amount of protein (g per 100 g of food)
White rice, cooked	2.6
Pasta, cooked	7.7
White bread	7.9
Semi-skimmed milk	3.4
Cheddar cheese	25.4
Poached egg	12.5
Rump steak, grilled	31.0
Peanuts	25.6

beans and lentils), cereals (wheat, maize and rice) and nuts. In general, proteins from animal sources have a higher biological value than proteins from plant sources, but the limiting amino acid varies.

The amount of protein in food varies, but the average daily intake of protein in the UK diet is 85 g for men and 62 g for women.

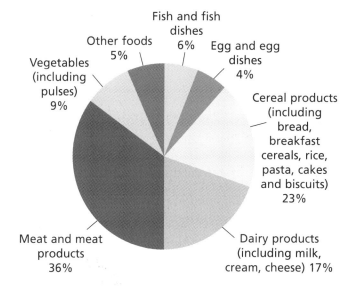

Figure 2.03 *Sources of protein in the British diet*

Source: www.nutrition.org.uk (accessed December 2008)

Complementary proteins

In the UK we eat a mixture of food with a variety of protein content. One type of protein food may be deficient in a particular amino acid, but when eaten with another protein food the amino acids of one protein may compensate for the other. The result is that the mixture becomes of a high biological value as the proteins complement each other – this is known as the **complementary action of proteins.** An example of this is baked beans on toast. Individually, beans and toast are of low biological value, but when eaten together they are of high biological value because the low lysine content of the toast is complemented by the higher lysine content of the beans.

Functions of protein

The three main functions of protein are:

- the growth of body cells, particularly during the growth spurts of adolescence and in a growing foetus

- the maintenance and repair of the body cells and tissues as a result of wear and tear or injury

- to provide a source of energy. If other sources of energy are lacking in the diet, protein is used first to meet energy needs. One gram provides 17 kJ (4 kcal).

Symptoms of deficiency

A deficiency of protein is extremely rare in the UK, because most people's diets contain plenty of protein and provide more than enough of the indispensable amino acids.

In developing countries protein deficiency can occur. **Protein energy malnutrition (PEM)** describes a range of disorders mainly affecting young children who have too little energy and protein in their diet. The two most common forms of PEM are Marasmus and Kwashiorkor. PEM is one of the greatest health problems in developing countries and around half of the child population does not reach the age of five.

Marasmus occurs in infants under one year of age who have been weaned off breast milk onto a diet containing too little energy and protein. As a result, the child becomes severely underweight and very weak and lethargic.

Kwashiorkor occurs in children who, after breast-feeding, are weaned onto a diet high in starchy foods that are low in energy and protein. Kwashiorkor often follows an acute infection such as gastroenteritis or measles. The body swells with **oedema** (water retention), the hair is thin and discoloured, and the skin may show patches of scaliness and pigmentation.

Symptoms of excess

If an excess of protein is consumed which is not required for growth and repair, it will be used as energy, and therefore can contribute towards a surplus of energy.

There is some evidence that a high protein intake may be harmful and may contribute to demineralisation of bones and a deterioration of kidney function in patients with kidney disease. Current recommendations are that adults should avoid protein intakes of more than twice the RNI. It had been thought that athletes may benefit from a high protein diet; this is not in fact the case as athletes need more energy (calories), which is best provided for by a diet high in carbohydrate.

High protein diets such as the Atkins Diet have been marketed as a treatment for **obesity.** This is because excess protein can be metabolised in much the same way as carbohydrate. Although in the short term these diets can be as good as high carbohydrate diets, they are harder to stick to, expensive, and have unpleasant side effects such as nausea, constipation and halitosis.

Activity 2.2

Review

Create a revision table on protein with the following headings:
- Functions
- Sources
- Structure
- Deficiency
- Excess

Activity 2.3

Practical opportunity

Plan a meal for two adults which is balanced (main meal, accompaniments, dessert).

Explain why your choices are balanced – directly referring to the nutrients in the food.

Calculate the protein content of the main meal. Analyse how far it meets the protein requirements of an adult.

In your next practical lesson, make the main meal only.

Novel sources of protein

In recent years, there has been a growing demand for protein that is suitable for vegetarians, and protein rich foods that are low in fat. The response to this by the food industry is the development of meat alternatives – novel sources of protein. These meat alternatives are discussed in detail in Topic 4. Some novel sources of protein are described below.

- Miso is a fermented condiment made from soya beans, rice or barley grains, salt and water.

- **Mycoprotein** (commonly known as quorn) is produced by fermentation of an organism (*Fusarium graminearum*) to produce fine fibres, which are formed together to produce a meat alternative.

- Soya dairy alternatives – soya milk is made from soaking soya beans in water.

- Tempeh is a mass of soya beans that have been allowed to ferment – essentially, it is fermented soya bean paste. It is solid, has a white fluffy outer layer and can be sliced.

- **Textured Vegetable Protein (TVP)** has been developed from the protein of a number of plants, especially the soya bean. It is composed of bundles of short fibres of extruded soya protein.

- Tofu is produced from ground soya beans that have been sieved. The proteins coagulate, producing a soft cheese-like product.

- Wheat protein comes from gluten which is extracted and processed to resemble meat. Its trade name is Wheatpro.

Activity 2.4

Practical opportunity

High Biological Value protein foods such as meat, fish and poultry can be expensive.

Identify a range of dishes suitable for main meals which use high biological protein food from less expensive sources, such as eggs, cheese and pulses (lentils, beans, chick peas).

In your next practical lesson, choose one of your dishes and make it.

CHECK YOUR UNDERSTANDING

Check that you understand the meaning of the following key terms by defining each in a sentence.

macronutrient	amino acid
peptide link	indispensable amino acid
dispensable amino acid	high biological value
low biological value	limiting amino acid
complementary action of proteins	PEM
Marasmus	Kwashiorkor
oedema	

Section 2   Fats

Introduction

In this section, we will explore the most energy-dense nutrient: fat. Eating fat is essential for a balanced diet and has many vital functions, including helping the body keep warm and providing essential fatty acids. We will investigate the sources and dietary function of fats and the essential fatty acids. We will also examine different types of fat, including **cholesterol**, and explore the possible link between fat and coronary heart disease.

The term 'fat' includes both fats and oils. Fats and oils are essentially the same, but fats tend to be solid at room temperature whereas oils are liquid.

Fats supply the most concentrated source of energy to the diet. Fat provides 37 kJ (9 kcal) of energy per gram. This is more than double that provided by either protein or carbohydrate, which provide 17 kJ/g (4 kcal) and 16 kJ/g (3.75 kcal) respectively.

Sources of fats

Figure 2.04 *Fatty foods*

Fats and oils can be **visible** in some foods such as fat on meat or as a layer of butter on bread. Some fats are **invisible** and cannot be seen easily. In milk, egg yolk, mayonnaise and gravy, the fat is an emulsion throughout the food, making it difficult to see. In food products, invisible fat is found in crisps, biscuits and cakes.

Foods that contain the largest quantities of fat usually come from animal products such as meat and meat products, cheese, cream, oily fish, chocolate, and eggs. However, avocados are also high in fat and most nuts and seeds are good sources, too. Readymade food products such as pastries, biscuits and cakes are also a rich source of fat in the diet.

Vegetable and plant oils, lard, fat spreads and butter contain large quantities of fat and are often used in the preparation and cooking of food.

Activity 2.5

Research

Construct a web diagram identifying foods that have a high fat content per 100 g.

Use a computer program, food tables or the internet to help you identify high fat foods and think about how often you eat these foods.

Current advice from COMA suggests that an average woman should not consume more than a total fat intake of around 76 g/day and an average man should consume no more than 100 g/day.

Can you calculate your total daily fat intake?

Functions of fats

- Fats provide a concentrated source of energy – 37 kJ (9 kcal) of energy per gram. Fat supplies more energy than the same weight of protein or carbohydrate.

- It provides the body with a long-term energy store known as adipose tissue. Adipose tissue is stored under the skin and around some internal organs. It cushions and insulates the body from cold.

- Fat around organs such as the kidneys helps to protect them.

- Fat is an essential component of all cell membranes in the body.

- Fat provides a source for the fat-soluble vitamins A, D, E and K.

- Fat contains the essential fatty acids **linoleic acid (omega 6)** and **alpha linolenic acid (omega 3)**. We will investigate their function later in this section.

In addition to dietary function, fat has a critical role in enhancing the flavour, texture, and aroma of the food we eat. It gives many qualities to food products including crispness, tenderness and enrichment.

Fat delays gastric emptying and fatty foods take longer to digest than other nutrients. This can prevent hunger sensations for longer so a person feels satisfied and full for a longer period.

Structure of fats and oils

To understand the functions and concern about fat in the diet we must study the basic structure of a fat molecule. Chemically, fat is a **triglyceride**. Nearly all fats we eat are triglycerides. Triglycerides consist of three fatty acid molecules combined with one glycerol molecule (see Figure 2.05).

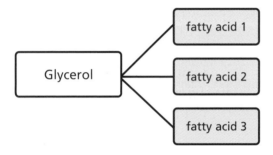

Figure 2.05 *Composition of a triglyceride*

Fatty acids are chains of carbon and hydrogen atoms. About 16 different fatty acids can be found in food. Different combinations of fatty acids make different types of fats and oils. The carbon atoms in the fatty acid molecules can be linked by single or double bonds. It is the bonding that allows us to classify the different types of fats. Most fats contain a mixture of **saturated**, **mono-unsaturated** and **polyunsaturated** fatty acids.

Fats can be divided into two groups – saturated fats and **unsaturated** fats.

Saturated fats

Saturated fats are simply fats that contain mainly saturated fatty acids. They have no double bonds between any of the carbon atoms in the carbon chain.

Figure 2.06 shows a saturated fat molecule with 10 carbon atoms called capric acid. Saturated fats are usually solid at room temperature; capric acid has a melting point of 32°C (90°F). Saturated fats with longer chains generally have higher melting points. Palmitic acid

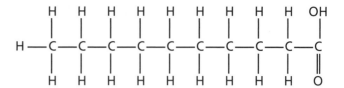

Figure 2.06 *Carbon chain of the saturated fatty acid capric acid*

has a chain length of 16 carbon atoms and its melting point is 63°C (145°F). Saturated fats are very stable molecules and are unlikely to react with other chemicals. The fat molecules can be packed close together due to their linear shape, giving them a rigid structure.

Saturated fats are usually found in red meat, butter, milk, cheese and eggs. However, coconut oil, palm oil and palm kernel oil are also very rich in saturated fats. Research suggests that saturated fat can raise blood cholesterol.

Unsaturated fats

Sometimes the chain of carbon atoms has some hydrogen atoms missing. This creates an unsaturated molecule and results in a 'double-bond' between two of the carbon atoms in the chain. The double bond gives unsaturated fatty acids special properties. It puts a bend or curve in the otherwise straight carbon chain. This allows the molecules more movement as they cannot be packed together easily. As a result, fats made with unsaturated fatty acids, like vegetable oils, are liquid at room temperature.

There are two further types of unsaturated fats:

Mono-unsaturated fatty acids

These are a type of unsaturated fat and have one double bond. The prefix 'mono' means one. Avocados,

Figure 2.07 *Avocados contain mono-unsaturated fatty acids*

cashews and peanuts are also good sources of monounsaturated fatty acids.

A good example of a mono-unsaturated fatty acid is oleic acid. Olive oil is a rich source of oleic acid. It has a chain of 18 carbon atoms, with one double bond between the ninth and tenth atom. At room temperature, olive oil is a clear liquid, but when chilled it becomes cloudy and may start to solidify. Figure 2.08 shows a mono-unsaturated fatty acid; the double bond can be seen here between the seventh and eighth carbon atoms.

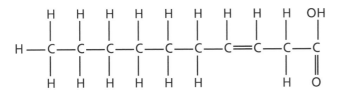

Figure 2.08 *Carbon chain of a mono-unsaturated fatty acid*

The double bond is also an area of weakness in the molecular structure of oil. Saturated fatty acids are stable and unlikely to react chemically, but the double bond in an unsaturated fatty acid creates an opportunity for oxidation to occur.

Polyunsaturated fatty acids

Polyunsaturated fatty acids have two or more double bonds in the carbon chains. The prefix 'poly' means

Figure 2.09 *Some vegetable oils are a good source of polyunsaturated fatty acids*

two or more. Corn, soya and sunflower oils are good sources of polyunsaturated fatty acids. Figure 2.10 shows the double bonds in the carbon chain of a polyunsaturated fatty acid.

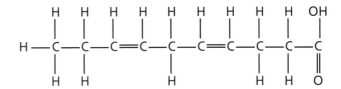

Figure 2.10 *Carbon chain of a polyunsaturated fatty acid*

The double bonds within a fatty acid chain reduce the stability of the molecule. They have more double bonds than monounsaturated fats so polyunsaturated fatty acids are far more likely to react with oxygen. This means polyunsaturated fats tend to go rancid when exposed to the air and sunlight for long periods; this is a sign of oxidation. Repeated exposure to high temperatures can also increase oxidative damage.

Activity 2.6

Practical opportunity

Figure 2.11 *Fruit and vegetables*

Government advice is to reduce fat consumption. Produce a dish which is low in fat and outline the reasons why it meets the current advice. Calculate the fat content of the dish.

Omega 3 and omega 6 fatty acids

Polyunsaturated fatty acids can be sub-divided further into a group that are identified by the word 'omega' followed by a number. The number indicates the location of the first double bond at one end of the carbon chain. Two well-known polyunsaturated fats are omega 3 and omega 6 fats. These are sometimes expressed as *n-3* and *n-6*. They are both essential fatty acids and their function and sources will be explored later in this section.

Trans and cis fatty acids

Unsaturated fatty acids also exist in two different structures called the trans and cis. These structures are identified by the position of the hydrogen atoms to the double bonds.

Trans fatty acids have the hydrogen atoms on opposite sides of the double bond. The prefix 'trans' means 'across'. This gives the molecule a more linear appearance, like saturated fats. **Cis fatty acids** have the hydrogen atoms both on the same side of the molecule. This causes the molecule to look like it is bent and curved.

Most unsaturated fatty acids exist naturally in the cis form but during food manufacturing processes the cis fatty acids may be changed to trans fatty acids. Trans fats are created by a process called **hydrogenation**.

Hydrogenation

The process of hydrogenation is used in the food industry to turn vegetable oil into a solid substance. It improves the shelf life of the fat and reduces the likelihood of oxidation. During hydrogenation, vegetable oils are hardened by processing them with hydrogen gas. The double bonds are converted into single bonds during the process and unsaturated fats can be made into saturated fats.

Figure 2.13 *Foods containing hydrogenated oil*

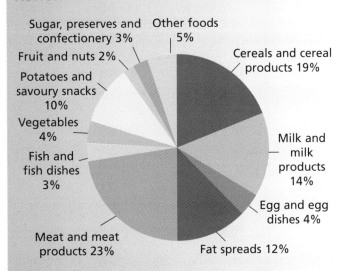

Figure 2.14 shows the conversion process that occurs in hydrogenation. The hydrogen gas and unsaturated molecule combine and the double bond disappears. The new fat produced is called a trans fatty acid.

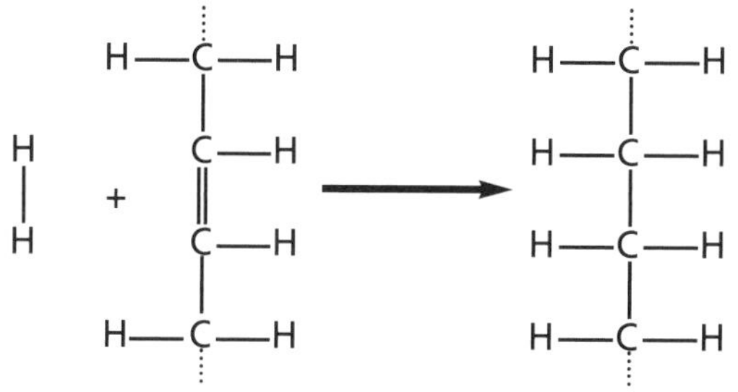

Figure 2.14 *Conversion process during hydrogenation*

Figure 2.15 *Sunflower oil is a source of essential fatty acids*

Partially hydrogenated oil is widely used in baking and processed foods, including fat spreads, cakes, biscuits and some readymade meals.

Like saturated fats, artificially created trans fats have been associated with coronary heart disease. Due to concern about the potential harmful effects of a high intake of trans fatty acids, some food manufacturing processes have changed, resulting in a reduction in the trans fatty acid content of some foods. Several food manufacturers use 'free from hydrogenated fats' as a marketing claim.

Small amounts of natural trans fats occur in milk and beef. These natural trans fats do not appear to be as unhealthy as the artificial trans fats.

Essential fatty acids

Two polyunsaturated fatty acids are essential for health – linoleic acid and alpha linolenic acid. **Essential fatty acids** must be consumed in the diet, as the body cannot manufacture them. In the body, the essential fatty acids can be converted into arachidonic acid, or eicosapentaenoic acid (EPA) and docosahexaenoic acid (DHA) which have essential roles. We sometimes refer to the essential fatty acids as omega 3 or omega 6; this indicates the position of the double bonding on the molecules.

Sources of essential fatty acids

Alpha linolenic acid (omega 3 fatty acid) is sometimes expressed as α-linolenic acid. Rapeseed oil (canola), mustard seeds, pumpkin seeds, soya bean, walnuts, green leafy vegetables and grains are all good sources of α-linolenic acid. Linseeds and linseed oil are also particularly rich sources of α-linolenic acid.

Linoleic acid (omega 6 fatty acid) is found in oils made from sunflower, corn, soya, pumpkin and wheat germ. Coldwater and oily ocean fish including tuna, salmon and sardines are also good source of polyunsaturated omega 3 fats.

Functions of essential fatty acids

- The essential fatty acid alpha linolenic acid is converted to eicosapentanoic acid (EPA) which is important for proper nerve function. EPA is claimed to be beneficial in reducing the symptoms of arthritis and the risk of heart disease.

- Docosahexanoic acid (DHA) is also produced from alpha linolenic acid and is essential for the proper functioning of the brain. It also assists in the development of the nervous system in the foetus before birth and the visual abilities during the first six months of life.

- Linoleic acid is converted into arachidonic acid, from which hormone-like chemicals known as prostaglandins are produced. Prostaglandins regulate many body processes, including inflammation and blood clotting.

- Essential fatty acids regulate body cholesterol metabolism.

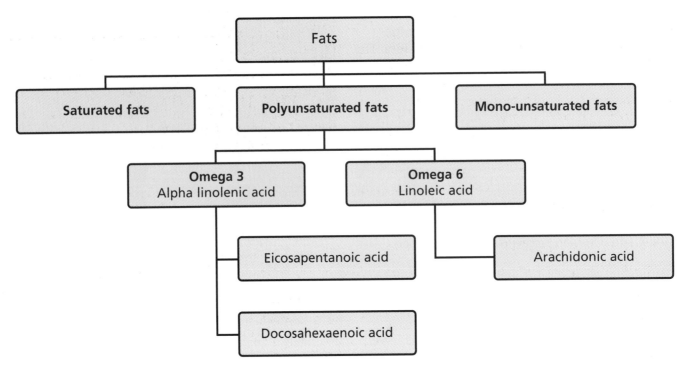

Figure 2.16 *Summary of the types of fat*

Fat in the diet

We will now explore the role of fat in the diet and its possible association with coronary heart disease. In countries in the developed world, such as Europe and North America there is concern that people are eating too much fat. A high fat intake, and in particular a high intake of saturated fat, has been associated with a raised blood cholesterol level, which is a potential risk factor in the development of coronary heart disease. Obesity also develops with the increased consumption of energy-dense foods and a lack of activity. Obesity increases the risk of developing heart disease, Type 2 diabetes, high blood pressure and osteoarthritis.

Cholesterol

Cholesterol is a type of fat but it does not produce any energy. It is found in all animal cells and tissues but is not found in vegetables or plants. Cholesterol has an essential role in the structure of cell membranes and production of bile for the absorption of fats, and is an essential component of many hormones. Most of the cholesterol in the body is manufactured by the liver.

Cholesterol is transported by proteins around the body. These complex molecules are called lipoproteins. There are two main types of protein and cholesterol molecules: **low density lipoprotein (LDL)** and **high density lipoprotein (HDL)**.

LDL cholesterol has been linked to coronary heart disease. LDL cholesterol may form plaques on artery walls, which can lead to atherosclerosis and blocked arteries. HDL cholesterol may help protect against heart disease.

However, dietary cholesterol is not clearly linked to levels of cholesterol in the blood. The type and amount of dietary fats eaten may affect levels of blood cholesterol. Blood cholesterol is closely associated with the amount of saturated fat in the diet, as saturated fat raises blood cholesterol. Unsaturated fats are less likely to raise blood cholesterol and indeed, may lower it. Consumption of monounsaturated fats including olive oil has been shown to help keep LDL cholesterol levels low and HDL cholesterol high.

Activity 2.9

Research opportunity

Devise a simple questionnaire to find out about the consumption of fat and fatty foods among your friends and family. Analyse your results and write some conclusions.

Required intakes of fat

It is thought that around 42 per cent of energy in the typical British diet is from fat – a figure that needs to be reduced. COMA (Committee on Medical Aspects of Food Policy) recommends that no more than 35 per cent of daily energy requirement should come from fat. Most of the fat consumed is from animal origin. The report also puts emphasis on reducing the amount of saturated fat in the diet and recommends that no more than 11 per cent of energy intake should come from saturated fatty acids. The goal for essential fatty acids is about 1–2 per cent of total energy intake. A detailed table of the COMA recommendations regarding the average contribution of different fatty acids in the UK diet can be found in Topic 1 (pages 6–7).

Activity 2.10

ICT opportunity

There are several simple ways to reduce fat intake. Produce a flyer informing the consumer of ways in which they can reduce their fat intake during the purchase, preparation and cooking of food.

CHECK YOUR UNDERSTANDING

Check you understand the meaning of the following key terms. Write a sentence using each word.

cholesterol	cis fatty acids
hydrogenation	monounsaturates
linoleic acid	alpha linolenic acid
low density lipoprotein	high density lipoprotein
omega 6	polyunsaturates
saturated fats	omega 3
trans fatty acids	fatty acids
unsaturated	visible fat
invisible fat	triglycerides

Section 3 Carbohydrates

Figure 2.17 *Carbohydrate foods*

Introduction

Carbohydrates are one of the three macronutrients. The two main groups of carbohydrates are sugars and starches. All carbohydrates are made up of carbon, hydrogen and oxygen. Sugars and starches are our major source of food energy. Approximately 1–2 per cent of the human body is made up of carbohydrate.

The main function of carbohydrates is to provide energy. However, too much energy in the diet can lead to a person becoming overweight. Note however that carbohydrate provides less energy than fat or alcohol. The RNI for carbohydrates can be found in Topic 1.

Sugars

Sugars are classified according to their structure and are divided into monosaccharides, **disaccharides** and polysaccharides, according to the size of the molecule.

Monosaccharides

Figure 2.18 *Fruit contains glucose and fructose – both monosaccharides*

Monosaccharides are simple sugars. The chemical formula for monosaccharides is $C_6H_{12}O_6$. There are three monosaccharides:

1 **Glucose** occurs naturally in fruit and plant juices and in the blood of living animals. Most carbohydrates in food are converted to glucose during digestion.

2 **Fructose** occurs naturally in some fruit and vegetables and especially in honey. It is the sweetest sugar and is a component of sucrose.

3 **Galactose** is found with glucose as lactose, the sugar which is present in milk.

Disaccharides

Figure 2.19 *Sugar beet contains sucrose – a disaccharide*

Disaccharides consist of two monosaccharide molecules joined together with the elimination of one molecule of water. The chemical formula for disaccharides is $C_{12}H_{22}O_{11}$. There are three disaccharides:

1 **Sucrose** is made up of one molecule of glucose and one molecule of fructose. It occurs naturally in sugar cane and sugar beet. It is also found in fruit and vegetables. 'Sugar', whether white or brown, is pure sucrose.

2 **Lactose** consists of one molecule of glucose and one molecule of galactose. It is the sugar present in milk. It is less sweet than sucrose or galactose.

3 **Maltose** consists of two molecules of glucose. Maltose forms when grain is germinated for the production of malt liquors such as beer.

Polysaccharides

Polysaccharides are made up of many monosaccharide molecules (usually glucose) joined together. They are also known as complex carbohydrates. The chemical formula of starch is $(C_6H_{10}O_5)_n$ where 'n' is a large number. The two main types of polysaccharides are:

1 **Starch** – the main food reserve in plants. It consists of many molecules of glucose. Starch exists in granules of a size and shape characteristic to each plant.

2 **Glycogen** – similar to starch but is made from glucose by animals rather than plants. Small amounts are stored in the liver and muscles as an energy reserve.

Sources of carbohydrates

Starchy foods such as bread, rice, pasta, cereal, pulses and potatoes are a good source of carbohydrate. Starches account for almost 60 per cent of the total carbohydrate intake in the average British diet.

Food and drink containing sugars such as those found in milk, fruits and vegetables, jam, confectionery, table sugar and some soft drinks are also a source of carbohydrate. Sugars account for almost 40 per cent of the total carbohydrate intake in the average British diet.

The average daily intake of carbohydrate is 272 g for men and 193 g for women, which provides just over 42 per cent of energy in the diet.

Figure 2.20 below shows sources of total carbohydrate in the British diet from a report entitled 'The Dietary and Nutritional Survey of British Adults' by Gregory et al. (1990). Figure 2.21 shows the sources of sugar in the British diet.

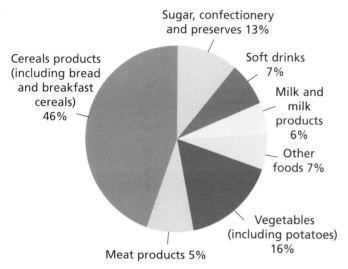

Figure 2.20 *Sources of total carbohydrate in the British diet*
Source: The Dietary and Nutritional Survey of British Adults, HMSO

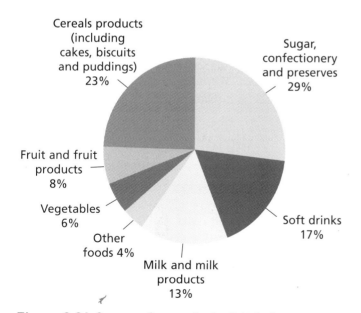

Figure 2.21 *Sources of sugars in the British diet*
Source: The Dietary and Nutritional Survey of British Adults, HMSO

Activity 2.11

Review

The table below shows the amount of carbohydrate per 100 g of food.

Analyse the table and explain in your own words what it tells us about carbohydrate consumption in the UK diet.

Food	Sugar g/100 g	Starch g/100 g	Total g/100 g
Whole milk	4.8	0	4.8
Meat	0	0	0
Sugar	105	0	105
Honey	76.4	0	76.4
Baked beans	5.9	9.4	15.3
Banana	20.9	2.3	23.2
White bread	2.6	46.7	49.3
Cornflakes	8.2	77.7	85.9
Milk chocolate	56.5	2.9	59.4

Source: Manual of Nutrition, Food Standards Agency

Functions of carbohydrate

- Carbohydrate provides a source of energy. One gram of carbohydrate provides 16 kJ (3.75 kcal) of energy. Glucose is oxidized in the body's cells and energy is released.

- Carbohydrate also acts as a protein sparer because it provides energy. Protein can be then be released to complete its primary function of growth and repair, rather than provide energy.

Symptoms of deficiency

Some people adopt a low carbohydrate diet in an attempt to lose weight, with the carbohydrate intake replaced with an increased consumption of fats and proteins. It is difficult to isolate the effect of a low carbohydrate diet on the body, but research suggests there are implications for reducing the consumption of fruit and vegetables and the subsequent nutrients they provide.

Symptoms of excess

Eating many sugary foods between meals is associated with increased tooth decay. The 1991 COMA report made recommendations regarding sugar consumption using the terms **intrinsic sugar** and **non-intrinsic** sugar. This has led to some manufacturers using these terms on food labels and some health professionals, usually dentists, referring to sugar in these terms.

Intrinsic sugars are sugars which form a vital part of certain unprocessed food (i.e., enclosed in the cell), the most important being whole fruits and vegetables.

Non-intrinsic sugars are not located within the cellular structure of a food and can be further divided into:

- milk sugars, occurring naturally in milk and milk products

- non-milk extrinsic sugars (NMES), which includes fruit juices, honey, and 'added sugars', which comprise both recipe sugars and table sugars.

The term **hidden sugar** may be used to refer to the fact that a product contains added sugar or non-milk extrinsic sugars.

The dietary guidelines issued by COMA on the consumption of non-milk extrinsic sugars are explored later in this chapter in the section on Energy. However, it is important to note that the advice suggests that the consumption of NMES should be reduced because of the risk of tooth decay.

Activity 2.12

Discussion/research
List some foods that contain hidden sugars.

Dietary fibre (non–starch polysaccharide)

Note that in this book we use the term **dietary fibre**; other sources of information may use the terms 'non-starch polysaccharide', or fibre.

Dietary fibre is a polysaccharide found in the cell walls of vegetables, fruits, pulses and cereal grains. The term dietary fibre is given to a mixture of substances which cannot be digested in the small intestine in humans, but pass into the large bowel where they are fermented by bacteria.

Fibre-rich foods are often recommended in weight-reducing diets. They contain fewer calories than foods with a high fat content, and when eaten they give a feeling of fullness and satiety.

Examples of dietary fibre are:

- **cellulose** – this consists of many thousands of glucose units. It is the main structural carbohydrate of plants. It is found in all foods which are vegetable in origin

- **pectin** – present in apples and many soft fruits. It is also present in root vegetables such as turnips or sweet potatoes. It forms a stiff jelly and is important in the setting of jam. It is not fibrous but it may help to reduce the amount of cholesterol in the blood

- **beta glucan** – present in the bran of barley, oats, rye and wheat. It may be beneficial in lowering blood cholesterol.

Figure 2.22 *Grain is a source of dietary fibre*

Sources of dietary fibre

In the UK we get most of our dietary fibre from wholemeal and brown bread, wholemeal flour, brown pasta, brown rice, oats and barley. Cereal grains are rich in dietary fibre especially if the whole grain is used. Root vegetables such as potatoes (especially with skin on), carrots and turnips, fresh fruit, dried fruit, pulses and nuts are also rich in dietary fibre. Breakfast cereals, especially the high-fibre varieties, can make a significant contribution to dietary fibre intake. The table below shows the amount of dietary fibre per 100 g of food for a variety of foods.

Food	fibre g/100 g
Meat	0
Baked beans	3.7
Boiled carrots	2.5
White bread	1.5
Brown bread	3.5
White flour	3.1
Wholemeal flour	9
All bran	24.5
Rice Krispies	0.7
Brown rice	0.8
White rice	0.1
White spaghetti	1.2
Wholemeal spaghetti	3.5

Source: Manual of Nutrition, Food Standards Agency

Activity 2.13

Review

Look at the table above and rearrange the food in descending order, with the highest amount of fibre per 100 g of food first. What can you conclude from this table?

Functions of dietary fibre

- Cellulose adds bulk to the **faeces** because its water-binding capacity greatly assists the passage of waste products and indigestible material through the intestines, thus preventing **constipation**. A high intake of fibre-rich foods may protect against bowel cancer.

- Polysaccharides such as pectin in fruit and beta glucan in oats may slightly reduce the level of cholesterol in blood.

- Diets high in dietary fibre are beneficial to diabetics because dietary fibre slows down the release of glucose into the bloodstream.

Symptoms of deficiency

A diet deficient in dietary fibre can result in low stool weight and contribute towards constipation; this could lead to an increased risk of bowel cancer.

Symptoms of excess

Excess consumption of dietary fibre rarely occurs in the UK. High intakes in countries such as Africa may result in a condition called 'large bowel volvulus'. A high consumption of cereals, especially wheat which contain phytic acid, can interfere with the absorption of some minerals.

Activity 2.14

Review

Create a revision table on sugars, starches and dietary fibre with the following headings:

Functions	Sources

Activity 2.15

Review and practical opportunity

Produce an informative leaflet explaining the health benefits of dietary fibre; include some recipe ideas.

In your next practical lesson, choose one of your recipes and make it.

CHECK YOUR UNDERSTANDING

Check you understand the meaning of the following key terms. Write a sentence using each word.

monosaccharide	disaccharide
polysaccharide	starch
glycogen	protein sparer
dietary fibre	cellulose
pectin	beta glucan
faeces	constipation
intrinsic sugar	non-intrinsic sugar
hidden sugar	

Section 4 | The micronutrients

Vitamin A

Figure 2.23 *Sweet potatoes are rich in vitamin A*

Introduction

We now explore the contribution that **micronutrients** make to a healthy diet. We will look at the dietary function and sources of **fat-soluble** and **water-soluble** vitamins. The effects of deficiencies and excesses of vitamins will be considered and you will develop an understanding of the value of vitamin supplements in the diet. You will also examine the effects of storage, preparation and cooking on the vitamin C content of fruit and vegetables.

Vitamins

The term vitamin comes from the Latin word *vita* meaning life, and describes a group of nutrients that control important metabolic reactions in the body. Vitamins are substances which are required in small amounts to sustain life. Vitamins are involved in the formation of hormones, enzymes, proteins, nerves and genetic materials. Most vitamins must be consumed in the diet because the body cannot manufacture them. A **deficiency disease** is a disease caused by a lack, or poor absorption, of a nutrient, for example, a vitamin. In this section, we will explore the deficiency diseases associated with a diet lacking certain vitamins.

Vitamins are measured in minute quantities. The term milligram (mg) or microgram (μg) is used. The amount of a vitamin absorbed into the body each day is difficult to measure because the vitamin content of a food product is affected by the freshness, condition and storage of the ingredients. The processing and cooking methods applied can also affect vitamin content. Drugs, alcohol and smoking can reduce the absorption of vitamins. People who consume large quantities of alcohol are often deficient in certain vitamins.

Vitamins are divided into:

- fat-soluble vitamins – includes vitamins A, D, E and K

- water-soluble vitamins – includes the B-vitamin complex and vitamin C.

Vitamin A is a fat-soluble vitamin. It is not normally affected by heat and is stable during most cooking methods. It is essential for growth and development.

Sources of vitamin A

There are two sources of Vitamin A:

1 Animal sources (**retinol**) – found in eggs, oily fish, liver, full fat milk, butter and cheese.

2 Vegetable sources (β-**carotene**) – found in carrots, sweet potatoes, apricots, cantaloupe melon, broccoli, spinach, pumpkin and all other green and orange fruits and vegetables.

Broccoli is a good source of vitamin A, but the chlorophyll (green) camouflages the yellow carotene colour. If chlorophyll was absent broccoli would be yellow or orange.

In the UK diet, about 75 per cent of our vitamin A is supplied in the form of retinol and 25 per cent as β-carotene. The animal sources provide a significant supply of retinol.

Margarine is a product obtained from vegetable oils and/or animal fats. By law, it must be **fortified** with both vitamin A and vitamin D. 'Fortification' means that vitamins or minerals have been added to the food, irrespective of whether they were present originally. Most people consume fat spreads that have a lower fat content than traditional 'block' margarines. However, spreads and reduced fat spreads are also fortified by manufacturers with vitamins A and D, although this is not required by law.

During digestion in the small intestines, a significant amount of β-carotene is converted into retinol. It is more easily absorbed into the body as retinol. Retinol can be stored in the liver for two years.

Functions of vitamin A

- Vitamin A aids vision, especially in the dark. Retinol is associated with the protection and maintenance of the retina in the eye. The retina is a light-sensitive tissue lining in the back of the eye, which allows vision in dim light. **Rhodopsin** is a pigment in the retina. Vitamin A is needed for the formation of rhodopsin, also known as visual purple.

- Vitamin A maintains mucous membranes that line any openings to the body, such as the nose, throat, lungs, mouth, stomach and urinary tract. It also helps in the formation of tissue, bone and skin and in cell formation. Vitamin A is important for growth and is essential for embryo development. Both an excess and deficiency of vitamin A are known to cause birth defects.

- Vitamin A is involved with the maintenance of the immune system. It helps prevent infections and fight infections by producing white blood cells and increases the activity of antibodies.

- Dietary intake studies suggest an association between diets rich in beta-carotene and a lower risk of some types of cancer. Carotenoids, which are another form of vitamin A, are powerful **antioxidants**. Antioxidants block some of the damage to body cells caused by **free radicals**, which are the by-products of metabolism, the process when the body converts food into energy. The removal of free radicals by antioxidants may reduce the risk of coronary heart disease.

Symptoms of deficiency

A deficiency of vitamin A is rare in the UK. **Night blindness** is the name given to the inability to see well in dim light and is associated with a deficiency of vitamin A. If untreated, the condition can lead to blindness. (Since carrots are a good source of beta-carotene, there is truth in the old adage that carrots help you see better in the dark.) The deficiency increases the risk of severe illness, and even death, from common childhood infections such as diarrhoea and measles in developing countries. Poor growth in children and slow bone development is evident.

Vitamin A deficiency is associated with a weakened immune system and a vulnerability to infection. The skin and moist membranes of the body will dry and rupture easily. If the tear glands in the eye become affected by this condition, they may become blocked, leading to permanent blindness. This condition is a significant problem in some parts of the world.

Vitamin A and blindness

Vitamin A deficiency in children under five years of age is common in developing countries. The World Health Organisation estimates that 100–140 million children are vitamin A deficient and that 500,000 of these children become blind every year. Of these, half die within 12 months of losing their sight. One approach to this problem is the development of genetically modified rice that is rich in beta-carotene. The modified rice would enable people who cannot afford a varied diet containing sufficient natural sources of vitamin A, to meet their dietary needs and reduce the risk of blindness.

Symptoms of excess

Retinol can be toxic in large quantities. Pregnant women should avoid consuming large amounts of vitamin A as research suggests it may harm the developing baby. Pregnant women should avoid eating liver or liver products such as pâté because these products are very high in vitamin A. They should also avoid taking vitamin supplements that contain vitamin A.

Some research suggests that a large intake of vitamin A over many years may adversely affect the bones, contributing to osteoporosis and making them more likely to fracture with increased age.

Vitamin D

Vitamin D is stored in the liver and fatty body tissues. The main form of vitamin D is **cholecalciferol**. Cholecalciferol is found in certain foods and can be produced in the body by the action of sunlight on the skin.

Figure 2.24 *Eggs and oily fish are rich in vitamin D*

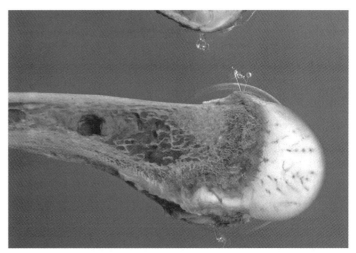

Figure 2.25 *Rickets*

Sources of vitamin D

For most people, the main source of vitamin D is sunlight. Because of this association, vitamin D is sometimes called the 'sunshine vitamin'. Ultra-violet light from the sun reacts with a substance in the skin to produce vitamin D. Around 15 minutes of exposure to sunshine, three times a week, will enable the body to manufacture all the vitamin D that it needs. Once manufactured to adequate levels, vitamin D is stored in the body.

Dietary sources of vitamin D include dairy produce, liver, oily fish and eggs. As mentioned earlier, spreadable fats and margarines are fortified with both vitamin A and vitamin D. Many breakfast cereals have voluntary enrichment of vitamin D. These can be important dietary sources of the vitamin for children and older people who are housebound.

Functions of vitamin D

- Vitamin D, together with calcium and phosphorus, develops and maintains bones and teeth.

- It also helps with the healing of fractured bones and may prevent brittle bone disease or osteoporosis in later life.

- Vitamin D helps the absorption of calcium from the intestine.

Symptoms of deficiency

Rickets is a deficiency of vitamin D that occurs in babies and toddlers. It is characterised by the development of bow-shaped legs, due to soft and weakened bones. The bone is unable to calcify or harden adequately so bends and deforms (see Figure 2.25). In adults, a deficiency of vitamin D can lead to an adult version of the disease called **osteomalacia**. Osteomalacia can cause the bones to fracture easily and severe pain in the back, legs and rib bones may develop. A poor intake of vitamin D hinders the absorption of calcium, which may increase the risk of rickets and osteoporosis.

Vitamin D deficiency is more likely to develop in young children, pregnant women and breastfeeding women because there are additional demands on the body. Pregnant or breastfeeding women risk a deficiency as their requirement for the vitamin increases to sustain their child. Mothers who prolong breastfeeding without ensuring their vitamin D requirements are met by dietary sources or supplements are likely to put their children at risk of a deficiency. Breast milk is not a good source of vitamin D and if the maternal supply is low the risk of deficiency increases in the baby.

People with darker skin are at greater risk of vitamin D deficiencies because increased pigmentation in the skin reduces the ability of the skin to manufacture vitamin D from sunlight. Inadequate sunlight exposure coupled with insufficient calcium and vitamin D intake during periods of rapid growth has produced some cases of rickets among children in the UK.

Asian women are particularly at risk of deficiency as their skin does not manufacture vitamin D effectively from sunlight and they may obtain very little sunlight on their skin if they cover up when outdoors, for example, by wearing a veil. The poor exposure to sunlight and a low dietary intake of vitamin D may result in a deficiency. Research indicates that 9 in 10 adults of South Asian origin may be vitamin D deficient in the UK.

Elderly people who are housebound or living in a nursing home may obtain little exposure to sunlight and are at greater risk of vitamin D deficiency. As mentioned above, in order to receive sufficient amounts of vitamin D, elderly people should sit in the sun during the summer months for 15 minutes each day.

Individuals with intestinal problems which reduce the absorption of vitamin D, such as coeliac disease, may also become deficient.

Symptoms of excess

Excess vitamin D is not excreted in the urine but is stored in soft tissues. Large doses of vitamin D have been associated with increased quantities of calcium in the blood, heart and kidneys. This can be dangerous. Symptoms of this toxic build up include nausea, vomiting and loss of appetite.

Vitamin E

Figure 2.26 *Nuts are rich in vitamin E*

Vitamin E is not a single substance but is a member of the family of fat-soluble vitamins. It is stored in the liver and body tissue. Some members of the vitamin E family are called **tocopherols**. Tocopherols are found in every cell membrane in the body.

Vitamin E is an antioxidant and is used in food production to prevent fats from becoming rancid. Fats will become rancid following exposure to oxygen and light, so antioxidants are added to food to slow this process down.

Vitamin E is very stable to heat at high temperatures and because it is fat-soluble it will not dissolve in water.

Sources of vitamin E

Foods that contain vitamin E include sunflower oil, olive oil, nuts, egg yolk, bananas, lettuce, spinach, onions, prawns and salmon.

Functions of vitamin E

- There is some evidence to suggest vitamin E protects body tissues from damage caused by unstable substances called free radicals. Free radicals can harm cells, tissues, and organs.

- The ability of vitamin E to prevent cancer, heart disease, dementia, liver disease and stroke is still uncertain.

- Vitamin E is important in the formation of red blood cells and helps the body to use vitamin K.

Symptoms of deficiency

Vitamin E deficiencies are not very common. A deficiency of vitamin E is difficult to pinpoint but possible symptoms include slow wound healing, lack of energy, poor concentration, irritability and muscle weakness.

Symptoms of excess

Too high an intake of vitamin E in the diet may lead to a loss of appetite.

Vitamin K

Vitamin K is a fat-soluble vitamin that can be stored in the liver.

Sources of vitamin K

Good supplies of vitamin K are found in green leafy vegetables such as green peas and beans, broccoli and spinach, and in vegetable oils and cereals. Small amounts of vitamin K are found in red meat and milk. Vitamin K is also made by bacteria in the large intestine.

Figure 2.27 *Green, leafy vegetables are rich in vitamin K*

Functions of vitamin K

● The blood-clotting process requires the presence of a number of different chemicals, called clotting factors. Vitamin K is involved in the production of clotting factors and, because it is required for blood clotting, also helps wounds to heal properly.

● Vitamin K is very important for bone health, as it can increase bone density and may prevent osteoporosis.

Symptoms of deficiency

Deficiency is rare, as vitamin K is manufactured in the body. Signs of deficiency include a tendency to bruise easily and bleeding, as the blood may take longer to clot in a person suffering a vitamin K deficiency. Newborn babies are at risk of developing a condition associated with vitamin K deficiency. VKDB (Vitamin K Deficiency Bleeding) is a rare condition where a newborn baby may develop bruising or bleeding as a result of low levels of Vitamin K. Three factors may contribute to this condition:

1 during pregnancy, insufficient vitamin K may reach the foetus across the placenta

2 breast milk contains low levels of vitamin K

3 there is an inadequate supply of bacteria in the intestine of newborns to produce vitamin K.

The deficiency is almost completely preventable by giving a single dose of vitamin K soon after birth, and this treatment has been offered to all UK mothers of newborn babies since the 1960s.

Symptoms of excess

There is little evidence to draw conclusions on the possible effects of taking high doses of vitamin K supplements each day.

Vitamin B1 (thiamin)

Figure 2.28 *Beans are rich in vitamin B1*

Vitamin B1 or **thiamin** is a water-soluble vitamin that cannot be stored in the body's muscle tissue. Body stores of thiamin are limited and a regular intake is therefore necessary.

Sources of vitamin B1

There are many sources of vitamin B1, including lean meats (particularly pork), milk, cheese, fortified bread and cereals, brown rice, dried beans, potatoes, spinach, nuts, peas and yeast. A significant amount of thiamin can be lost if vegetables are overcooked.

Thiamin is added to some breakfast cereals as the processing of cereals can destroy the vitamin. In the UK, white and brown flour is fortified with thiamin by law. More than two-thirds of our thiamin intake comes from plant sources, including bread, which is a significant source in the UK diet.

Functions of vitamin B1

- Thiamin is important in the process of energy release. It plays a vital role in helping the body to convert carbohydrates and fat into energy. Thiamin is part of an enzyme system that makes energy available to nearly every body cell.

- Thiamin is necessary for the transmission of nerve signals between the brain and the spinal cord. It also helps with the maintenance of nerve cells and several brain functions including memory.

- Thiamin is essential for normal growth and development of the body. It helps to maintain proper functioning of the heart, muscle and digestive systems.

- The requirement for thiamin increases if the body requires an increase of energy. During pregnancy and lactation, more energy is required so thiamin intake should be increased accordingly. Athletes also require more thiamin for increased energy release.

Symptoms of deficiency

Thiamin deficiency can lead to many problems including nerve damage, wasting and death. **Beri beri** is a deficiency disease associated with severe thiamin deficiency. A mild deficiency of thiamin can cause tiredness, headaches, muscle weakness, nerve damage, confusion, memory loss and enlargement of the heart. Thiamin deficiency is rare in developed countries but can be caused by alcoholism.

Symptoms of excess

It is unlikely an individual will consume excessive amounts of thiamin unless they are taking supplements. Toxicity is rare as excess thiamin is excreted in the urine. Long-term excessive use can produce symptoms of hyperthyroidism – headache, irritability, trembling, rapid pulse and insomnia.

Vitamin B2 (riboflavin)

Vitamin B2 or **riboflavin** is a water-soluble vitamin of the B group. Riboflavin is destroyed by light and loss will occur if foods are exposed to sunlight for long periods. Riboflavin is stable when heated, but will leak into cooking water. The process of pasteurisation results in milk losing about 20 per cent of its riboflavin content. Alkalis, such as baking soda (sodium bicarbonate), also destroy riboflavin.

Figure 2.29 *Leafy vegetables are rich in vitamin B2*

Sources of vitamin B2

Riboflavin is found inside every animal and vegetable cell. Its presence inside cells ensure riboflavin is found in a wide range of foods, including poultry, lean meat, eggs, milk, fish, yoghurt, yeast, soy beans, legumes, almonds, leafy green vegetables and fortified breads and cereals.

Functions of vitamin B2

- Riboflavin is essential for releasing energy from food.

- It is vital for growth and development of the body and is involved in the production of red blood cells and hormones.

- Riboflavin helps to keep skin, eyes, the nervous system and mucous membranes healthy.

Symptoms of deficiency

Riboflavin deficiency is rare in the developed world. However, where there is a shortage of food in developing countries, symptoms of riboflavin deficiency will be evident among children. These symptom include skin disorders, dry and cracked lips, bloodshot eyes and poor growth.

Other groups likely to suffer riboflavin deficiency are older people with a poor diet and people who exercise excessively.

Symptoms of excess

No toxic side effects of excessive intake of riboflavin have been reported. Riboflavin is a water-soluble vitamin, so excess amounts are excreted in the urine.

Vitamin B3 (niacin)

Niacin or vitamin B3 is sometimes referred to as nicotinic acid. It is a water-soluble vitamin that is slightly more stable when heated than either thiamin and riboflavin.

Figure 2.30 *Foods rich in vitamin B3*

Sources of vitamin B3

Niacin is found in a wide range of foods including poultry, lean meat, peanuts, pulses, potatoes, milk, eggs, broccoli, carrots, avocados, tomatoes, dates, sweet potatoes and mushrooms. A significant amount of niacin is lost during the milling process to convert grains into flour. As a result, white and brown bread flours and some breakfast cereals are fortified with niacin by food manufacturers.

In addition to food sources, niacin can be made in the body by the amino acid tryptophan. Foods containing a good source of tryptophan, and therefore contributing to niacin intake, include eggs, milk and cheese.

Functions of vitamin B3

- Niacin is essential in the metabolism of carbohydrates, fats and proteins to produce the energy used for body growth.

- Niacin maintains a healthy skin and keeps the digestive and nervous system working well.

- It is essential to the production of hormones including oestrogen and insulin.

Symptoms of deficiency

Daily supplies of niacin are required and an increased intake is required during pregnancy and lactation. Deficiency is very rare in developed countries but a serious condition called **pellagra** can develop in individuals who lack niacin in their diet. The symptoms of pellagra can be identified as the 'three D's':

- dermatitis – a disorder producing rough red skin on the neck, hands and feet

- dementia – including loss of memory and depression

- diarrhoea – including abdominal pains and a loss of appetite.

Symptoms of excess

Continual high doses of niacin can lead to liver damage and peptic ulcers.

Activity 2.16

Investigative opportunity

Figure 2.31

Look at a selection of breakfast cereal packets and produce a table showing the amount of vitamins found in a single serving of each product.

Which breakfast cereals are the 'best' sources of vitamins? You should also consider which cereals contain high levels of sugar and minerals.

Vitamin B6 (pyridoxine)

Vitamin B6 or pyridoxine is the name given to a range of compounds involved in metabolism and the maintenance of the immune system. Vitamin B6 is lost in cooking water and is destroyed by heat, sunlight and air.

Sources of vitamin B6

Vitamin B6 is found in lean meat, eggs, chicken, fish, beans, nuts, whole grains and cereals, bananas and avocados.

Functions of vitamin B6

- Vitamin B6 is required for the formation of red blood cells and helps to maintain nerve function.

- Vitamin B6 has an important role in the immune system and the formation of antibodies.

- Vitamin B6 is required for the use and storage of energy from proteins and carbohydrates. It assists with the conversion of the amino acid tryptophan to niacin.

Symptoms of deficiency

A deficiency of vitamin B6 has been associated with skin disorders including dermatitis and acne, mouth sores, confusion, depression and anaemia.

Symptoms of excess

There has been concern over the large quantities of vitamin B6 taken as a supplement by some individuals. Taking large amounts of vitamin B6 each day over a long period can lead to **peripheral neuropathy**. This is a condition which can cause damage to the nerves that run from the brain and spinal cord to the rest of the body. Peripheral neuropathy can cause a loss of feeling in the arms and legs, or a tingling and numbness in the hands and feet. The condition is usually reversible if the high dose is stopped.

Vitamin B12

Vitamin B12 is a water-soluble vitamin which is stable when heated to 100°C but it is sensitive to sunlight. Vitamin B12 is also known as **cyanocobalamin** and **cobalamin**.

Figure 2.32 *Shellfish are a source of vitamin B12*

Sources of vitamin B12

Vitamin B12 is found mostly in animal products including eggs, shellfish, poultry, meat, dairy produce and liver. There is no vitamin B12 in vegetables or cereals so many cereal products are fortified with it.

Lacto vegetarians must consume dairy products to receive adequate daily supplies and vegans should consume cereals fortified with vitamin B12 or tempeh (fermented soybeans).

Functions of vitamin B12

- Vitamin B12 is used in the metabolism of fats, proteins and carbohydrates for cell growth.

- It is involved in the metabolism of folic acid and the maintenance of the nervous system.

- Vitamin B12 is needed for the manufacture of red blood cells and supports the immune system.

Symptoms of deficiency

Vitamin B12 deficiency is known as **pernicious anaemia**. The body needs iron, vitamin B12 and folic acid to produce a regular supply of red blood cells. A lack of one or more of these nutrients can result in pernicious anaemia. Pernicious anaemia is most common in the elderly and vegans. The symptoms include tiredness and fatigue, tingling and numbness in the hands and feet, loss of memory, chest pain and confusion. It can take several years for the symptoms to develop and they are reversible if treated promptly.

Vitamin B12 is vital for a healthy nervous system, which is why a deficiency can also cause inflammation of the nerves and mental deterioration.

Symptoms of excess

An excess of vitamin B12 is stored in the liver and excreted in the urine each day. There are no known harmful effects.

Folic acid

Figure 2.34 *Bread may be fortified with folic acid*

Figure 2.33 *Many vegetables are sources of folic acid*

Folic acid is part of a family of compounds called folates. Folic acid is a water-soluble vitamin and leaches into cooking water during boiling. Daily supplies are required to maintain health.

Sources of folic acid

Many vegetables contain folic acid including spinach, sprouts, broccoli, green beans and potatoes. Pulses, peas and beans are also a good source. Some bread and breakfast cereals are fortified with folic acid.

Fortification

'Fortification' or a 'fortified food' refers to the addition of one or more nutrients to a food, whether or not it is normally contained in the food. It makes the food a 'richer' source of nutrients.

Mandatory fortification is the addition of a nutrient to a food product by law. During the Second World War, there was concern about public health and the need to ensure the nation remained healthy if food supplies

became restricted. To address this concern certain vitamins and minerals were added to white and brown flour (niacin, thiamin, iron and calcium) and margarine (Vitamin A and D). Many vitamins are also added to infant milk powders.

The purpose of mandatory fortification of bread and flour with folic acid is to reduce the number of neural tube defects (see below). In 2007, the Food Standards Agency agreed that mandatory fortification of bread and flour with folic acid should be introduced in the UK. This has meant the folic acid intake of everyone who eats bread and flour products in the UK, including pregnant women, has increased.

However, there is concern that the fortification of bread will conceal vitamin B12 deficiency in the elderly. According to SACN, in the UK vitamin B12 deficiency is common in people aged 65 years and over, and is usually caused by a failure of the intestine to absorb vitamin B12. Folic acid can hide a vitamin B12 deficiency by improving one of the symptoms of the vitamin B12 deficiency, pernicious anaemia. This can make it difficult for a doctor to spot the vitamin B12 deficiency disease in an older person. If someone has a prolonged undiagnosed vitamin B12 deficiency, it can cause damage to the nervous system and lead to severe disability.

Activity 2.17

Discussion

Is the fortification of bread and flour with folic acid a good idea?

Functions of folic acid

- Pregnant women need a good supply of folic acid. The development of the spinal cord in the embryo requires a regular supply of folic acid. Ideally, folic acid should be consumed every day before conception and for the first 12 weeks of pregnancy to meet this need.

- Folic acid is essential for the formation of red blood cells.

- Folic acid works with vitamin B12 in the process of cell division.

Symptoms of deficiency

Folic acid can reduce the risk of having a baby born with **spina bifida**. Spina bifida means 'split spine' and is often referred to as a neural tube defect. The series of small bones that make up the backbone are designed to protect the spinal cord. In spina bifida, the backbones do not close round the spinal cord and the nerves may bulge out and become damaged.

The Scientific Advisory Committee on Nutrition (SACN) estimates that there are between 700 and 900 pregnancies affected by neural tube defects each year. It is thought that many affected pregnancies are terminated. Taking a folic acid supplement may prevent the development of the condition in many of these pregnancies. Pregnant women or those thinking of having a baby should take 0.4 mg (400 micrograms) of folic acid each day.

Symptoms of excess

Symptoms of excess folic acid intake are rare but include gastrointestinal problems and sleep disturbances. As mentioned elsewhere, some research suggests that large amounts of folic acid can mask or hide the damaging effects of vitamin B12 deficiency and the development of pernicious anaemia.

Vitamin C (ascorbic acid)

Vitamin C is a water-soluble vitamin which can be stored in the liver and body tissues in limited supplies. It is commonly referred to as **ascorbic acid.**

Sources of vitamin C

The main source of vitamin C is fresh fruit and vegetables. Good sources include citrus fruits (oranges,

Figure 2.35 *Citrus fruits are sources of vitamin C*

lemons, limes, and tangerines), cantaloupe melon, strawberries, blackcurrants, green peppers, tomatoes, broccoli, kiwi fruit, dark green leafy vegetables and peppers.

Potatoes are a significant source of vitamin C in the UK diet because they are consumed in large quantities. An average serving of boiled new potatoes will provide 90 per cent of the recommended daily intake of vitamin C.

Functions of vitamin C

- Vitamin C is required for growth and helps to make collagen, an important protein found in skin, ligaments, and the walls of blood vessels.

- It is essential for repair of body tissues including the healing of wounds and development of scar tissue.

- Vitamin C is required for the repair and maintenance of cartilage, bones, and teeth.

- Vitamin C assists in the formation of red blood cells by helping the absorption of iron from the intestines. Iron is an important building block of red blood cells.

- Vitamin C has a vital role in the immune system and the function of lymphocytes to fight infections.

- Vitamin C is an antioxidant. It works with vitamin E, another antioxidant, to block some of the damage caused by free radicals, which are by-products that result when the body converts food into energy. This action may reduce the risk of coronary heart disease.

Symptoms of deficiency

Deficiency of vitamin C makes the individual more prone to infection, slows the metabolism and reduces the appetite. Wounds are slower to heal and dental and gum problems can develop.

Vitamin C has a protective role in the body and helps to prevent the deficiency disease **scurvy**. This disease was first discovered in sailors, whose lengthy sea voyages left them without adequate supplies of fresh fruit and vegetables for extended periods. When body stores of vitamin C fall below 300 milligrams, spongy gums, tooth loss and bleeding from all mucous membranes will develop.

Symptoms of excess

Taking large amounts of vitamin C can cause stomach pain and diarrhoea.

Effects of storage, preparation and cooking

Vitamin C is found in the watery parts of fruits and vegetables and we will now explore how vitamin C can be retained in fruit and vegetables during storage,

Figure 2.36 *Pre-packed salads retain vitamin C for longer*

preparation and cooking. All water-soluble vitamins are easily dissolved in water and unstable and are affected by a range of factors including heat, light, alkalinity, oxygen, enzyme activity. Vitamin C is the most sensitive vitamin to destruction by these factors. Fruit and vegetables are a good source of vitamin C and can be exposed to these factors, thereby reducing their vitamin content.

Storage

Condition of the fruit and vegetables

Avoid purchasing bruised or damaged fruit and vegetables as cell walls are broken and enzymes released. All fruit and vegetables contain enzymes that control the processes of ripening and spoilage. The enzyme **ascorbic acid oxidase** will destroy the vitamin C content. Ascorbic acid oxidase is released from plant cells by bruising, cutting and slicing, and exposure to the air destroys vitamin C. However, in some fruits there is less enzyme action and many of the enzymes are neutralised by the natural acids contained in the fruit or vegetables.

Age of fruit and vegetables

The quantity of vitamin C can vary according to the age and variety of the fruit and vegetables, so always choose young fruit and vegetables, as they will contain the greatest quantity of vitamin C. Unripe fruit is much lower in vitamin C than ripe fruit. The ideal fruit is harvested ripe and eaten shortly afterwards. The amount of vitamin C present in vegetables is greatest during periods of rapid growth in spring and early summer.

Use shortly after purchase

Ripening will continue after purchase and exposure to light and warmth will accelerate the loss of vitamin C. Homemade fruit juices should be consumed within two to three days as the vitamin C content will fall due to oxidation, even in refrigerated conditions. Cut raw fruits and vegetables should be stored in an airtight container or bag and refrigerated for only a short period. Pre-packed bags of salad usually have a modified atmosphere, which slows the process of oxidation down, but once opened will deteriorate rapidly and vitamin C loss will be significant.

Store in cool, dark places

Enzymes are active at room temperature and this is why most fruits and vegetables should be stored in the refrigerator to reduce the amount of deterioration that will occur after purchase. As mentioned above, the action of ascorbic acid oxidase is slowed but not stopped by refrigeration. Sunlight can also destroy vitamin C and although the quantities of vitamin C found in milk are not large, leaving milk exposed to sunlight will reduce its vitamin C content.

Preparation

Minimal preparation

Every time you cut, slice or chop fruit and vegetables cells walls are damaged and enzymes released which destroy vitamin C. Rip or tear when possible as this reduces cell wall damage. Using a blunt knife will also damage more cells than necessary, so use a sharp, stainless steel vegetable knife.

Cook potatoes in their skins to reduce damage to cell walls. Peeling and soaking potatoes before cooking will increase the amount of vitamin C lost. Research suggests that peeled potatoes lose 10 per cent more vitamin C than unpeeled during boiling.

Vitamin loss is greater when vegetables are cut into small pieces. Smaller pieces have more surface area exposed to the air and greater cell damage, which releases more enzymes for oxidation. Avoid fine chopping, slicing and dicing to retain more vitamin C.

Blanching

The process of freezing slows down enzyme activity but does not prevent it. The only way to prevent enzyme activity is blanching. **Blanching** is immersing the prepared fruit and vegetables in boiling water or steam for a specific amount of time and then cooling rapidly. About 25 per cent of the vitamin C in vegetables can be lost by blanching but the process will destroy more enzymes that would otherwise continue their activity even when frozen.

Processing methods

The process of pasteurisation reduces the vitamin C content of fruit juices and milk. Food manufacturers voluntarily fortify some fruit juices with vitamin C to restore their vitamin content.

Figure 2.37 *Some juices are fortified with vitamin C*

There is a significant loss of vitamin C in dried foods. It is estimated that 50 per cent of vitamin C is removed with the water during the drying process.

The canning process results in some loss of vitamin C in fruit and vegetables. However, the fruit and vegetables chosen for the canning process are very fresh and in prime condition so losses are not as large as expected. Canned tomatoes, gooseberries or blackcurrants retain a significant amount of vitamin C and are often overlooked as an important source.

Cooking

Avoid cooking and eat raw

Research suggests that as much as 75 per cent of the vitamin C found in green vegetables is lost during cooking. Around 25 per cent of the vitamin C is lost by simply boiling or steaming food for a few minutes. Serve fruits and vegetables raw whenever possible.

Avoid soaking in cold water

Because vitamin C is water soluble, it will leach out of fruit and vegetables if they are placed in water. Washing and soaking fruit and vegetables before cooking considerably reduces their vitamin C content.

Use minimal amounts of water

The smallest amount of water should be used in cooking vegetables to prevent vitamin C from dissolving away. Generally, the more water used the more water-soluble vitamin will be lost. Some vegetables such as cabbage and spinach have a much larger surface area from which the vitamin can be lost. When cooking leafy vegetables, use a small quantity of water, avoid immersing all the leaves in the water and use a saucepan with a lid, as the steam generated will complete the cooking process quickly. Peeled and chopped potatoes have a smaller surface area than leafy vegetables, and the gelatinisation of the starch reduces the movement and loss of some vitamin C.

Place fruit and vegetables in boiling water

By placing vegetables into a small amount of very hot water immediately after preparation, the enzyme oxidase is destroyed before it can have a significant effect on the vitamin C content of the vegetables. When vegetables are placed in cold water and brought to the boil slowly, the enzyme can destroy a large proportion of the vitamin C before the heat destroys the enzyme. In addition, a large amount of the vitamin C will leach out into the water, as the cooking process is extended. The use of the cooking water to make gravies, soups and sauces can help to ensure that some of these water-soluble vitamins are consumed.

Reduce cooking time

Always cook fruit or vegetables for the minimum time required as a prolonged cooking process can reduce the vitamin C content. Use a tightly fitting saucepan lid on the saucepan to speed up the cooking process. If the vegetables require mashing or pureeing after cooking this should be completed immediately and the food served at once; further processing after cooking prolongs the rate of oxidation.

Choose an appropriate cooking method and equipment

All cooking methods reduce vitamin C content. Steaming uses very little water so in theory the loss of water-soluble vitamins should be smaller. However, if longer cooking times are required more vitamin C will be destroyed.

Figure 2.38 *Stir frying helps retain vitamin C content*

The use of a pressure cooker is probably the most effective cooking method to use when cooking fruit and vegetables to conserve vitamins. The pressure cooker increases the temperature at which water boils to 120°C. Although some vitamin C is lost due to the increase in temperature, the significant shortening of the cooking time retains vitamin C.

Cooking utensils made of Pyrex, stainless steel, aluminum or enamel or lined with a nonstick coating have little effect on vitamin content. The use of iron or unlined copper saucepans can destroy vitamin C.

Avoid adding bicarbonate of soda to cooking water

Vitamin C or ascorbic acid is a weak acid and is easily destroyed by a mild alkali such as bicarbonate of soda. Bicarbonate of soda may be added to preserve the green colour in cooked vegetables and help reduce acidity when stewing sour plums or rhubarb, but this will destroy the vitamin C.

Serve immediately

To avoid further vitamin C loss, cooked vegetables should not be kept warm for long periods before serving. Research suggests that approximately 25 per cent of the vitamin C of cooked vegetables is lost by keeping vegetables warm for 15 minutes, and 75 per cent on keeping them warm for 90 minutes. Avoid reheating food, as this will reduce vitamin C further.

Activity 2.18

Review

The table below shows the amount of vitamin C found in different types of potatoes and after different cooking methods had been applied.

Each of the batches of potatoes was prepared as described and the vitamin content measured.

Potatoes	Vitamin C (mg/100g)
Raw potatoes (new spring)	63
Raw potatoes (old winter)	50
Plunged into 200 ml boiling water, lid on pan, boiled for 15 minutes	35
Soaked for 2 hours, plunged into 200 ml boiling water, lid on pan, boiled for 15 minutes	21
Plunged into 200 ml boiling water, lid on pan, boiled for 60 minutes	8
Plunged into 1 litre boiling water, lid on pan, boiled for 15 minutes	20
Plunged into 200 ml cold water, lid on pan, boiled for 15 minutes	10
Plunged into 200 ml boiling water, lid on pan, boiled for 15 minutes, keep warm for 30 minutes after cooking	3

1 Which method of cooking retains the most vitamin C?
2 Which method of cooking and serving results in the greatest loss of vitamin C?
3 Look at the table and identify the factors that could affect the retention of vitamin C.
4 Vitamin C is destroyed by the release of enzymes during the preparation of potatoes. How can this be reduced?
5 Give one reason why new potatoes contain more vitamin C than old potatoes.
6 Describe the effect of mashing on the vitamin C content of potato.

Activity 2.19

Practical opportunity

Prepare a salad or vegetable dish demonstrating the skills required in food storage, preparation and cooking to retain vitamin C.

Vitamin supplements

As mentioned at the beginning of this section, vitamins are substances that are essential in tiny quantities for energy release, growth and development. The need for vitamins in the diet is crucial, so to meet this need many people take vitamin supplements.

A Food Standards Agency (FSA) report stated that £220 million was spent on vitamin and mineral supplements in 2006. In addition, the report also revealed that 43

Figure 2.39 *Vitamin supplements*

per cent of UK adults had taken vitamin or mineral supplements during the previous 12 months, with usage highest among the 50–65 age group. The most popular supplements in 2006 were cod-liver oil capsules and multivitamins. However, sales of 'mega dose' vitamin and minerals supplements are increasing.

The dangers of vitamin overdose

Large doses of vitamins can have toxic effects. Vitamin A is a fat-soluble vitamin stored in the liver, but if consumed in large quantities it can eventually reach toxic levels and cause liver damage. The water-soluble vitamin C can cause diarrhoea at levels of 2000 mg a day; some people consume large amounts in the hope of preventing the common cold.

Groups that may need vitamin supplements

Experts suggest that apart from small groups of people with special dietary needs, most people do not need to take vitamin supplements. We receive adequate vitamins from eating a balanced diet.

Women who are planning to get pregnant

The government advises women who are planning to get pregnant to consume folic acid supplements. Women who have conceived should continue taking the supplement for the first 12 weeks of pregnancy. Folic acid is believed to prevent the development of spina bifida.

People with limited exposure to sunlight

Some groups of people may have limited exposure to sunlight and therefore lack vitamin D. This includes Asian women who may be required to keep their skin covered for cultural reasons and housebound elderly people. Vitamin D can be taken in supplement form to avoid deficiency.

Vegans

A vegan is a type of vegetarian who does not eat any animal flesh or animal products, including fish, dairy products or eggs. Vegans may need to take vitamin B12 in tablet form to reduce the risk of pernicious anaemia.

People who are malnourished due to illness

Illness or surgery can cause some people to have difficulty eating or swallowing. They may be advised to take supplements to ensure they maintain a balanced diet.

Elderly people

Increasing age does not automatically create the need to take vitamin supplements. However, supplements are necessary if an individual has problems eating due to loss of appetite or problems with chewing, swallowing or digestion.

Athletes in training

Some people undertaking intense training or sporting activities may need to take extra vitamins to support their increased energy requirements.

Concentrating on single vitamins as a key to good health is a mistake. Health is best promoted through a balanced diet. Many studies have shown that vitamin supplements do not affect the body in the same way as the vitamins found in food. For the general population, the most important advice is to increase fresh fruit and vegetable consumption, as these are rich in both vitamins and minerals.

Healthy Start scheme

Figure 2.40 *The Healthy Start logo*

Healthy Start is a government-funded scheme launched in November 2006. Low-income families are issued with vouchers every week, which can be exchanged for milk, fresh fruit, fresh vegetables and infant formula milk. Free vitamin supplements are available on this scheme. These are provided for vitamins A, C and D for children, and vitamins C and D and folic acid for pregnant and lactating women.

Activity 2.20

Research opportunity

Investigate the range of vitamin supplements at one of the following: supermarket, internet retailer or specialist retailer.

Record the range of vitamin supplements offered and their cost.

Look at the key vitamins and examine the suggested dosage and compare the products to the RNI.

What marketing claims are made? Are there any warnings about excessive intake?

Activity 2.21

Review by case study

Each of the following people is suffering from a vitamin deficiency disease.

Read each case study and name the vitamin that may be deficient.

Suggest some remedial actions that could be taken to the diet or lifestyle to prevent or reduce the symptoms.

Joe – student

Joe has spent most of his student loan on beer and junk food. Money has been in short supply recently and Joe has purchased a large quantity of rolled oats which he consumes twice a day as porridge. At least he isn't hungry anymore! He has started to suffer with dental problems and sore gums. His skin has deteriorated and become dry, wounds have failed to heal and old scars have started to break down.

Jack – pensioner

Jack was admitted to hospital after a fall which resulted in a fracture to his hip. He had been feeling generally weak for six months before the fall and had bone pains, often in the back, hips or legs. Recently this has developed into muscle pains and weakness. Jack does not enjoy cooking and seems to exist on cakes and biscuits. Jack often stays indoors during the day.

Josie – vegan

Josie is fifty and is a strict vegan. She eats no dairy products and meat. She does eat a plentiful supply of fresh fruit and vegetables. Over the last year, she has started to suffer with digestive problems and has been feeling tired, looking pale and becoming easily breathless. She has also experienced numbness and tingling sensations in her fingers.

CHECK YOUR UNDERSTANDING

1 Check you understand the meaning of the following key terms. Write a sentence using each word.

antioxidants	ascorbic acid oxidase
beri beri	rhodopsin
rickets	blanching
scurvy	cholecalciferol
fat-soluble vitamins	osteomalacia
peripheral neuropathy	deficiency disease
niacin	thiamin
spina bifida	sunshine vitamin
tocopherols	water-soluble vitamins
β-carotene	riboflavin
pernicious anaemia	fortification
retinol	free radicals
night blindness	

2 Complete the following exercise using some of the key words and phrases shown above.

There are two main groups of vitamins – _____ and _____. Vitamin B1 is also known as _____. A deficiency of Vitamin B1 is called _____ _____. This disease is very rare in developing countries. The over-consumption of vitamin B6 has been associated with the condition _____ _____. Vitamin B12 deficiency is linked to the condition _____ _____. The other B vitamins _____ and _____ are usually in good supply as the _____ of cereal products and flour is completed by food manufacturers.

Vitamin C is associated with the deficiency disease _____. The enzyme _____ _____ _____ will destroy vitamin C in fruit and vegetables.

Vitamin A is found in two forms _____ and _____. Vitamin A helps to make a substance called _____, this helps vision in poor light. The fat-soluble _____ _____ works with calcium to produce strong bones and teeth. A deficiency of vitamin D in children is called _____ and in adults is called _____.

Section 5   Minerals

Introduction

About 6 per cent of the body is made up of minerals – inorganic substances required by the body for a variety of reasons. Some minerals are needed in larger amounts than others and these are called the **major minerals**. There are eight major minerals:

1 iron

2 calcium

3 phosphorus

4 magnesium

5 sodium

6 potassium

7 zinc

8 chloride.

Others such as manganese, chromium, cobalt, iodine, fluoride, selenium and copper are required in smaller quantities and are called **trace elements**. Trace elements are no less important than other minerals; they are simply needed in smaller quantities.

Eating a balanced and varied diet will ensure an adequate supply of most minerals for healthy people. The minerals studied at A2 in unit G004 Nutrition and Food Production, are:

● iron

● calcium

● phosphorus

● potassium

● zinc

● magnesium

● fluoride

● sodium

● iodine.

Each person has different requirements for minerals – the RNI for minerals is found in Chapter 1. However, it should be noted that some groups of people may have higher requirements for certain minerals, for example, those suffering from certain medical conditions, those recovering from illness and some athletes. It is important that these groups of people receive sufficient amounts of the mineral they are at risk of being deficient in.

Function of minerals

Figure 2.41 *Minerals aid development of the skeleton*

● Minerals are required for the formation and development of the skeleton and teeth.

● Minerals in the form of soluble salts control the essential constituents of body fluids and cells.

● The components of enzyme systems require certain minerals.

● The clotting of blood requires certain minerals.

● Minerals are required for the normal functioning of muscles and nerves.

Iron

A healthy adult body contains about 4 g of iron, which is found in haemoglobin, myoglobin, the liver, spleen and bone marrow. Iron accounts for about 0.1 per cent of the mineral elements in the body. Iron is stored in the liver, spleen and bone marrow. This store is an important source of iron for babies, because a baby's diet in the first six months of life consists only of milk, which contains very little iron.

Sources of iron

Figure 2.42 *Meat is a good source of iron*

Iron is found in animal and plant sources. Iron from animal sources (**haem iron**) is better absorbed than iron from plant sources (**non-haem iron**). The main sources of iron are meat, offal, dried fruit, red kidney beans, curry powder, cocoa, bread, cereal products, potatoes and vegetables. In the UK bread and many breakfast cereals are fortified with iron, and these make a valuable contribution to iron intake.

Absorption of iron

Only about 10 per cent of the iron consumed is actually absorbed by the body. Non-haem iron is present in the food as ferric iron, which cannot be absorbed by the body. Before it can be absorbed, it has to be changed into ferrous iron. Vitamin C is required in this process.

Non-haem iron also readily binds with other substances present in food and as a consequence the iron reacts with the substance and an insoluble complex is formed that cannot be absorbed by the body. This ultimately hinders the absorption of iron.

The table below shows how iron combines with substances found in particular foods to form new complexes that hinder the absorption of iron.

Iron combines with this substance	Food source (i.e the substance is found in these foods)	Insoluble complex formed hindering the absorption of iron
Oxalate	Spinach	Iron oxalate
Phosphate	Rhubarb, egg yolk	Iron phosphate
Phytate	Wholegrain cereals, pulses	Iron phytate
Tannin	Tea, pulses, spices, condiments	Iron tannate

Source: Adapted from Jill Davies, Cooking Explained, *published by Longman, 1997*

The table below shows the iron content in milligrams per 100 grams of some types of food.

Food	Iron content mg per 100 g
Eggs	2
White bread	1.7
Wholemeal flour	4
Spinach	1.6
Boiled potatoes	0.4
Pigs kidney (fried)	9.1
Oats	3.8
Cooked beef	3
Lambs liver (fried)	7.7
Canned sardines	2.3
Cheddar cheese	0.4

Source: Adapted from Michael E. J. Lean, Food Science, Nutrition and Health, *7th ed. published by Hodder Arnold (2006)*

Activity 2.22

Review

- Rearrange the table in descending order with the highest amount of iron per 100 g of food first. What can you conclude from this table?

Functions of iron

- Iron is needed for the formation of haemoglobin in red blood cells, which transport oxygen from the lungs to body tissues.

- Iron is required for normal energy metabolism, and for metabolism of drugs and foreign substances that need to be removed from the body.

- The immune system also requires iron for normal function.

Symptoms of deficiency

A lack of iron leads to low iron stores in the body and eventually to iron deficiency anaemia. Some iron is present in the muscle protein myoglobin; the rest of the iron content in our body is stored in the spleen, liver and bone marrow. When there is insufficient iron in the bloodstream, the body uses bone marrow reserves. If the iron stored in the bone marrow is low, red blood cells do not form properly and as a consequence less haemoglobin is available to transport oxygen throughout the body. The symptoms of this are fatigue, dizziness, irritability, headaches, difficulty in concentrating, shortness of breath during exercise, a pale appearance, brittle nails, and cracked lips.

Loss of blood due to injury or large menstrual losses increases iron requirements. Women of childbearing age and teenage girls should ensure that they have enough iron in their diet to compensate for iron losses during menstruation.

Symptom of excess

Large quantities of iron can be harmful. Iron is stored as ferritin but if too much iron is stored as ferritin then siderosis, which causes heart and liver damage, can occur. This is extremely rare in the UK but can occur in countries such as Africa because of the use of iron cooking pots in which cereals such as maize are cooked.

Activity 2.23

Investigation

Anaemia can be a problem for teenage girls. Explain what is meant by anaemia and describe what can be done to reduce the risk of anaemia.

What iron-rich foods should be included in the diet of a person suffering from anaemia?

What advice on diet would you give to teenage girls?

Write a report on your findings (maximum 500 words).

Activity 2.24

Practical opportunity

Choose an interesting dish that is high in iron and which would appeal to a teenage girl.

Calculate the iron content of the dish and its contribution to the amount of iron needed per day for a teenage girl.

In your next practical lesson make your chosen dish.

Calcium

Figure 2.43 *Milk, yoghurt and cheese are sources of calcium*

Calcium and phosphorus account for about 75 per cent of the mineral elements in the body. A sufficient supply of calcium is crucial for health, particularly in times of growth, such as childhood, adolescence, pregnancy, and also during lactation (breastfeeding).

Sources of calcium

Calcium is found in milk, cheese, yoghurt and other dairy products (but not butter). White and brown flour are fortified with calcium by law, so bread and other products made from white and brown flour are important sources of calcium in the UK diet. Calcium is also found in some vegetables such as broccoli, fish (if the bones are eaten, e.g. sardines, canned salmon), almonds and brazil nuts, pulses, soya products such as tofu and tempeh, and sesame seeds.

The table below shows the calcium content in milligrams per 100 grams of some types of food.

Food	Calcium content mg per 100 g
Cheese	739
Milk	118
Boiled eggs	57
Butter	18
Canned sardines	540
Raw white fish	14
Raw beef	5
White bread	177
Wholemeal bread	106
Boiled rice	18
Boiled spinach	160
Oranges	47
Boiled cabbage	33
Boiled old potatoes	5
Apples	4

Source: Adapted from Food Science, Nutrition and Health, *published by Hodder Arnold*

Activity 2.25

Review

Rearrange the table in descending order with the highest amount of calcium per 100 g of food first. What can you conclude from this table?

Absorption of calcium

Calcium is easily absorbed from milk and dairy products because:

- vitamin D promotes the absorption of calcium

- when protein is broken down into amino acids during the digestive process, it combines with calcium to form calcium salts which are easily absorbed

- lactose (the sugar present in milk) increases calcium absorption.

Calcium is less easily absorbed from plant foods because:

- the calcium may be bound by phytates found in wholegrain cereals and pulses, and oxalates found in spinach and rhubarb

- fibre also binds calcium

- saturated fatty acids form insoluble soaps with calcium.

Functions of calcium

- Calcium is the main constituent of **hydroxyapatite**, the principal mineral essential for building and maintaining healthy bones and teeth.

- Calcium is needed for contraction of the muscles, including the maintenance of a regular heart beat, and for nerve function.

- It is involved in blood clotting.

- It is needed for the activity of several enzymes.

Symptoms of deficiency

Calcium deficiency symptoms include muscle aches and pains, muscle twitching and spasm, muscle cramps and reduced bone density. Vitamin D is essential for proper absorption and utilisation of calcium. Too little calcium in the diet of children can result in stunted growth and rickets. In adults, too little calcium in the diet can result in osteomalacia. Both conditions cause softening and weakening of the bones and can result in a tendency to fractures.

As people age, some loss of calcium from bone is normal and bone mass slowly decreases. Severe loss can lead to bones that are weak, brittle and easily broken – a condition known as osteoporosis, that frequently affects older women. Calcium intake is important in achieving peak bone mass in early life, but it is equally important for older women who may be at risk from osteoporosis.

Symptoms of excess

High intakes of vitamin D can cause calcium to be deposited in the soft tissues of the body causing **hypercalcaemia**. The symptoms of hypercalcaemia are loss of appetite, nausea, vomiting, thirst and alternating diarrhoea and constipation.

Phosphorus

Phosphorus is present in all body cells, with the majority found in bones and teeth.

Sources of phosphorus

Phosphorus is found in many foods but the main sources are milk and milk products, bread and other

Figure 2.44 *Bread is a source of phosphorus*

cereal products, meat and meat products. Phosphates are added to a number of processed foods.

Functions of phosphorus

- Phosphorus is essential for bone and tooth structure. Calcium phosphate provides the strength of bones and teeth.

- It is needed for the release of energy from cells. When glucose is oxidized, the energy produced is stored in phosphate compounds that break down to give energy when required.

Symptoms of deficiency

Phosphorus is found in so many foods that it is unlikely to be in short supply in UK diets; dietary deficiency is therefore unknown.

Symptom of excess

Unmodified cow's milk should not be given to babies, as it contains more phosphorus and calcium than human milk. The high phosphorous content of cow's milk may reduce the absorption of calcium, leading to twitching of the face, hands and feet, a condition known as tetany. Maintaining a balance between phosphorus and calcium is therefore important when feeding babies.

Potassium

Potassium is found in the fluids within the body cells.

Sources of potassium

Potassium is present in almost all foods; the main sources are potatoes, vegetables, fruit, bananas and juices.

Figure 2.45 *Bananas are a source of potassium*

Functions of potassium

- Potassium has a complementary action with sodium in the functioning of cells, including nerves.

- It is essential for water and electrolyte balance.

- Potassium has a beneficial blood pressure-lowering effect in people with raised blood pressure because it can counter the effects of sodium.

Symptoms of deficiency

Potassium is present in almost all foods so there is rarely a deficiency. Frequent use of diuretics or laxatives may result in large losses of potassium and in severe cases of deficiency, heart failure may occur.

Symptoms of excess

Most of the potassium is absorbed and any excess is excreted through the kidneys in the urine.

Zinc

Zinc is present in many enzymes, and is present in all tissues of the body.

Research has been carried out which suggests that selenium and zinc may form part of the body's defence against free radicals, by helping to protect against heart disease and some types of cancer. Free radicals are substances that have been linked to various chronic diseases. They are produced naturally by the body but are also present in cigarette smoke.

Sources of zinc

Figure 2.46 *Shell fish are a source of zinc*

Zinc is found in many foods but the main sources are red meat, fish (particularly shell fish), cheese, pulses and unrefined cereals. It is easily absorbed from meat, which provides about a third of the intake of zinc in the UK diet. Zinc is less easily absorbed if large amounts of phytic acid and fibre are consumed.

Functions of zinc

- Zinc is an essential constituent of over 100 enzymes, and plays a part in protein and carbohydrate metabolism.

- It is needed for the functioning of the immune system and in the structure and function of the skin and, therefore, in wound healing.

Symptoms of deficiency

The body is unable to store zinc, so a daily intake is required. A deficiency of zinc can lead to retarded physical and mental development in adolescents.

Delayed puberty and small stature have been linked to zinc deficiency, though it is unlikely this is due to zinc deficiency alone.

Symptoms of excess

Zinc excess is extremely rare, but zinc toxicity has occurred when water is stored in galvanised containers.

Magnesium

Magnesium is present in all tissues including bone, where it is present as magnesium phosphate.

Sources of magnesium

Figure 2.47 *Cabbage is a source of magnesium*

Magnesium is present in many foods, especially those which are vegetable in origin because magnesium is found in chlorophyll, the green pigment in plants. Therefore, dark green leafy vegetables are a rich source, but less than half is absorbed because much of it is bound and not readily available for absorption. Grains and nuts are also rich in magnesium.

Functions of magnesium

- Magnesium is an essential constituent of all cells and is needed for the functioning of some enzymes involved in normal energy metabolism and electrolyte balance.

- It is also needed for nerve, muscle and brain function.

Symptoms of deficiency

Magnesium deficiency is rare and is most likely to occur from excessive losses due to diarrhoea rather than from low intakes.

Symptom of excess

There are no known symptoms of excess.

Activity 2.26

Research and practical opportunity

Find **two** recipes for each of the following categories. Write out the recipe only, highlighting the mineral rich food.

- high in phosphorus
- high in potassium
- high in magnesium
- high in zinc.

In your next practical lesson, make one of the recipes you have found.

Fluoride

Figure 2.48 *Fluoride is added to water and toothpaste*

Fluoride is not found in many foods. In the UK, a small amount of fluoride is added to the water supply in areas where the fluoride content is low (about 1 part per million [ppm]).

The addition of fluoride to toothpaste is now very common and is especially important in those areas where the water supply is low in fluoride.

Sources of fluoride

Drinking water is an important source of fluoride; the only other sources in the diet are tea, fish where the bones are eaten (such as canned sardines or salmon), and seafood. Fluoride is also found in most types of toothpaste.

Functions of fluoride

Figure 2.49 *Fluoride helps prevent dental decay*

- Fluoride contributes to the maintenance of bone health by supporting bone mineralisation.
- By combining with calcium phosphate to form calcium fluorapatite, fluoride protects the teeth by hardening tooth enamel, thereby increasing resistance against dental decay (caries)
- Fluoride is especially important in the development of teeth in children under the age of eight.

Symptoms of deficiency

If fluoride is deficient in the diet, or not present in water, then there will be less protection against dental decay. In areas where water is fluoridated, the incidence of dental decay in children has fallen dramatically.

Symptoms of excess

Very large amounts of fluoride can cause mottling and crumbling of teeth, and changes to the bones – a condition called fluorosis.

Sodium

Sodium in the form of **sodium chloride** (salt) is found in both food and the body itself. According to the British Nutrition Foundation, the average intake of salt in the UK is 11.0 g/day for adult men and 8.1 g/day for adult women, compared with the recommendation of 6 g per day for adults (Scientific Advisory Committee on Nutrition, 2003). Intakes among children are also higher than the recommended amount of 3 g per day.

Figure 2.50 *Salt is added to food during and after cooking*

Work is underway to reduce the amount of salt present in the food supply. For example, a reduction in bread, soups and snacks has already been achieved and industry targets have been set for other foods, including meat products and biscuits.

The public also has a role to play, as about 20 per cent of salt consumed is added at home during cooking and at the table (source: www.nutrition.org.uk).

Sources of sodium

The sodium content of most raw foods is very low, but salt is often added to processed foods. Bacon, sausages, pies and most meat products are high in added salt. Kippers or smoked fish are high in salt. Salt is added to butter, margarine, canned vegetables, bread and breakfast cereals. In addition, people add salt to food when they cook, and may also add it at the table.

Functions of sodium

- Sodium and potassium are involved in the transmission of nerve impulses and muscle contraction.

- Sodium is present in the soft tissues and body fluids and helps regulate body water content and electrolyte balance.

Symptoms of deficiency

Low intakes of sodium results in muscle cramps; a deficiency of sodium is linked with heat exhaustion. Excess sweating, due to exercising in a warm environment for example, may cause sodium depletion. Therefore, sodium intake may need to be increased slightly for a short period to replace the sodium lost in sweat.

Symptoms of excess

Too much sodium in the diet may lead to high blood pressure, which is a risk factor for heart disease and stroke. A low salt diet may be used in the treatment of high blood pressure. Babies and young children cannot tolerate high sodium diets because their kidneys are not sufficiently developed to excrete the excess. It is important therefore that salt is not added to food given to babies and young children.

Activity 2.27

Research and ICT opportunity
Produce an informative leaflet on how to reduce the salt content of the diet. Include information on the problems that can occur with a diet too high in salt.

Iodine

Iodine is an essential constituent of hormones produced by the thyroid gland in the neck, but only 2.9 g of iodine is required in a lifetime.

Sources of iodine

The amount of iodine in plant foods such as vegetables and cereal grains depends upon how much is present in the soil or water. Rich sources of iodine are seafoods and edible seaweed; some iodine is also found in meat, eggs, milk and dairy products.

Functions of iodine

- Iodine is required for normal neurological development and for energy metabolism.

- Iodine is absorbed in the thyroid gland in the neck where it is converted into two hormones – triiodothyronine and thyroxine. These hormones control many metabolic processes and the rate of energy production in all cells.

Symptoms of deficiency

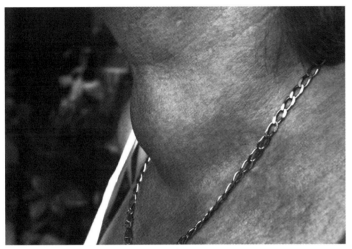

Figure 2.51 *Goitre is caused by iodine deficiency*

Insufficient iodine in the diet can result in the thyroid gland swelling to compensate. The swollen neck is called a **goitre**. Children born to severely iodine deficient mothers may be mentally retarded (cretinism). Nowadays, iodine deficiency is very rare in the UK; however, worldwide, iodine deficiency is one of the three biggest dietary deficiency diseases along with iron and vitamin A deficiency.

Symptom of excess

Excessive intakes of iodine can have toxic effects on the thyroid gland.

Activity 2.29

Research

Although the following trace elements are not studied as part of the A2 OCR specification, they are still needed in small amounts by the body.

Find out some information about the source, function, deficiency and excess of the following trace elements:

- selenium
- copper
- chromium
- manganese
- cobalt.

Interrelationship between iron and vitamin C

Vitamin C, present in fruit and vegetables, aids the absorption of iron because it reduces ferric iron to the absorbable ferrous state. (Most of the iron we eat is in the ferric state but in order to be absorbed adequately, it needs to be changed to a reduced ferrous state.)

Activity 2.28

Review/summary

Create two revision tables – one for the major minerals, the other for the trace elements. Use the headings shown below.

Do not use more than one side of A4 for both tables.

Mineral name	Function	Source	Symptoms of deficiency	Symptoms of excess

Figure 2.52 *Orange juice aids absorption of iron*

Vitamin C assists by promoting reduction to the ferrous state because it is a reducing agent. The blood carries absorbed iron to the bone marrow where some is used for the formation of red blood cells. Haem iron from meat and some fish is much better absorbed than the non-haem iron found in vegetables.

Activity 2.30

Review

In your own words, explain the effect that some foods have on the absorption of iron.

Interrelationship between calcium and vitamin D

Vitamin D is essential for calcium absorption along with the parathyroid hormone. A deficiency of vitamin D will result in poor calcium absorption, which in young children causes the disease rickets and in adults osteomalacia. Calcium, vitamin D and phosphorus are all needed for building and maintaining healthy bones and teeth.

CHECK YOUR UNDERSTANDING

Complete the following exercise using some of the key words and phrases shown below.

free radicals	trace elements	thyroxine	thyroid
iron	fluids	cells	enzyme
blood	potassium	nerves	salts
haemoglobin	calcium	hydroxyapatite	rickets
osteomalacia	tetany	muscles	selenium
major minerals	goitre	tooth enamel	calcium fluorapatite
sodium chloride	teeth	skeleton	metabolic processes
chlorophyll			

Some minerals are needed in larger amounts than others these are called the _____. Others are required in smaller quantities and are called _____. Overall minerals have the following general functions.

● The formation and development of the _____ and _____.

● As soluble _____ which control the essential constituents of body _____ and _____.

● The components of _____ systems.

● The clotting of _____.

● The normal functioning of _____ and _____.

_____ is needed for the formation of _____ in red blood cells, which transports oxygen from the lungs to body tissues. _____ is the main constituent of _____, the principal mineral in bones and teeth. Too little calcium in the diet of children can result in stunted growth and _____. In adults, too little calcium in the diet can result in _____. Phosphorus is present in all body cells and the majority is found bones and teeth. It is thought that the high phosphorous content of cow's milk may reduce the absorption of calcium. This then could lead to twitching of the face, hands and feet known as _____. _____ has a complementary action with sodium in the functioning of cells, including nerves. Zinc is present in many enzymes, and is present in all tissues of the body. Some research has been carried out which suggests that _____ and zinc may form part of the body's defences against _____. Fluoride protects teeth by hardening _____ by combining with calcium phosphate to form _____ increasing the resistance against dental decay (caries). In food and in the body sodium is present in salt as _____. Iodine is absorbed in the _____ gland in the neck where it is converted to two hormones – triidothyronine and _____. These hormones control many _____ and control the rate of energy production in all cells. If there is insufficient iodine in the diet, the thyroid gland swells to compensate. The swollen neck is called a _____. Magnesium is found in _____, the green pigment in plants. Therefore, dark green leafy vegetables are rich sources of magnesium.

CHECK YOUR UNDERSTANDING

Check you understand the meaning of the following key terms. Write a sentence using each word.

major minerals	trace elements	enzymes
haemoglobin	myoglobin	haem iron
non-haem iron	metabolism	menstruation
ferritin	siderosis	anaemia
hydroxyapatite	rickets	osteomalacia
osteoporosis	peak bone mass	hypercalcaemia
tetany	diuretic	laxative
free radicals	calcium fluorapatite	fluorosis
sodium chloride	triidothyronine	thyroxine
goitre	chlorophyll	

Section 6   Energy

Introduction

Energy is crucial for every process in the body – it is required for movement of all muscles, maintaining body temperature and transmitting nerve impulses. The body obtains energy from food. Glucose molecules from digested food combine with oxygen to produce energy. Large quantities of excess energy are stored as fat in the body.

In this section, we will explore the role of energy in the body and the sources in the diet. We will also investigate the factors affecting the amount of energy an individual requires and the consequences of consuming too much energy.

It is important to remember that energy is *not* a nutrient – the three main nutrients of fat, carbohydrates and protein *provide* energy. When these nutrients are digested, the energy is released. The amount of energy in each nutrient group varies:

- 1 g of fat gives 37 kJ/9 kcal

- 1 g carbohydrates give 16 kJ/3.75 kcal

- 1 g of protein gives 17 kJ/4 kcal.

Fats are the most energy dense.

Energy is measured in either kilocalories or kilojoules:

- a **kilocalorie** (Kcal) is a unit of heat. One kilocalorie is required to raise the temperature of 1 g of water by 1°C.

- **kilojoules** are much smaller units used for measuring energy. One calorie is equal to 4.18 kilojoules. A kilojoule is the international measurement used to work out how much energy is in food or how much energy is expended during exercise.

Why does the body need energy?

Most of the energy released in the body is used for essential processes. About 60–70 per cent of the energy consumed is required for the following processes:

- to keep the body warm – chemical reactions in the body produce heat

- to enable nerve cells to carry impulses from muscles to the brain, and the correct functioning of the brain

- to maintain breathing, pump blood around the body, excrete (remove) waste from the body and release hormones

- to digest, absorb, transport and store food

- to create body cells and tissues, fight infection and repair damage to tissues.

About 30–40 per cent of the energy consumed is needed for muscle movement. The single biggest use of energy by the body is in movement.

Figure 2.53 *Movement requires energy*

Sources of energy

Figure 2.54 *Energy-rich food*

Good sources of energy in the diet tend to be foods that are high in fat and sugar. They can be single foods including butter, margarine/spreads, cheese, cream, red meats, nuts and seeds, or oils from vegetable, nut and animal sources. Sugar and honey are also high in energy.

In addition, many manufactured food products contain high levels of energy. These include biscuits, cakes, confectionary and some carbonated drinks that are rich in sugar. Fatty foods including chocolate, pizza, pies and pastries are good sources of energy. Cooking food by frying and roasting can also increase its energy content.

Recommended nutrient sources of energy

The source of energy in the diet may increase the risk of certain diet-related diseases. The recommendations from the Committee on Medical Aspects of Food and Nutrition Policy (1991) (COMA) are still used today.

The table below shows the recommended population averages for protein, carbohydrate and fat as a percentage of total daily dietary energy and the average adult intakes.

Activity 2.31

Research opportunity

Investigate the energy content of the popular foods listed below. Each food represents a serving of 100 g.
Rank the foods from 1–12 in order of their energy content, with 1 being the greatest.
Use food tables (use a nutrition program or the internet) to compare your ranking to the actual energy content of the food products.

potato crisps	banana	cheddar cheese
apple	fried potatoes	stewed minced beef
ice cream	peanut butter	skimmed milk
white bread	red wine	grilled pork sausages

Which food contained the greatest and the least amount of energy?
Using the food tables, suggest a low-energy daily menu for a student. Calculate the energy content.
How does it compare to the Estimated Average Requirement for Energy (EAR) of 2755 kcal for a male aged 15–18 years and 2110 kcals for a female aged 15–18 years?

	Diet containing alcohol (recommended percentage)	Diet not containing alcohol (recommended percentage)	2000/2001 Average British adult intakes (actual percentages)	
			Men	**Women**
Protein	15	15	16.5	16.6
Total carbohydrate	47	50	47.7	48.5
– non-milk extrinsic sugars*	10	11	13.6	11.9
Total fat	33	35	35.8	34.9
– saturated fatty acids	10	11	13.4	13.2
– polyunsaturated fatty acids	6	6.5	6.4	6.3
– trans fatty acids	2	2	1.2	1.2
– monounsaturated fatty acids	12	13	12.1	11.5

*NMES – free sugar not bound in foods, e.g., table sugar, honey and sugars in fruit juices, but excluding milk sugar. Sugary foods and non-milk extrinsic sugars are the main causes of dental caries.
Alcohol should provide no more than 5 per cent of energy in the diet.

Sources: Department of Health (1991) *Dietary Reference Values for Food Energy and Nutrients in the United Kingdom,* HMSO, London.
The National Diet and Nutrition Survey: Adults Aged 19–64 years, (2003), HMSO, London.

In the table we see that the average total carbohydrate intakes are similar to the recommendations. However, intakes of non-milk extrinsic sugars such as those found in table sugar, drinks, preserves and confectionary, are higher than the COMA recommendation. The total dietary fat intake for women is just below the recommendation and intakes of trans fatty acids are well below the target level for both men and women. This is good news but more could be done to reduce saturated fat intake.

Energy balance

The energy balance is concerned with the intake of energy and the expenditure of energy by the body. When an individual's energy intake is equal to their energy expenditure, their body weight will remain stable. Individuals who consume more energy than required will, over time, gain weight and those who consume less energy than required will lose body weight. The concept of **energy balance** is concerned with having an energy intake that matches energy expenditure so there is no weight gain or loss. It is important because an imbalance can be associated with diet-related conditions such as obesity.

Energy requirements vary between individuals. The speed at which the body uses energy is known as the **metabolic rate**. Individuals with a fast metabolic rate burn energy more quickly. The **basal metabolic rate** (BMR) is the energy required for supporting the basic processes required for life, such as the heartbeat and maintaining body temperature.

Normal energy balance

This occurs when energy intake and expenditure is equal and balanced. This will result in a stable weight, with no weight gain or weight loss (see Figure 2.55).

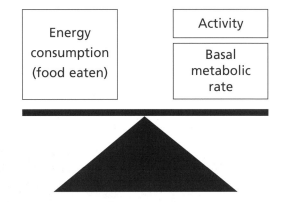

Figure 2.55 *Normal energy balance*

Negative energy balance

This occurs when energy intake or food intake is less than **energy expenditure**. In this situation, weight loss will occur because a negative energy balance is created (see Figure 2.56).

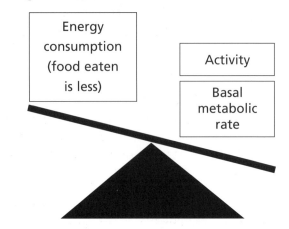

Figure 2.56 *Negative energy balance*

Positive energy balance

This occurs when energy intake is greater than energy expenditure. The surplus energy will be stored, resulting in weight gain.

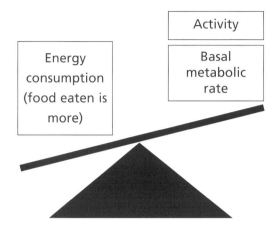

Figure 2.57 *Positive energy balance*

The basal metabolic rate is affected by a range of factors, which we will explore now.

Factors affecting individual energy requirements

Figure 2.58 *Babies have a higher metabolic rate*

Rate of growth and age

Young children have higher relative metabolic rates and require more energy in relation to their size than adults do. This is because they are generally more active and are growing rapidly. The energy required for growth is greatest during the first three months of life, when it accounts for about 35 per cent of energy requirements. This falls rapidly during childhood and mid-adolescence, when only 1–2 per cent of energy requirements are necessary for growth and by the late teens, the amount needed is insignificant.

The older we become the less energy we require. With increasing age energy requirements decrease, due in part to a reduction in physical activity and **lean body mass**. Lean body mass is everything in the body except fat – bone, organs, skin, nails and all body tissue including muscles and water.

Body size and gender

Men require more energy than women do because they tend to have a larger overall body size and surface area. In general, the larger the body size or surface area the greater the energy expenditure. Larger bodies require more energy to keep warm. Large muscles and long bones require more energy for movement than smaller body frames.

Activity level

Sedentary occupations including office workers, drivers, shop workers and those following an inactive lifestyle require less energy. Moderately active occupations including light industrial workers require more energy than sedentary occupations. By contrast, some very active occupations such as builders' labourers and steel workers require major physical exertion and therefore have the largest energy requirement.

Athletes who train for long periods will require a greater-than-average energy intake.

The amount of energy used to complete different activities varies. Some activities use more kilocalories than others because they exercise more muscles and require the body to work hard. Below are some examples of the amount of energy a person weighing 60 kg may use if completing the activity for 30 minutes.

Activity	Energy used
Ironing	69 kcal
Cleaning and dusting or walking (strolling)	75 kcal
Golf	129 kcal
Walking (briskly)	150 kcal
Cycling	180 kcal
Aerobics	195 kcal
Swimming (slow crawl)	195 kcal
Running (10 minutes/mile)	300 kcal
Running (7.5 minutes/mile)	405 kcal

Source: www.nutrition.org.uk

Exercising in hot weather or a warm environment will burn more kilocalories because the heart has to work harder to pump more blood to the skin to cool down, using more energy in the process. However, exercising in hot weather can lead to heat stroke if the body temperature rises too rapidly.

Pregnancy

Figure 2.59 *Pregnancy requires more energy*

Pregnancy requires extra energy to ensure the healthy growth and development of the foetus, uterus, and breast tissue. A pregnant woman has a larger tissue mass which will increase energy demand for movement, particularly for weight bearing activities after 25 weeks. This extra energy only amounts to an extra 200 kcals a day throughout a 40 week pregnancy. The production of milk for breast feeding (lactation) also requires extra energy. During lactation, energy is required for the production of breast milk and for the energy content of milk. Throughout lactation, an extra 450–480 kcals is required each day.

Illness and disease

The metabolic rate rises if the body has a fever. During a fever, the attempt by the body to reduce the

temperature by 1°C will increase basal metabolic rate (BMR) by about 10 per cent.

Body composition

Lean body tissue (muscle) is metabolically more active and uses more energy than fatty (adipose) tissue. Individuals with more lean body tissue are more likely to burn off excess energy.

Hormonal imbalance

Hormones help to regulate metabolism. The thyroid gland secretes hormones to regulate many metabolic processes, including energy expenditure. Energy expenditure is the rate at which kilocalories or kilojoules are burned. An overactive thyroid gland can increase the metabolic rate and individuals may need to consume more energy to address the imbalance. An underactive thyroid slows metabolism because the thyroid gland doesn't release enough hormones. The symptoms of an underactive thyroid include unusual weight gain, lethargy, depression and constipation.

Environmental conditions

Food plays a role in the prevention of hypothermia since it is the fuel source for producing body heat. A high-energy intake is required when working or living in an extremely cold environment.

Energy intake

Energy requirements vary considerably between different groups, much more than nutrient intakes. The EAR intakes suggested in Topic 1 are only a recommendation or guide.

Effects of energy imbalance

We have already investigated the concept of energy balance and the factors that can affect an individual's energy requirements. We will now explore the effects of an imbalance of energy on the body.

Dietary energy

Body weight is influenced by energy intake and energy expenditure. All dietary energy is digested and converted into glucose – the fuel the body needs to function. Glucose can be stored in the liver and muscles as glycogen. Only a small quantity of glycogen is stored in the liver and muscles and excess glucose is converted into fat and stored under the skin.

Energy from dietary fat is more likely to be stored as fat in the body than energy from dietary carbohydrates. Fat is energy dense and is converted into glucose and then into body fat much more efficiently than the conversion of carbohydrates and protein into body fat. Most dietary carbohydrate is stored as glycogen or used directly as energy.

If a person regularly consumes less energy than they use up, they will lose weight. An inadequate energy intake over a period of time can result in malnutrition.

Incidence of obesity

Obesity is a condition in which excessive fat accumulates in adipose tissue and impairs health. It is defined in adults as a body mass index (BMI) above 30. In England, 22 per cent of men and 23 per cent of women are now obese and well over half of all adults are either overweight or obese – almost 24 million adults. Obesity is also increasing in children.

Obesity is caused by an imbalance of energy intake. If a person regularly consumes more energy than they use up, they will start to gain weight and eventually become overweight or obese.

Changes in society have undoubtedly contributed to the growth of obesity. There has been a significant change in the proportion of people employed in manufacturing, farming and other physically demanding jobs; more people do less physically demanding jobs but their energy intake is too high. Car ownership has increased and the distance children and adults walk or cycle has declined. An increase in leisure time has not necessarily meant an increase in sport or physical activity.

Research has shown that in 2005, the three main activities completed by men and women in Great Britain were sleeping, working in their main job and watching television and videos/DVDs or listening to music. Lifestyle changes in adults have affected children too. Many children spend a considerable amount of their leisure time watching television and playing computer games; less time is spent playing sport.

Consumption of high-energy foods plays a major role in what makes people gain weight. The convenience of fast food restaurants, pre-packaged foods and soft drinks affect our food choices and many of these products are high in fat and calories. Large servings also increase energy consumption. A diet high in energy rich foods coupled with a decrease in physical activity has contributed to the growth of obesity in the UK.

Measuring obesity

For adults and children, **body mass index (BMI)** is used as the measure of obesity. The BMI is a statistical measurement that compares a person's weight and height. It is a tool that can be used to tell how healthy a person's weight is. The World Health Organisation sets out the BMI weight ranges used in the UK. The calculation is based on an individual's body weight divided by the square of their height.

Among adults, the following categories are used to indicate being overweight and obese:

Description BMI (kg/m²)
BMI is less than 18.4 – underweight for height.
BMI is between 18.5 and 24.9 – an ideal weight for height
BMI is between 25 and 29.9 – over the ideal weight for height.
BMI is between 30 and 39.9 – obese.
BMI is over 40 – very obese.

Activity 34

Investigative opportunity
Visit a website with a body mass index (BMI) calculator and calculate the BMI of the following individuals. Describe their weight using the terms 'very obese', 'obese', 'overweight', 'ideal weight' or 'underweight'.

	Height	Weight
John	175cms	80kgs
Andy	160cms	110kgs
Isabel	160cms	55kgs
Michelle	159cms	65kgs
Rachel	177cms	57kgs

What advice would you give to each individual about their weight?

Impact of obesity

Obese people have an increased risk of developing serious health conditions such as coronary heart disease, gall bladder disease, hypertension, type 2 diabetes and some cancers. They are likely to have a shorter life expectancy.

The distribution of the body fat is very significant in assessing the health risks associated with obesity. Men tend to accumulate fat around their waist, sometimes referred to as 'apple shape', whereas women accumulate fat around the hips, sometimes referred to as 'pear shape'.

Weight management

There is no easy solution to weight loss as a variety of approaches are required to help an individual lose weight and maintain their ideal weight. The weight loss should be gradual – no more than 1 kg a week. To achieve this goal, energy intake needs to be reduced by about 1,000 kcal per day. When weight is reduced, the body's basic metabolic rate will fall slightly so less energy is required to maintain the smaller body mass. To maintain permanent weight loss, fewer calories have to be consumed forever!

Activity 2.35

Research

Figure 2.60 *A low calorie meal*

Investigate some low calorie or low fat products. Are they value for money?

Choose some popular food products and compare the calorie or fat content to the regular versions. Products you might consider include milk, cheese, fat spreads, yoghurts, cream, biscuits and cakes.

Write some notes about each comparison you make, considering the food item's cost and energy or fat content.

Eating fewer calories is the first step and can be achieved by eating foods that contain fewer calories than are required for metabolism and physical activity. This does not mean eating less food but eating foods with fewer calories. High calorie foods are sometimes referred to as **high energy dense foods** as they contain about 225–275 kcal per 100g. They tend to be high in fat and/or sugar and are causes of weight gain and obesity. To lose weight, stored calories have to be used up. Exercise alone is not usually sufficient to achieve weight loss – eating fewer calories is crucial.

Changing eating habits

There are a number of behavioural changes that will lead to an individual losing weight and maintaining weight loss:

● Fat and carbohydrates are important sources of energy in the diet and reducing intake of these nutrients will result in weight loss.

● Choose low fat options and check the number of calories on a food product label before purchase.

● Frequent snacking can lead to weight gain. Food products are sold at a number of retail outlets, including garages, which can increase the temptation to snack.

● Eat just three meals a day and nothing in between.

● Always sit down at designated meal times and avoid eating snacks 'on the go', as these are often high energy dense foods.

● Those wishing to lose weight should avoid second helpings during meal times.

● Food prepared with cooking methods involving fat or oils should be avoided.

There are many helpful suggestions to reduce energy intake in the diet and for some individuals making one or two simple changes can prevent weight gain. An important element to any diet is to plan food purchases and ensure that plenty of fruit and vegetables are incorporated into the diet.

The portion sizes of some products have increased and the option for a larger portion is more widely available. Individuals wishing to lose weight should choose smaller portions and small sizes of food products. Avoid 'eating with fingers', as fast foods and snack products are usually high in calories.

Increase exercise

Figure 2.61 *Exercise helps weight loss*

Individuals who are overweight should try to lose weight by using their stored body fat to provide energy and increase their energy output. This really means eating less and increasing physical activity.

It is estimated that up to one-third of boys and one-third to a half of girls may not do enough physical activity. A report by the Chief Medical Officer made the recommendation that adults should complete at least 30 minutes of at least moderate activity on five or more days a week. Exercise increases the amount of muscle in the body which will burn more energy. There are many local and national initiatives to encourage individuals to exercise more, but the key to success is that the exercise becomes a routine and is appropriate for the individual.

The simplest way to increase physical activity is to incorporate more physical activity into daily routines, for example, walking or cycling instead of driving or taking the bus. Taking up more active hobbies such as gardening, walking and dancing is also helpful in reducing weight.

More radical steps to reduce obesity include the use of prescribed medication to reduce appetite or reduce the absorption of fats. Gastric surgery reduces the size of the stomach and fat can be removed surgically from the abdomen. However, the long-term success of all these methods is only possible when behaviour changes in eating patterns and choice of food are permanent.

Inadequate weight

A lack of energy from food can result in loss of weight and if this situation persists, then an individual will become malnourished and eventually starve. In the UK, unlike the developing world, we rarely encounter individuals who face starvation due to the consumption of insufficient food.

Various illnesses or circumstances can contribute to malnutrition and we have already explored these in Topic 1. Research suggests that elderly women have a greater risk of malnutrition than elderly men do.

Inadequate food intake may also be due to a psychological eating disorder. The condition **anorexia nervosa** is the deliberate loss of weight, usually by avoiding foods containing energy. Individuals will deliberately vomit, take laxatives or appetite-suppressing drugs, or do excessive amounts of exercise to lose weight. A normal BMI for an adult is 20–25. A BMI slightly above this is overweight and below is underweight. Adults with anorexia have a BMI below 17.5.

CHECK YOUR UNDERSTANDING

Check that you understand the meaning of the following key terms by defining each in a sentence.

anorexia nervosa
body mass index (BMI)
energy expenditure
high energy dense foods
kilojoules
metabolic rate
negative energy balance

Basal Metabolic Rate
energy balance
glycogen
kilocalorie
lean body mass
obesity
positive energy balance

Exam-style questions

Proteins

1 Explain the term high biological value protein.

(2 marks)

2 Discuss the implications of excess protein and a deficiency of protein in the diet.

(10 marks)

Fats

1a Describe four functions of fat in the diet.

(4 marks)

1b Explain the term saturated fatty acid

(2 marks)

1c Name an essential fatty acid and its food source.

(2 marks)

Carbohydrates

1 Explain the benefits of dietary fibre in the diet.

(6 marks)

Vitamins

1 Describe two good sources of vitamin A

(4 marks)

2 Explain the value of vitamin supplements in the diet.

(10 marks)

Minerals

1 Minerals are essential micronutrients. Identify four minerals necessary for good health.

(4 marks)

2 Describe the functions of the minerals identified in question 1.

(8 marks)

Energy

1a Identify four good sources of energy in the UK diet.

(4 marks)

1b Explain the term energy imbalance.

(6 marks)

1c Explain four factors that affect energy requirements.

(8 marks)

(Total of 70 marks)

NUTRITIONAL AND DIETARY NEEDS OF DIFFERENT GROUPS

Learning objectives

By the end of this chapter you will be able to:

- describe the nutritional and dietary needs of babies, pre-school children, young children, adolescents, adults, the elderly, vegetarians, and pregnant and lactating women
- explain how and why nutritional and dietary needs change over the course of a lifetime
- plan suitable and well balanced meals for those groups listed above.

Figure 3.01

Introduction

All individuals need a variety of nutrients, in differing amounts, to maintain health and reduce their risk of diet-related disease. Each person's nutritional requirement, i.e. the amount of each nutrient they require, varies, because each nutrient has a particular function in the body and some are needed in larger quantities than others are. Individual nutritional requirements will depend upon a person's age, sex, level of physical activity and state of health.

This chapter will identify the nutritional needs of the following groups of people:

- babies
- pre-school children
- young children
- adolescents
- adults
- the elderly
- vegetarians
- pregnant women
- lactating women.

We will also look at the dietary needs of each of the above, taking into account their particular nutritional needs, and using that information to plan meals and choose the most appropriate foods.

Babies (0–12 months)

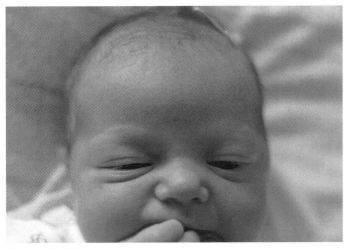

Figure 3.02

During the first 4 to 6 months of life, babies go through a period of rapid growth and development. Breast milk (or infant formula) contains all the nutrients required during this period. Breast feeding is recommended by the Department of Health and should ideally continue for the first year, and especially for the first three months of life. Current advice is not to give solid foods to babies before the age of 6 months, but often this process begins sometime between 4 and 6 months. When babies are introduced to solid foods and a mixed diet this is called **weaning**. During weaning the baby should be gradually introduced to a wide variety of foods.

Nutritional needs of babies

Initially, babies rely on their mother's milk or formula milk to satisfy their nutritional needs. During the early months of life, babies draw upon iron stores they have accumulated before birth but these stores are rapidly depleted and it is important that the diet given during weaning contains enough iron to meet the baby's needs for growth and development. Requirements for protein, the B vitamins, magnesium, zinc, sodium and chloride also increase between 6 and 12 months.

Dietary needs of babies

During weaning, a baby should be gradually introduced to a variety of foods such as infant cereals, puréed fruit and vegetables, egg yolk and finely chopped meat.

Eggs must be cooked until they are solid and should not be given to babies under 6 months.

It is important that sugar and salt are not added to foods that are prepared at home. Home-prepared and cooked food is preferable to commercial baby foods, which may be sweetened or salted.

Milk remains an important part of a baby's diet, but cows milk should be avoided because of the risk of gastrointestinal bleeding. As stated above, iron is the main nutrient that may be lacking. Only a small amount of iron is found in milk, so babies need to be given iron-rich foods when they are weaned such as fish, minced meat, cereals and eggs.

Pre-school children (12 months to 4 years)

Figure 3.03

At around 12 to 18-months-old, a child can eat a mixed diet that is not so different from that of the rest of the family. This is a transitional period where the diet gradually changes from a baby's diet to an adult-type diet.

Nutritional needs of pre-school children

Energy requirements increase during this time because young children are active and growing rapidly. The requirement for protein increases a little. There is an increased need for all the vitamins except vitamin D because it will now be synthesised in the skin, following exposure to sunlight. Slightly lower amounts of calcium, phosphorus and iron are needed. There is an increased requirement for all the other minerals except zinc.

Dietary needs of pre-school children

It is crucial to balance the need for a diet that will benefit a child's future health and one that ensures growth and development. Milk and dairy products remain an important source of calcium and Vitamin D. Pre-school children should be given whole milk, not skimmed or semi-skimmed. Semi-skimmed milk may be given after the age of 2 years, but skimmed milk should not be given to children under the age of five.

Sensible patterns of eating should be established at this time, with meals taken at regular times and a wide variety of foods introduced. Encouraging children to choose a variety of foods will ensure they obtain the wide range of nutrients they need to stay healthy. Snacks should consist of nutritious food such as carrots, bread, cheese and yoghurt, rather than fatty, salty or sugary foods. This will help to establish good eating habits as the child gets older.

Care needs to be taken over the amount of fibre (non-starch polysaccharide or NSP) eaten by young children. A diet that is too bulky because of over-consumption of high-fibre foods could result in a child being unable to eat enough food to satisfy its energy needs.

School-age children (4 to 10 years)

School-age children are growing fast and are also very active. They have high energy and nutrient needs, particularly during periods of rapid growth and development. The nutritional requirements of children can be divided into two broad groups and need to be considered separately because there are some differences in the nutrient requirements between the ages of 4 to 10.

4–6 years

Energy requirements increase and there is a greater need for protein, all the vitamins except vitamins C and D, and all the minerals except iron. The requirement for vitamin C remains the same as for pre-school children.

Figure 3.04

The action of sunlight on the child's skin is the major source of vitamin D. Asian children may be at risk of vitamin D deficiency because of low vitamin D intake from food and/or inadequate exposure of skin to sunshine.

7–10 years

There is a marked increase in requirements for energy and protein. There is no change in the requirement for thiamin, vitamin C or vitamin A; however, the requirements for the other vitamins and minerals are increased.

Activity 3.1

Research opportunity
Parents need to encourage young children to eat a variety of foods, and establish good routines and sound eating habits. Suggest some strategies parents can use to achieve these aims and make meal times a positive experience for young children.

Dietary needs of school-age children

School-age children require a healthy, balanced diet, rich in fruit, vegetables and starchy foods. They should be eating at least five portions of fruit and vegetables each day. However, consumption is sometimes less in children, particularly in lower income groups, so it is important to encourage children to try a variety of fruit and vegetables.

The family is the main influence on eating habits early in life and it is difficult to change habits once they are established. It is therefore important that the whole family adopts a healthy lifestyle and avoids salty, sugary and fatty foods. If children do eat foods and drinks containing sugar it is best to have them only at meal times. Eating sugary foods frequently between meals causes dental decay. Snack foods such as cakes, biscuits, crisps, chocolate and sweets are often high in sugar and saturated fat, and low in certain vitamins and minerals, so their consumption should be limited.

To achieve a high energy intake, energy rich foods should be eaten as part of small and frequent meals. This may be necessary for younger children (4–6-year-olds), who do not have large enough stomachs to cope with big meals. Children's weight gain should be gradual, in line with height increases, so that they grow to be an acceptable weight for their height.

Milk and dairy products remain essential for tooth development and, together with vitamin D, help to make bones stronger.

Iron deficiency anaemia is associated with frequent infections, poor weight gain and delay in development. If iron-rich foods such as liver and red meat are not popular with children, other sources such as dark green leafy vegetables, pulses, nuts, bread and some fortified breakfast cereals should be included in the diet.

Activity 3.2

ICT opportunity

It is important that school-age children consume five portions of fruit or vegetables a day. Design a leaflet to explain the importance of fruit and vegetables in the diet and include some recipe ideas that may encourage a reluctant child to eat vegetables.

The maximum amount of salt children should consume varies by age. From 4 to 6 years the maximum salt intake should be 3 g a day and for children aged 7 to 10 years the maximum is 5 g a day.

Adolescents (11 to 18 years)

Figure 3.05

Adolescence is a period of considerable change, centred on **puberty**, the process during which there is a spurt of physical growth leading to an increase in height and weight, changes in body composition and sexual development. Adolescents have high nutritional needs and therefore large appetites. It is important that this appetite is satisfied with foods of a high nutritional value, and that well balanced meals are eaten regularly. The nutritional requirements of adolescents can be divided into two broad groups and need to be considered separately because there are some differences in the nutrient requirements between the ages of 11 and 18.

Activity 3.3

Review

Read the sections on the nutritional requirements for babies, pre-school children and school-age children. Summarise this information by copying and completing the table below.

Age group	Specific nutrients needed	Food sources
Babies		
Pre-school children		
School-age children		

Describe the differences and similarities in the nutritional requirements for the groups.

Nutritional needs of adolescents

11–14 years

For both boys and girls, energy requirements continue to increase and protein requirements increase by approximately 50 per cent. By the age of 11, the vitamin and mineral requirements for boys and girls start to differ. For boys there is an increased requirement for all the vitamins and minerals. For girls there is no change in the requirement for thiamin, niacin and vitamin B6, but there is an increased requirement for all the minerals. Girls have a much higher iron requirement than boys once **menstruation** starts, and blood loss occurs every month.

The maximum amount of salt children should be consuming varies by age and from the age of 11 years the maximum is 6 g a day.

15–18 years

Boys: Energy and protein requirements continue to increase, as do the requirements of a number of vitamins – thiamin, riboflavin, niacin, vitamins B6, B12, C and A. There is an increased requirement for the minerals magnesium, potassium, zinc, copper, selenium and iodine. Calcium requirements remain high as skeletal development is rapid.

Girls: The requirements for energy, protein, thiamin, niacin, vitamins B6, B12 and C, phosphorus, magnesium, potassium, copper, selenium and iodine all increase. Girls have a higher requirement than boys for iron (due to menstrual losses) but a lower requirement for zinc and calcium.

Boys and girls have the same requirement for vitamin B12, folate, vitamin C, magnesium, sodium, potassium, chloride and copper.

Dietary needs of adolescents

As with the other age groups, eating a variety of foods is important for adolescents. Obesity in adolescence is becoming increasingly common, so eating sensibly to avoid this risk should be encouraged. Foods high in energy such as pasta, rice, potatoes and bread, and those high in protein such as meat, fish, eggs, nuts, pulses, should be consumed.

Calcium needs are higher during adolescence because of bone development – about 45 per cent of the adult skeleton is laid down during these years.

Iron requirements are particularly high because there is an increase in lean body mass, blood volume and haemoglobin. Girls will need to take care to consume iron-rich foods to make up for iron lost in menstruation.

Knowledge of nutrition and which foods to eat and which to avoid will benefit health during adolescence and into adulthood.

Adolescent girls who become pregnant are at a particular risk of developing nutrient deficiencies, and it is essential that they consume additional nutrients for their baby's growth as well as for their own.

Activity 3.4

Practical opportunity

Explain the current dietary guidelines for healthy eating.

Explain the nutritional requirements for adolescents.

Using this information create a menu for five main meals for a school canteen, which address both the current dietary guidelines and adolescents' nutritional requirements.

In your next practical lesson, make one of your choices.

CHECK YOUR UNDERSTANDING

Check that you understand the meaning of the following key terms:

weaning   **puberty**   **menstruation**

Adults (19 to 50 years)

The nutritional needs of adults differ from those of children because adults are no longer growing. At the adult stage of life nutrients are needed for energy requirements, to maintain and repair body tissue and for normal bodily functions.

Nutritional needs of adults

Energy requirements are lower for both men and women compared with adolescents, as are the requirements for calcium and phosphorus. There is also a reduced requirement in women for magnesium, and in men for iron. The requirements for protein and most of the vitamins and minerals remain virtually

Figure 3.06

unchanged compared with adolescents. Lastly, the requirement for selenium in men increases slightly.

Dietary needs of adults

In the UK adults are more likely to be at risk of over nutrition than under nutrition. The dietary energy required by an adult should equal exactly the energy required for body maintenance and physical activity. Energy sources should be obtained from starchy carbohydrate foods such as potatoes, rice, pasta and bread, not sweet carbohydrate foods such as cakes, biscuits and pastry. Making the correct choice will help maintain energy balance.

The Eatwell plate (see Topic 1) gives the following good advice on the dietary needs of adults:

1 Base your meals on starchy foods.

2 Eat lots of fruit and vegetables.

3 Eat more fish.

4 Cut down on saturated fat and sugar.

5 Try to eat less salt – no more than 6 g a day.

6 Get active and try to be a healthy weight.

7 Drink plenty of water.

8 Don't skip breakfast.

The elderly

Figure 3.07

According to the British Nutrition Foundation, the elderly can be divided into two groups – those under 75 years are described as the 'young' old, and those over 75 as the 'old' old. There is very little difference between the nutritional requirements of most adults and the elderly. However, as we get older we tend to become less active, so the main difference is that energy expenditure decreases. The elderly are the fastest growing sector in society and ensuring they receive an adequate diet can help to ensure they stay in good health – and is therefore of increasing relevance. The personal circumstances and state of health of older people also needs to be considered, because this can affect what they are able to eat.

Activity 3.5

Discussion
Carry out some research into why some elderly people suffer from an inadequate diet.
Discuss your findings with the rest of your group.

Nutritional needs of the elderly

Because of a reduction in physical activity, energy requirements may decrease gradually after the age of 50 in women and 60 in men. Protein requirements decrease for men but continue to increase slightly in women. The requirement for vitamins remains the same but an elderly person's diet is more likely to be deficient in vitamin C, D and folate. Elderly people may not consume enough green leafy vegetables, which would account for the lack of folate in their diet. Those who are housebound may be lacking in vitamin D due to limited exposure to sunlight, so foods rich in vitamin D and calcium should be included in the diet. Vitamin C deficiency may result if a person has difficulty in peeling fruit and vegetables. An elderly person's diet will benefit from the recommended amounts of iron, zinc and calcium. **Anaemia** can occur in elderly people due to poor absorption and blood loss as a result of injury, so foods rich in iron should be included in the diet. Zinc is needed for a healthy immune system and to help with wound healing of pressure sores and leg ulcers; a lack of zinc may be a factor in causes of dementia.

Adequate intakes of calcium should be included in the diet of the elderly for good bone health. Elderly people who are well should restrict saturated fat intakes but fat restrictions are less likely to be beneficial in those over 75. Fat restriction is not appropriate for people who are frail or have weight loss or a very small appetite. Some elderly people may suffer with constipation and bowel problems due to reduced gut mobility and inactivity, and the consumption of cereals can help with this. Dehydration can interfere with digestion and may lead

Activity 3.6

Review

Figure 3.08

It is a good idea for the elderly to have a store cupboard of essential items in case they are unwell, or unable to get out due to adverse weather conditions. What items would you recommend they keep in their store cupboard and why?

Activity 3.7

Research opportunity

Figure 3.09

Find out about the 'Meals on Wheels' service provided by the Women's Royal Voluntary Service (WRVS).

to constipation; drinking a variety of drinks will maintain water intake and reduce the risk of dehydration.

Dietary needs of the elderly

The elderly should eat meals based upon starchy foods – pasta, potatoes, rice and bread – as these are filling sources of carbohydrate. Oily fish is a useful source of protein and may help reduce the risk of **thrombosis**.

There are huge benefits from eating fruit and vegetables as they provide valuable vitamins, minerals, fibre and antioxidants, which mop up damaging free radicals (see Topic 2). Some degenerative diseases that are common in later life, including cancer, vascular diseases, degenerative eye diseases and possibly neuro-degenerative diseases like Parkinson's, may be exacerbated or even caused by free radical damage. The crucial antioxidant vitamins (A, C and E) and minerals (zinc, copper, manganese and selenium) found in fruit and vegetables can halt the damaged caused by free radicals. Fruit and vegetables may also help to lower blood pressure, because the potassium they contain increases sodium (salt) excretion. Potassium is found in many fruits and vegetables including bananas, citrus fruits, raisins and other dried fruits, potatoes and avocados.

A daily intake of iron is very important and should come from haem (meat, offal) and non-haem sources (fortified cereals, dried fruit, pulses and green leafy vegetables). Absorption of iron is increased by consuming vitamin C at the same time, for example by drinking a glass of fruit juice with meals. Zinc is very important in the diet of the elderly and is found in meat and meat products, seafood, milk and dairy products, wholemeal bread, lentils, eggs, nuts, sweetcorn and rice.

Calcium-rich foods are needed for good bone health and sources include milk, cheese and other dairy products, green leafy vegetables, sesame seeds, canned fish (such as sardine and salmon where the bones are eaten), dried fruit and baked beans.

Elderly people should aim to eat at least one well-balanced meal a day, although this does not necessarily have to be a hot meal. It is useful for the elderly to have a freezer containing some ready-made meals and bread and a well-stocked store cupboard containing such items as long-life milk, cereals, canned foods, pulses and pasta, in case of illness or becoming housebound. An easy-to-operate microwave may be useful.

Activity 3.8

Practical opportunity

Write a report on the elderly (maximum of 500 words) that includes:

- an explanation of the nutritional needs of an elderly person
- recipes for two suitable hot main meals and two suitable hot puddings, with reasons why they meet the nutritional needs of the elderly.

In your next practical lesson, make one of your choices.

CHECK YOUR UNDERSTANDING

Check that you understand the meaning of the following key terms by defining each in a sentence.

thrombosis   anaemia   constipation

Vegetarians

Between 3 and 7 per cent of the UK population are vegetarian, with women more likely to be vegetarian than men. In an **omnivorous** diet, foods of animal origin such as meat, fish, eggs and dairy products are consumed. These provide substantial amounts of food energy, protein, calcium, iron, zinc and vitamins A, D and B12. The nutritional content of a vegetarian diet may be reduced when appropriate substitutions are not made for those foods omitted from the diet that are animal in origin. People become vegetarians for a variety of reasons.

Activity 3.10

Review

Create a mind map of some reasons why a person might be a vegetarian.

The definition of vegetarian is someone who does not eat food of animal origin, but a vegetarian diet can take many different forms:

- Pesco-vegetarian – all red meat and poultry are excluded but fish and other animal products are still consumed.

- Lacto-ovo-vegetarian – all meat, fish and poultry are excluded but milk, milk products and eggs are still consumed. Most UK vegetarians follow a lacto-ovo vegetarian diet.

Activity 3.9

Review

Read the sections on the nutritional requirements for adolescents, adults and the elderly. Summarise this information by copying and completing the table below.

Age group	Specific nutrients needed	Food sources
Adolescents		
Adults		
The elderly		

Describe the differences and similarities in the nutritional requirements for the groups.

- **Lacto-vegetarian** – all meat, fish, poultry and eggs are excluded. Milk and milk products are consumed.

- **Fruitarian** – all foods of animal origin as well as pulses and cereals are excluded. The diet mainly consists of raw and dried fruits, nuts, honey and olive oil.

- **Vegan** – all foods of animal origin are excluded. The diet mainly consists of grains, vegetables, vegetable oils, cereals, pulses such as beans and lentils, nuts, fruit and seeds. Non-food animal products, such as leather, may also be avoided.

A well-planned and varied vegetarian diet is needed in order to supply adequate energy and sufficient amounts of nutrients. Different food restrictions will apply depending on the particular type of vegetarian diet followed and problems may occur if those foods excluded are not replaced by suitable alternatives in terms of the nutrients they supply.

Nutritional requirements of vegetarians

Vegetarians must consume an adequate intake of essential nutrients. Protein from animal sources is of high biological value and contains all of the amino acids needed by the body. A vegetarian diet that includes milk or eggs will contain sufficient protein of a high biological protein. Protein from plant sources, with the exception of soya, has a low biological content, which means that one or more of the essential or indispensable amino acids needed by the body are missing (see Topic 2 for more information on proteins). However, if proteins from different plant sources are eaten together, the amino acid content of the plant proteins will complement each other. A deficiency in amino acids in one plant protein can be compensated for by the amino acids in another.

Vegans need to ensure they consume adequate quantities of calcium, iron, vitamin D, iodine and vitamin B12, as these nutrients are more difficult to obtain from plant sources. Although most vitamins are provided by foods of plant origin, vitamin B_{12} is found only in foods of animal origin. The body's requirement for vitamin B12 is only a few micrograms per day, but it is essential that vegans and those who avoid all animal foods include a source of vitamin B_{12} in their diet, usually by taking a vitamin B12 supplement. There may be a problem with adequate intakes of vitamin D among vegetarians. Low vitamin D status may be due to a combination of low exposure to sunlight and the type of vegetarian diet followed, particularly if milk and milk-products are excluded.

Great care is needed if babies are to be weaned on to a vegan diet. The diet must be planned to ensure it contains sufficient fat and protein. Soy-based infant formula can be given on the advice of a GP or health visitor, and children under 2 years of age should take supplements of vitamin drops containing vitamins A, C and D. Foods fortified with vitamin B12 should be included in the diet and, if necessary, a vitamin B12 supplement taken.

Following a vegetarian diet is becoming more common among adolescents. Care needs to be taken to ensure protein and energy requirements are met because adolescence is a period of rapid growth and development.

Activity 3.11

Review

The nutrients shown in the table below are important in a vegetarian diet. Copy the table and identify the animal and plant sources of each nutrient.

Nutrient	Animal Sources	Plant Sources
Protein		
Calcium		
Iron		
Vitamin A		
Vitamin B12		
Vitamin D		

Dietary requirements of vegetarians

Figure 3.10 *Vegetarian sources of protein: soya products*

Becoming a vegetarian does not simply mean avoiding meat. It is important to substitute foods that contain the nutrients which would have been provided by meat.

A vegetarian diet is not necessarily healthier than an omnivorous diet. Both can be healthy – the key is to achieve a balanced diet that is low in saturated fat and which includes at least five portions of fruit and vegetables a day, coupled with a healthy lifestyle that includes not smoking, taking moderate exercise and avoiding obesity.

Calcium is present in milk, cheese and dairy products, so vegetarians who consume milk and milk products are likely to have adequate intakes of calcium. However, vegans may not have an adequate intake of calcium because relatively few other foods contain large amounts. In addition, the availability of calcium from some plant sources may be reduced by fibre, phytate or oxalate present in food. These form complexes with the calcium, making it insoluble and unable to be absorbed by the body. Vegans need to consider other sources of calcium such as almonds, sesame seeds, pulses, pulse products, such as tofu (a very rich source of calcium), tempeh and vegan cheese, which is made from soya flour.

Lacto-ovo-vegetarian diets usually contain adequate amounts of iodine, because it is found in milk and eggs, but vegans are at risk of low intakes. Vegans will need to obtain iodine from edible seaweeds or iodised salt.

Haem iron is easily sourced from red meat and offal. Non-haem iron is obtained from sources such as eggs, cereal foods, green vegetables, nuts and pulses. It is important to remember that if vitamin C is consumed from fruit, fruit juices and vegetables this will enhance the absorption of non-haem iron; for example, having beans on toast and a glass of orange juice at the same meal. Female vegetarians need to take care that they consume sufficient quantities of iron.

A vegetarian diet provides on average 35 per cent of food energy as fat. In most vegan diets the amount of energy provided by fat is 10 per cent.

Zinc is found in a variety of plant and animals sources such as meat, poultry, dairy products, bread and other cereal products, and seafood. Care needs to be taken with bread and cereal products, pulses, nuts and seeds, because many of these foods are also high in phytate, which is an inhibitor of zinc absorption.

Vegans need to ensure that they take Vitamin B12, either as a supplement, in fortified foods such as yeast extract, fortified soya milk or fortified breakfast cereal.

Vitamin D is found naturally in only a few foods, all of which are of animal origin – meat, oily fish such as mackerel and sardines, eggs, whole milk and its products. Products such as breakfast cereals, yoghurts and all margarines are fortified with vitamin D and these can be consumed by vegans and vegetarians who do not consume milk or milk products. Vegetarians who receive little exposure to the sun have a greater need to ensure that they include dietary sources of vitamin D.

CHECK YOUR UNDERSTANDING

Check you understand the meaning of the following key terms. Write a sentence using each word.

pesco-vegetarian	lacto-ovo-vegetarian	lacto-vegetarian
fruitarian	vegan	omnivorous

Activity 3.12

Review

Discuss the dietary implications of becoming a vegan.

Activity 3.13

Practical opportunity

Plan a main meal suitable for an adult vegan.

Calculate the protein content of the meal and compare it with the reference nutrient intake for protein for adults.

Evaluate your findings.

In your next practical lesson, make your meal.

A carefully planned and well-balanced vegetarian diet should provide all the necessary nutrients throughout life. However, a vegetarian diet may not be appropriate for babies and young children because this is a time of rapid growth and development. A wide range of foods should be given daily, following the same guidelines as for adults. It is important to ensure an adequate amount of foods containing all the essential nutrients are consumed, such as milk, cheese, margarine, pulses and peanut butter. Milk, milk products and eggs provide sufficient calcium, vitamin B12, vitamin D and riboflavin. If a vegetarian or vegan diet does not include these foods then these nutrients will need to be provided by supplements or fortified foods.

Pregnant women

A woman's nutritional needs change during pregnancy because her diet must provide for the growth and development of the foetus. Physiological changes occur to ensure the mother has enough energy to carry the extra weight of pregnancy and sufficient nutrients to aid development of the foetus. Maintaining a healthy diet in pregnancy will also prepare the woman for birth.

Nutritional needs of a pregnant woman

A pregnant woman should ensure her diet contains sufficient energy, protein, iron, calcium, folate and vitamins C and D, as any deficiencies in obtaining these nutrients may lead to a reduction in the woman's

Figure 3.11

own stores of nutrients. There are increased requirements for some, but not all, nutrients during pregnancy. Women intending to become pregnant or who are pregnant are advised to take supplements of folic acid (also called folate) for the first 12 weeks of pregnancy to reduce the risk of neural tube defects in the developing foetus. Neural tube defects occur when the development of the spine or brain is incomplete and include spina bifida and anencephaly. Additional energy and thiamin are required only during the last three months of pregnancy. Mineral requirements do not increase, though iron supplements may sometimes be given.

Dietary needs of a pregnant woman

Most of the extra nutrients needed during pregnancy are provided by a healthy balanced diet, which should consist of:

- fresh fruit and vegetables – dark green vegetables are a good source of folate

- starchy carbohydrates – bread, pasta, potatoes and cereals

- dairy products – milk, yoghurt and cheese

- lean meat and fish.

Fish is an excellent source of essential fatty acids, although current advice is not to consume more than two portions of oily fish per week.

It is also important to maintain fluid levels, as this keeps the body hydrated, preventing tiredness and headaches, and maintains good bladder and kidney health.

Preparing food carefully and safely is very important. Meat must be cooked thoroughly and all fruit and vegetables should be washed before eating to avoid **toxoplasmosis**, a condition which can affect the unborn baby.

It is very difficult to get the recommended amount of folic acid from diet alone. Folic acid is found in dark green vegetables, wholegrain cereals, oranges, grapefruit, bananas, beans, pulses, milk, yogurt and yeast or malt extracts. Current advice is that women who are planning to become pregnant or who are pregnant should take 400 mcg of folic acid until the twelfth week of pregnancy. It is possible to continue taking folic acid after this date but medical advice should be sought.

Most women will obtain sufficient quantities of iron from a balanced and varied diet. Haem iron is easily sourced from red meat and offal. Non-haem iron is obtained from eggs, cereal foods, green vegetables, nuts and pulses. It is important to remember that if vitamin C is consumed from fruit, fruit juices and vegetables this will enhance the absorption of non-haem iron.

Eating during pregnancy

- Shark, swordfish and marlin should be avoided and intake of tuna limited to no more than two tuna steaks per week, or four medium-sized cans. This is because of the levels of mercury found in these foods, which can harm the baby's developing nervous system.

- Pregnant woman are advised not to take supplements of vitamin A or eat liver (which is extremely rich in vitamin A) due to the possible risks of birth defects.

- Brie, Camembert, mould-ripened goats' and sheep's milk cheeses such as chèvre and blue-veined cheeses such as Stilton should be avoided because of the possible risk of listeria, which can lead to premature

birth and miscarriage. Pâté should be avoided for the same reason.

- Ready meals must be cooked until piping hot and well stirred, since they are also a potential source of listeria.

- Unpasteurised milk should be avoided; only drink pasteurised or UHT milk.

- Eggs should be well cooked before being eaten. Raw eggs should not be eaten because of the risk of salmonella.

- Liver and liver products should be avoided during pregnancy as they contain high levels of vitamin A, which can be harmful to the body.

- There is some evidence to suggest that it may be safer to avoid peanuts in pregnancy if the woman's partner has a peanut allergy.

- Recent advice from the Food Standards Agency about caffeine suggests that pregnant women should limit their intake of caffeine. It is recommended that a pregnant woman should drink no more that four cups of coffee a day. It is also important to remember that some fizzy drinks contain caffeine so it is advisable to switch to non-caffeine alternatives.

- Current advice is that low to moderate alcohol consumption that equates to approximately 1.5 units a day does not have any adverse effect on the unborn baby. Continuous heavy drinking however can cause permanent brain and developmental damage in the foetus.

Activity 3.14

ICT opportunity
Create a leaflet to advise pregnant women about foods to eat and foods to avoid during pregnancy.

Lactating women

The production of breast milk by a woman is called **lactation**. Breast milk provides all of the nutrients needed by a baby from birth up to around the age of four months. It is therefore essential that the mother's diet is sufficient to enable her to produce milk for her baby.

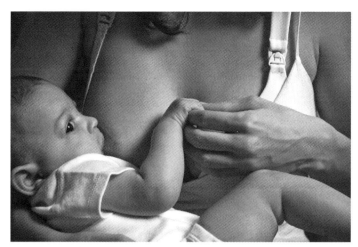

Figure 3.12

Dietary needs during lactation

Ideally, the same balanced and healthy diet followed during pregnancy should be continued during lactation. The emphasis should be on foods rich in starchy carbohydrates, protein, calcium and iron. Fluid is very important, so it is recommended that eight to twelve glasses of water a day are drunk, as this helps the body produce the milk needed to feed the baby. Caffeine and alcohol can pass from the blood into breast milk, so intake of these should be limited.

Sometimes babies are sensitive to foods eaten by their mother. It is possible to establish if the baby is sensitive to what the mother eats or drinks if they become unsettled after feeds, cry or sleep badly.

Some mothers want to get back to their pre-pregnancy weight as soon as possible. However, it is advisable to lose weight gradually by combining a healthy low fat diet with moderate exercise and to wait until six weeks after the baby is born before embarking on a steady weight loss programme. Rapid weight loss may be harmful to the baby because the breast milk may not contain sufficient nutrients.

Soft cheeses and pâté no longer need to be avoided as they were in pregnancy. If there is a peanut allergy in the family then it may be beneficial to avoid eating peanuts when breastfeeding.

There is no evidence to suggest that small quantities of alcohol will affect the baby. However, if a woman is breastfeeding and is concerned, she should either avoid alcohol or wait a couple of hours after drinking before feeding her baby. Once the alcohol is out of the bloodstream, it will not appear in the breast milk.

Activity 3.15

Research and ICT opportunity

Create a PowerPoint presentation to explain the benefits of breastfeeding.

Nutritional needs during lactation

During pregnancy, fat reserves are laid down to provide some of the energy requirement needed for breast milk production. As the baby is weaned, a woman's energy requirements will reduce to pre-pregnancy levels. Current research suggests that an extra 300 to 400 kcal per day is enough for fully breastfeeding mothers during the first three months. Additional requirements are also needed for protein, all the vitamins (except B6), calcium, phosphorus, magnesium, zinc, copper and selenium.

Activity 3.16

Review

Copy and complete the table below to identify the sources of those nutrients that are most important in the diet during lactation.

Nutrient	Sources
Protein	
Starchy carbohydrates	
Iron	
Calcium	
Vitamin C	
Vitamin D	

Activity 3.17

Practical opportunity

Plan five different lunchtime snacks that are quick to prepare and that will provide the nutrients required by a lactating woman.

Choose one of the snacks to make in your next practical lesson.

Calculate the protein and energy content of your snack and compare it with the reference nutrient intake for protein and energy for lactating women.

Evaluate your findings.

Exam-style questions

1 Discuss the nutritional and dietary needs of children aged 4 to 12 years.

(25 marks)

2 Discuss the issues involved in meeting the dietary needs of elderly people.

(25 marks)

(Total of 50 marks)

PROPERTIES OF FOOD

Learning objectives

By the end of this chapter you will be able to:

- describe the choice, use and nutritional value of meat, fish, eggs, dairy products, alternative protein sources, cereals, pulses, fats and oils, fruit and vegetables, sugar and sugar substitutes
- explain the performance characteristics of eggs and flour
- describe the behaviour changes that may occur in the production of food products such as bread, cakes, sauces and pastry
- describe the role and function of additives in the food industry.

Introduction

This chapter is divided into four sections. The first section looks at the choice, use and nutritional value of the food commodities described above. The chapter then goes on to look at the performance characteristics of eggs and the properties of flour or starch in food preparation.

The third section looks at the common behaviour changes that can occur when food products are prepared and cooked.

The final section considers the use of food **additives**, which are ingredients used in the preparation of processed foods.

Section 1   Food commodities

Introduction

In this chapter you will look at the factors to be considered when choosing the following food commodities:

- meat
- fish
- eggs
- dairy products
- alternative protein sources
- cereals
- pulses
- fats and oils
- fruit and vegetables
- sugar and sugar substitutes.

You will also consider the nutritional value of each of these foods and explain their usefulness in the diet.

Meat

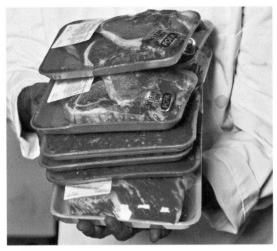

Figure 4.01

Most meat consumed in the UK comes from cattle, sheep, pigs, poultry and game. Poultry is the name given to birds that are reared for their meat, eggs or both. Game describes any animal or bird that is shot for sport.

Structure of meat

Lean meat is the muscle of the animal. The muscle fibres are bound together in bundles by thin sheets of **connective tissue**. Muscle fibres contain the proteins **myosin** and **actin**. Connective tissue is made up of proteins called **collagen** and **elastin**. Collagen is pearly white in colour, flexible and forms **gelatine** when cooked. This change helps meat to become tender. Elastin is yellow in colour, is not weakened by heat, and does not convert to gelatine when cooked.

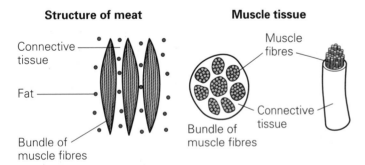

Figure 4.02 *Structure of meat*
Source: Jill Davies, Cooking Explained, Pearson Education Limited,
© Jill Davies 1997

A mixture of pigment in the muscle gives meat its colour. The main pigment is **myoglobin**.

Muscles that are used for physical activity contain large quantities of myoglobin and as a consequence are darker in colour. As red meat cooks, the myoglobin changes colour from a purple red to a greyish brown.

'Invisible fat' is found in the connective tissue of the muscles and is described as **marbling**. This fat helps to keep meat moist during cooking.

Nutritional value of meat

Around 20 per cent of the weight of lean meat is protein that is of high biological value. Fat is present in varying quantities, depending on the type and cut of meat. The fat content of poultry is low and contains a high percentage of unsaturated fats. The fat content of game is also very low.

Meat is a valuable source of iron, present as haem iron, and contains the minerals zinc, potassium and phosphorus and the vitamins thiamin, ribloflavin and niacin.

Lean meat contains very little vitamin A and almost no vitamin D, vitamin C or carbohydrate.

Activity 4.1

Review

	Lean beef	Lean lamb	Lean pork	Chicken
Energy Kj	517	679	512	508
Protein g	20	21	22	21
Fat g	5	9	4	4
Calcium mg	7	7	7	10
Iron mg	2	2	1	1
Niacin mg	5	6	7	8
Riboflavin mg	0.2	0.3	0.3	0.2

Source: Adapted from Michael E. J. Lean, Food Science, Nutrition and Health, *7th edition (Hodder Arnold, 2006)*

The table shows the composition of 100 g edible portion (raw weight) of meat and poultry. What observations can be made about the nutritional content of beef, lamb, pork and chicken?

Choice of meat

The species, age and part of the animal used in cooking will have an impact on the sensory qualities of meat – its taste and texture. Meat from a younger animal is tender and cooks quickly; meat from an older animal is tougher because of its age and needs a longer, slower method of cooking.

Types and cuts of meat

- *Beef* – most commonly used cuts are silverside, shin, steak, topside and brisket.

- *Pork* – most commonly used cuts are leg, chop and belly.

- *Bacon* and *gammon* are the cured flesh of a pig. The meat is cured by salting (which is done by a dry method and smoking) or by soaking in brine followed by smoking. Unsmoked bacon is brine cured but not smoked and has a milder flavour.

- *Lamb* – most commonly used cuts are chops, shoulder, leg, shank and breast.

- *Poultry* – chicken is the most popular type of poultry. Other types are duck, goose and turkey. Poultry has less connective tissue than red meat so is often more tender. The legs and wings of a bird do the most work and therefore tend to be darker and tougher due to the presence of myoglobin. The breast meat has less myoglobin and therefore becomes white during cooking.

- *Game* – there are two kinds of game – feathered (grouse, pheasant, partridge and ostrich) and furred (rabbit, hare and venison). Game is generally tougher than poultry, beef, pork and lamb, because game animals are wild and have an active life.

- *Meat products* – a wide variety of meat products are available, including curries, sausages, pies, burgers and pâté. Products such as gelatine and stock cubes are also by-products of the meat processing industry.

Activity 4.2

Starter activity
List as many types or cuts of meat as you can.

Activity 4.3

Practical opportunity
Chicken is a good choice of meat because it is low in fat.

Make a dish using chicken in your next practical lesson.

Storage

Fresh meat has a short shelf life and should either be frozen or eaten within a few days of purchase. It should be covered and stored in the bottom of the refrigerator, separate from uncooked meat, in order to avoid cross-contamination.

Cooking methods

Meat can be cooked in a variety of ways, and the method selected will depend upon the type and cut of meat.

Grilling

Grilling is suitable for tender cuts of meat, including chops, bacon, gammon and steak. It is a healthy method of cooking because any fat present can drip down and away from the meat.

Shallow frying

Shallow frying is suitable for tender cuts of meat, such as steak or chicken breasts cut into strips. It is a healthy method of cooking because it requires only a small amount of oil.

Roasting

Roasting is a dry method of cooking involving baking a whole joint of meat in the oven. A variety of meats can be roasted such as topside or silverside of beef, leg or shoulder of lamb, belly pork, leg of pork and chicken.

Braising

Braising means cooking meat or poultry on a bed of fried root vegetables with the addition of some stock. A variety of meats can be braised including brisket, breast or shoulder of lamb and belly or shoulder of pork.

Stewing

Stewing is cooking in a small amount of liquid, which is simmered slowly; the liquid is served with the meat. A variety of meats, such as shin of beef or gammon, can be stewed.

Meat is cooked to make it safe to eat by destroying any bacteria present and to improve its texture by making it tender and digestible. Although the tenderness of meat depends upon the age of the animal, it can be improved by cooking or by one of the methods described below.

- *Mechanical action* – the length of muscle fibres is reduced by mincing, or hitting with a hammer or cutting the meat into chunks.

- *Chemical action* – meat tenderisers can be added to the surface of the meat. These contain **proteolytic enzymes**, which digest muscle fibre and connective tissue.

- *Marinading* – an acidic, alkaline or salt solution can increase the amount of water meat can hold and make it more tender. Wine or lemon juice are often used as marinades, which are added prior to cooking.

Activity 4.4

Review

Explain the nutritional significance of meat.

Identify two cuts of meat suitable for roasting, frying, stewing, and braising.

CHECK YOUR UNDERSTANDING

1 Complete the following exercise using the key words and phrases shown below.

muscle	fibres	connective tissue
myosin	actin	collagen
elastin	gelatine	tender
myoglobin	marbling	invisible fat

Lean meat is the _____ of the animal. The muscle _____ are bound together in bundles by thin sheets of _____. Muscle fibres contain the proteins _____ and _____ . Connective tissue is made up of the protein _____, which is pearly white in colour, flexible and forms _____ when cooked. This change helps the meat to become _____. The other protein found in the connective tissue is _____, which is yellow in colour and is not weakened by heat. It does not convert to gelatine when cooked.

The colour of meat is due to a mixture of pigment in the muscle. Muscles are used for physical activity, so contain large quantities of the main pigment called _____, and therefore are darker in colour.

The fat found in the connective tissue of the muscles is called _____ and is described as _____. This fat helps keeps keep the meat moist during cooking.

2 Check that you understand the meaning of the following key terms by defining each in a sentence.

connective tissue	myosin	actin
collagen	elastin	gelatine
myoglobin	marbling	invisible fat
proteolytic enzymes		

Fish

Figure 4.03

Fish is classified into three groups: white, oily and shellfish. The government advises that individuals should aim to eat at least two portions of fish a week, one of which should be oily. The use of new technologies and improvements in modern trawlers has maintained the UK fish supply. Selected fish such as trout and salmon are also bred on fish farms, where large quantities can be produced to meet market demand. Much consideration is now given to producing a sustainable supply of fish such as Pollack.

Structure of fish

The structure of muscle in fish is made up from segments of short fibres called **myomeres**, which give fish its characteristic flaky texture. These segments are separated by fine connective tissue composed of collagen. The connective tissue is very fragile and converts to gelatine during cooking. The absence of tough elastin, its short fibres and conversion of collagen to gelatine during cooking means that fish is cooked very easily and is easily digestible. However, care needs to be taken not to overcook fish as it will fall apart.

Cooking improves the colour and flavour of fish and destroys harmful bacteria. However, fish can also be eaten raw, for example, sushi. Raw fish must be very fresh and finely sliced.

Nutritional value of fish

Fish is a good source of protein containing 15 to 20 g of protein per 100 g and is a good source of iodine. Small fish that are eaten whole, such as whitebait and some canned fish, provide calcium. Although many fish live in a salt-water environment, fish do not contain high amounts of sodium or chloride. Oily fish are a source of vitamin A and vitamin D. Fish liver oils contain vitamin E and *n-3* (omega 3) fatty acids.

Activity 4.5

Discussion

	Cod	Haddock	Plaice	Herring	Mackerel	Salmon
Energy value (kJ)	337	345	336	791	914	750
Protein (g)	18.3	19.0	16.7	17.8	18.7	20.2
% Energy from protein	92.3	93.6	84.5	38.3	34.8	45.8
Total fat (g)	0.7	0.6	1.4	13.2[a]	16.1[a]	11.0
% Energy from fat	7.7	6.4	15.4	61.7	65.2	54.3
PUFA (g)	0.4	0.3	0.3	2.7	3.3	3.1
Calcium (mg)	9	14	45	60	11	21
Iron (mg)	0.1	0.1	0.3	1.2	0.8	0.4
Vitamin A (μg)	2	0	0	45[b]	45[b]	13
Thiamin (μg)	0.04	0.04	0.2	0.01	0.14	0.23
Vitamin D (μg)	0	0	0	19.0	8.2	5.9

PUFA, polyunsaturated fatty acid.

[a]Value varies through the year, being highest in July–October.

[b]Expressed as retinol equivalents.

Source: Michael E. J. Lean, Food Science, Nutrition and Health, 7th ed. (Hodder Arnold, 2006)

The table shows the nutrient composition of 100 g of raw fish.

What observations can you make about the nutritional value of fish in the diet?

Oily fish have more than 5 per cent (5 g/100 g) fat in their flesh; white fish such as cod and halibut have less than 5 per cent fat in their flesh. Oily fish contain *n-3* fatty acids, most notably eicosapentaenoic acid (EPA) and docosahexaenoic acid (DHA) a well as alpha linolenic acid. Including fish in the diet, particularly oily fish, may be associated with a lower risk of cardiovascular disease, as the *n-3* fatty acids present in fish protect against heart disease.

Choice of fish

White fish

White fish store their fat reserves in the liver. Some types of white fish are described below.

- *Cod* – can be cut into steaks or filleted into portions. Usually fried or poached.

- *Coley* – has a coarse texture and a dry indistinctive flavour, so is often used in stews, soups or pies.

- *Haddock* – a versatile fish, which can also be smoked.

- *Hake* – due to over fishing, this is quite a scarce fish. It has a very delicate flavour.

- *Halibut* – a flat fish that has an excellent texture. Can be poached, boiled, grilled or shallow fried, and can be smoked.

- *Monkfish* – a firm, close textured fish, which can be cooked by a number of methods.

- *Plaice* – flat and oval in shape. Usually deep-fried or grilled.

- *Pollack* – a member of the cod family and a sustainable sourced fish. Can be cooked by a variety of methods.

- *Sea bass* – usually farmed, but sea bass is available around the coast of Britain. Has an excellent flavour and lean, white, very soft flesh. Can be cooked in a number of different ways, including whole.

- *Skate* – a very large and bony flat fish. It is served on the bone and either poached, shallow or deep fat fried.

- *Sole* – considered the best flat fish because it is very versatile. Cooked by poaching, grilling or frying.

Oily fish

Oily fish store their fat reserves in the flesh and the liver. Some types of oily fish are shown below.

- *Anchovies* – small round fish mainly tinned in oil and used for garnishing, snacks, salads and savouries.

- *Eel* – generally used in fish stew or the traditional delicacy of jellied eels.

- *Herring* – fresh herrings are served at breakfast and lunch and can be grilled, fried or soused (marinated).

- *Kippers* – these are split, salted, dried, smoked herrings, traditionally served at breakfast.

- *Mackerel* – served at breakfast or lunch and are traditionally grilled, fried, smoked or soused.

- *Salmon* – can be fresh, tinned and smoked.

- *Sardines* – small fish from the pilchard family. Can be eaten fresh or bought tinned.

- *Trout* – fresh trout can be poached, grilled, or fried and is available smoked.

- *Tuna* – can be eaten fresh or tinned in brine, oil or spring water.

- *Whitebait* – the young of herring; they are usually deep-fried and eaten whole.

Shellfish

Shellfish are divided into **crustaceans** and **molluscs**. Crustaceans have legs and a partially jointed shell. Molluscs have a hard outer shell and no legs. They may also be bivalves – a shell in two hinged parts. Shellfish have no backbone. Here are some examples of shellfish.

Molluscs

- *Cockles* – cockles are soaked in salt water and then steamed or boiled. Used in salads, soups or eaten on their own.

- *Mussels* – tender, delicately flavoured fish. Can be served hot or cold as a main dish or in a salad.

- *Oysters* – most oysters are eaten raw, so it is essential that they are fresh.

- *Scallops* – tender, highly flavoured fish. Scallops must be cooked quickly and are often served very simply fried in butter or oil.

Crustaceans

Crayfish – similar to large lobsters but without the claws. Can be served hot or cold.

Lobster – can be served hot or cold and in a number of dishes with sauces.

Scampi – these resemble small lobsters. Only the tail flesh is eaten and scampi are used mainly for garnishing and salads.

Prawns – used for garnishing fish dishes and for cocktails, canapés and salads.

Crab – used in cocktails and salads, or eaten on its own as dressed crab.

Cephalopods

Cephalopods is the name given to the squid and octopus family. They need to be prepared and cooked carefully, otherwise they can be tough.

Storage

Fish deteriorates very quickly after death because the lack of connective tissue makes the muscle protein more susceptible to spoilage. It is therefore essential that when buying fish it should be as fresh as possible. For this reason, most fish is placed on ice or frozen while still at sea, as this increases the shelf life of fish. Once purchased, fresh fish should be cooked, chilled or frozen as soon as possible.

Activity 4.6

Research
Find out what a consumer needs to check for to ensure the fish they are buying is fresh.

Cooking methods

Fish cooks very easily and quickly. It is often prepared beforehand by a fishmonger or fish specialist in a supermarket, and is sold whole, or cut into fillets, steaks or cutlets. The cut chosen will depend upon the method of cooking.

Cooking fish preserves its flavour and nutrients. There are a number of different cooking methods for fish.

Fillet   Steak   Cutlet

Figure 4.04 *Cuts of fish*

- *Frying* – fish can be coated in egg and breadcrumbs, batter or just flour, before being fried. Coating fish helps to retain its flavour and protects its delicate structure.

- *Grilling/barbecuing* – this method preserves flavour and is especially successful with whole fish, flat fish and oily fish. The fish should only be turned once to ensure it does not fall apart.

- *Baking* – baking fish helps to preserve its flavour and retains moisture. Baked fish may be stuffed or wrapped in foil or parchment.

- *Poaching* – fish can be poached in a small amount of liquid such as milk or stock. Using the cooking liquid as the basis of a sauce to serve with the fish will ensure that any nutrients lost in the cooking process are retained.

- *Steaming* – fish can be very successfully steamed in an electric steamer or on a lightly greased plate over a pan of boiling water.

- *Microwave cooking* – this method is well suited to cooking fish because it is quick so moisture, flavour and nutrients are retained, and cooking smells are minimal.

Fish can also be successfully preserved by a number of methods:

- *Salting* – a traditional method of preserving fish, for example, salt cod. Adding salt can improve the flavour of fish.

- *Marinating* – adding acid such as lemon juice or vinegar can improve the flavour of fish and increase its shelf life. Soused (rollmop) herrings are an example of marinated fish.

- *Drying* – drying fish in the sun is a traditional method of preserving used in many warm countries.

- *Smoking* – this gives a characteristic smell and flavour to the fish, as well as acting as a form of preservation; for example, smoked mackerel.

- *Canning* – usually used for small oily fish. The fish are prepared and then canned in a variety of mediums such as brine (salt water), spring water, tomato sauce or oil.

- *Freezing* – white fish freezes very successfully and can be processed and reformed into blocks and frozen. These blocks are usually made of fillets. Minced fish comes from trimming of fillets and recovery from the skeleton. The mince itself can be formed into blocks or used to fill spaces in the fillet blocks. A wide variety of processed fish products are available, for example, fish fingers and fish cakes, where blocks of fish have been cut into shapes and covered with batter or breadcrumbs.

Figure 4.05

Activity 4.7

Review

Look in some recipe books and make a list of as many fish dishes as you can.

Choose one to make in your next practical session.

Activity 4.8

Review

Explain the nutritive value of fish.

Identify the factors that need to be taken into consideration when cooking fish.

CHECK YOUR UNDERSTANDING

Check you understand the meaning of the following key terms. Write a sentence using each word.

crustacean	**mollusc**	**cephalopod**
myomeres	**collagen**	**gelatine**

Eggs

An egg supplies a developing chick embryo with all the nutrients needed during the early stages of growth. It is a valuable commodity because of the nutrients it contains and its variety of uses.

The egg consists of three main parts:

1 shell – equates to around 10 per cent of the egg and is made primarily of phosphate and calcium carbonate

2 egg white (albumen) – equates to around 60 per cent of the egg and is divided into thin white and thick white

3 yolk – equates to around 30% of the egg and is separate from the egg white by the **vitelline membrane**. The yolk is held in position by the **chalaza**.

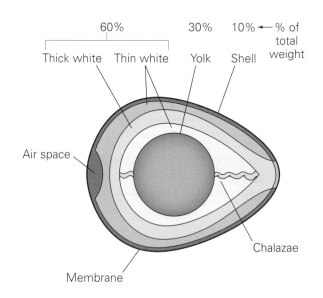

Figure 4.06 *Structure of a hen's egg*

Source: *Michael E. J. Lean,* Food Science, Nutrition and Health, *7th ed. (Hodder Arnold, 2006)*

Nutritional value of eggs

Eggs contain valuable amounts of iron and high biological value protein. They are also a good source of fat, vitamin A and calcium, and contain a small amount of vitamin D and B group vitamins. Eggs can therefore make a significant contribution to a healthy diet.

A medium-size egg has an energy value of 76 kcal, so the consumption of one egg daily would contribute around 3 per cent of the average energy requirement of an adult man and 4 per cent of the AER of an adult woman. Eggs do not contain vitamin C, carbohydrate or dietary fibre. The fat content of an egg is 10.8 per cent, which is found almost entirely in the yolk; less than 0.05 per cent fat is contained in the albumen. The types of fatty acid in an egg are approximately:

- 11 per cent polyunsaturated
- 44 per cent monounsaturated
- 29 per cent saturated.

Egg white

Egg white mainly consists of water, dissolved salts, and proteins called **ovalbumin**, **conalbumin** and **ovomucoid**. It also contains the B vitamin riboflavin.

Egg yolk

Egg yolk is approximately half water, one-third fat and one-sixth protein. It also contains calcium, iron, vitamin A, vitamin D, vitamin E, riboflavin, thiamin and niacin.

Eggs contain cholesterol but it has now been established that dietary cholesterol has little influence on blood cholesterol levels in healthy individuals. A hen's diet can be modified in order to enhance her eggs' nutritional value. For instance, flaxseed and fish oil are added to hens' feed to increase the n-3 (omega 3) fatty acid content, and it is possible to produce vitamin E-enriched eggs too.

Choice of eggs

The term 'egg' applies to all edible eggs of birds such as hens, ducks, quails, geese and gulls. Hens' eggs are most commonly eaten in the UK – around 26 million eggs are eaten each year and about 85 per cent of these eggs are produced in the UK.

Activity 4.9

Discussion

Nutrient	Nutrient content per 100 g
Energy (kJ)	612
Protein (g)	12.3
Fat, total (g)	10.9
Fat, saturated (g)	3.4
Fat, polyunsaturated (g)	1.2
Carbohydrate (g)	0
Water (g)	75
Cholesterol (mg)	450
Calcium (mg)	52
Iron (mg)	2
Sodium (mg)	140
Vitamin A (μg)	140
Thiamin (mg)	0.09
Riboflavin (mg)	0.47
Niacin (mg)	3.68
Vitamin C (mg)	0
Vitamin D (μg)	1.75
Vitamin E (mg)	1.6

The table shows the nutrient content of eggs per 100 g. What observations can you make about the nutritional value of eggs in the diet?

Eggs are graded by size and quality according to European Union regulations:

1 Small 53 g or under

2 Medium 53–63 g

3 Large 63–73 g

4 Very large – 73 g and above.

Activity 4.10

Research opportunity

Using sketches where appropriate, describe the characteristics of a fresh and stale egg, and explain how you can test an egg for freshness. You will need to carry out research using appropriate sources of information.

Eggs are tested for quality – only top quality 'A' grade eggs are available to the consumer. These eggs have to be naturally clean, fresh, internally perfect and with an air cell not exceeding 6 mm in depth. Eggs that are graded 'B' and 'C' are only used in manufacturing.

Eggs are usually sold in pre-packed boxes stamped with the packing date, size of egg and 'best before' date. More than 80 per cent of the eggs produced in the UK also carry the Lion Quality mark – a registered trademark – that shows the eggs have been produced to high food safety standards.

Figure 4.07 *Lion Quality mark*

Eggs should be kept in a refrigerator, ideally in their box or in a specialised compartment, away from other foods. If eggs are to be used for baking, they should be taken out of the refrigerator before they are used in order to allow them to come up to room temperature. Cracked eggs should not be used because bacteria may have entered the egg.

There has been much publicity about the systems of egg production in the UK. The main systems of egg production in the UK are:

- battery farming (intensive)
- deep litter (semi-intensive)
- barn
- free range.

Public knowledge and disapproval of intensive methods of egg production has meant consumers have begun to make an active choice to buy more barn and free range eggs.

Raw eggs have been the source of infection in a number of salmonella food-poisoning cases. The Department of Health has therefore issued guidelines regarding the consumption of raw eggs, as described below.

- Vulnerable people such as the elderly, infirm, pregnant women and children should not eat raw or lightly cooked eggs.

- Vulnerable people should also avoid uncooked foods such as mayonnaise, mousses and ice creams.

- Look for the Lion Quality mark, which will mean that the eggs have been produced to the highest standards of food safety.

- Hands should be washed before and after handling raw eggs.

Eggs are also available in liquid, frozen or spray-dried form and these forms are particularly useful to the caterer, for example, dried egg white is used to make meringues or royal icing, which is used to decorate traditional wedding or Christmas cakes.

Uses of eggs

Figure 4.08 *Eggs are used in a variety of dishes*

The cooking methods used for eggs are classified according to the three main performance characteristics of the egg:

- coagulation
- emulsification
- foaming.

More information on these characteristics can be found later in this chapter; this section will focus on the different uses of eggs in food preparation.

Coagulation

- *Coagulation* – when eggs are heated, the protein in the white and yolk starts to coagulate, which means that the liquid egg becomes firmer. As heating continues, the egg eventually becomes solid. Eggs cooked by boiling, poaching, frying, scrambling and omelettes all illustrate this process.

- *Thickening* – sauces, custards and soups can be thickened by adding egg and then heating. Adding egg enriches the nutrient content of a food.

- *Binding* – eggs are very useful to bind ingredients together. The addition of egg adds moisture to a mixture and holds the ingredients together. As the food is cooked, the egg coagulates and keeps the product whole. Examples of foods bound with egg are rissoles, burgers, meatballs and croquettes.

- *Coating* – eggs are used as a coating, usually mixed with breadcrumb. The egg enables the coating to stick to the surface of a product. It forms a protective barrier during cooking and can prevent the food from absorbing too much oil. Examples include fishcakes and fish fingers.

- *Glazing* – brushing egg over the surface of a baked item before cooking gives it a glossy golden brown finish, for example, scones and pastry products such as pies, pasties and sausage rolls.

- *Garnishing* – slices of hard-boiled eggs can be used as a garnish on dishes such as Kedgeree and curry.

Emulsification

Egg yolk is used to stabilise an emulsion – a mixture of oil and water. Adding egg yolk to a mixture of oil and water prevents the two liquids from separating because egg yolk contains lecithin, which acts as an emulsifier. An example of this is mayonnaise, which is an emulsion of oil and vinegar, held together by egg yolk.

Foaming

When egg white is whisked, it incorporates air and produces foam. This foam will gradually collapse but if it is heated the foam becomes permanent. Egg whites can be whisked to make meringues and soufflés, and can be folded into mousses. Whole egg can also be whisked, but does not incorporate air so well, although it can give fatless sponges a light and airy texture, for example, Swiss roll, sponge flan and sponge cake.

Activity 4.11

Practical opportunity

Copy and complete the table.

Use of Eggs	Examples of dishes
Coagulation	
Thickening	
Binding	
Coating	
Glazing	
Garnishing	
Emulsification	
Foaming	

In your next practical lesson, make one of the dishes.

CHECK YOUR UNDERSTANDING

Check you understand the meaning of the following key terms. Write a sentence using each word.

chalaza vitelline membrane ovalbumin

conalbumin ovomucoid coagulation

emulsification foaming

Milk and dairy products

Milk is the natural food for young mammals. It is also used in the development of a number of products made from milk, known as dairy products, including butter, cheese, cream and yogurt.

Milk and milk products (cheese and yogurt) are important sources of protein, B vitamins such as riboflavin and B12, and minerals such as calcium, zinc and magnesium. Vitamin A and small amounts of vitamin D are found in whole-milk products.

Data from the 2004 National Diet and Nutrition Survey (NDNS) of British adults aged 19–64 years show that milk and milk products in the diet provide:

- 43 per cent of calcium intake

- 33 per cent of riboflavin intake

- 35 per cent (men) and 42 per cent (women) of iodine intake.

Milk and milk products also provide:

- 27 per cent of vitamin A intake
- 11 per cent of magnesium intake
- 13 per cent of potassium intake.

Nutritional value of milk

Milk is a source of high biological value protein; the protein accounts for 3 per cent of the weight of the milk. The main proteins in milk are called **caseinogens**, **lactalbumin** and **lactoglobulin**.

Milk contains zinc, magnesium, potassium, phosphorus, vitamin B12, vitamin A, vitamin D and riboflavin. In the UK, milk is one of the major sources of calcium, contributing 43 per cent of calcium intake in adults (20 mg per 100 g).

Although milk contains fat, the amount depends upon the type of milk:

- whole milk (blue cap) – 3.9 per cent fat
- semi skimmed milk (green cap) – 1.6 per cent fat
- skimmed milk (red cap) – 0.1 per cent fat.

Milk also contains carbohydrate in the form of

Activity 4.12

Review

Analyse the table below and discuss the statement: Is milk the perfect food?

Composition of fresh milk

Nutrient	Amount per 100 g
Energy	271 kj
Carbohydrate	4.7 g
Fat	3.8 g
Protein	3.4 g
Water	88 g
Vitamin C	1.5 mg
Calcium	103 mg
Iron	0.1 mg
Niacin	90 mg
Riboflavin	170 mg
Thiamin	50 mg
Vitamin A	56 mg
Vitamin D	0.1 mg

Source: Adapted from Michael E. J. Lean, Food Science, Nutrition and Health, *7th ed. (Hodder Arnold, 2006)*

lactose; this accounts for about 5 per cent of the weight of milk.

Choice of milks

In the UK, cows milk is most commonly consumed,

Figure 4.09

although other types such as ewes and goats milk are also consumed. Most milk undergoes some form of heat processing such as pasteurisation, sterilisation or ultra high temperature (UHT) treatment to ensure that any harmful microorganisms are destroyed before the milk is consumed and to improve keeping qualities. Milk is available in a number of different types:

- **Pasteurised milk** is treated to a temperature of 71.7°C for 15 seconds and then cooled quickly to less than 10°C.

- **Sterilised milk** is preheated to 50°C, separated and standardised to produce whole, semi skimmed or skimmed milk. The milk is then bottled and passed through a steam pressure chamber at temperatures between 110°C and 130°C for 10 to 30 minutes and then cooled in a cold-water tank.

- **UHT milk** is **homogenised** and then heated to a temperature of at least 135°C for one second and then packed into cartons. Homogenised means the milk is forced through a fine aperture that breaks up the fat globules to an even size so that they remain distributed throughout the milk and don't form a cream layer on top of the milk. All three types of milk – whole milk, semi skimmed and skimmed – are available pasteurised or pasteurised homogenised.

- *Evaporated milk* is concentrated sterilised milk, which is usually canned and has twice the concentration of milk.

- *Condensed milk* is concentrated in the same way as evaporated milk, and sugar is added. It is not sterilised because the milk is preserved by the addition of sugar.

- *Dried milk powder* is produced by the water content of milk being evaporated off to produce a solid that has about 5 per cent water content.

- *Soya milk* is made from soya beans.

- *Goats milk* and *ewes milk* are obtained from goats and sheep respectively.

Uses of milk

Whole milk, semi skimmed, skimmed and UHT milk can be used in many ways.

- Soups – for example, cream of mushroom.

- Sauces – for example, parsley sauce, roux sauce.

- Batters – for example, pancakes, Yorkshire puddings.

- Puddings – for example, rice pudding, bread and butter pudding.

- Baked products – for example, bread, scones and cakes.

- Hot drinks – added to coffee, tea, lattes, cappuccinos and hot chocolate.

- Cold drinks – milk shakes and smoothies.

- Glazing – brushing over the surface of foods to be baked will give a smooth shiny finish.

In addition:

- Dried milk powder is a very useful store cupboard ingredient because of its keeping qualities. It is also useful when making bread in a bread maker.

- Soya milk is a useful alternative to cows milk and can be used by vegetarians, vegans and people with an intolerance to cows milk.

- Goats milk is nutritionally similar to cows milk and has a very distinctive taste. It can be useful for people with a lactose intolerance.

Activity 4.13

Practical opportunity

Make a dish which contains milk.
Calculate the calcium content of your chosen dish.

Activity 4.14

Research

A growing number of people have intolerance to dairy products.
Investigate the alternatives available to dairy products.
Do they provide an effective replacement to the equivalent dairy products?

Butter

Figure 4.10

Butter is a natural dairy product which is a water-in-oil emulsion made from cream.

Nutritional value of butter

Butter contains around 80 per cent fat, so is a high energy food. It also contains protein, vitamins A and D, and a small amount of calcium.

Choice of butter

There are two types of butter:

1 **Lactic butter (unsalted)** – the pasteurised cream is ripened before churning with a lactobacillus culture, which gives the butter a slightly acidic flavour and improves its keeping qualities.

2 **Sweetcream butter** – the cream is not ripened before churning and therefore the salt content needs to be higher to assist the keeping qualities.

Uses of butter

Butter has a number of uses:

● Spreading on bread, toast and crumpets.

● As a base for sauces, soups, making brandy butter and butter icing.

● Pastries – shortcrust, sweet shortcrust, puff and flaky.

● Shallow frying

● Basting – melted butter on fish and meat can be combined with herbs or spices.

● Glazing – on cooked vegetables such as potatoes and carrots.

Cream

Cream is made by separating the fat and solids from milk. It is a fat-in-water emulsion. The composition of

Figure 4.11

the different types of cream is controlled by law. Cream should be stored in a refrigerator and kept covered because it can easily absorb smells from other foods.

Nutritional value of cream

Protein is found in small amounts in cream. The fat content of cream varies according to the type. Carbohydrate is present as lactose, and cream also contains calcium and vitamins A and D.

Activity 4.15

Review

Look at the table below which shows the nutrient composition of milks and creams. What observations can be made about the nutrient composition of the different types of cream and milk?

Type	Energy Kcal	Protein g	Fat g	Carbohydrate g	Sodium mg	Calcium mg
Half cream	568	2.8	12.3	4.1	55	96
Single cream	813	2.6	19.1	3.9	50	91
Whipping cream	1536	2.0	39.3	3.0	42	62
Double cream	1847	1.7	48.0	2.6	39	50
Whole milk	274	3.3	3.9	4.6	43	118
Semi skimmed milk	195	3.5	1.7	4.7	43	120

Source: Michael E. J. Lean, Food Science, Nutrition and Health, 7th ed. (Hodder Arnold, 2006)

Choice of cream

There are many different types of cream available and all vary in terms of their fat content.

Cream	Fat content %
Clotted	55
Double	48
Extra thick double cream	35
Whipping	35
Sterilised cream	23
Aerosol cream	35
Single cream	18
Soured cream	18

Use of cream

The choice of cream depends upon its use. When cream is whipped, it is transformed from a liquid into a foam. The air bubbles that are introduced into the cream are stabilised by a thin layer of denatured milk protein. For cream to be whipped it must have a fat content of 38–42 per cent. If the fat content is too low, there will not be enough fat to enclose the air bubbles and form a foam. If the fat content is too high, the fat globules come into contact with each other too easily and instead butter granules are formed. Some types of cream are described below.

- *Clotted cream* – a thick and spreadable cream; it is slightly granular in texture and has a very rich texture. Traditionally served as part of a cream tea – scones spread with jam and clotted cream and served with a pot of tea. Clotted cream cannot be whipped.

- *Double cream* – can be poured over desserts or added to sauces. It can also float on the top of coffee. It can be whipped to one-and-a-half times its original volume and then piped as a decoration on cakes and desserts.

- *Extra thick double cream* – as its name suggests, it is thick and can be spooned over desserts, but it cannot be whipped.

- *Whipping cream* – can be piped and used in sweet dishes. Can also be used as a filling for cakes and pastries.

- *Sterilised cream* – usually found in cans. It is spoonable and, due to the sterilisation process, it has a very distinctive taste and a long shelf life.

- *Aerosol cream* – this cream may contain additives such as sugar. It is useful as an instant topping on flans, fruit and trifle, but must be served immediately because it collapses into a liquid within half an hour of being squirted from the can.

- *Single cream* – single cream will not whip; it is used as an accompaniment to desserts, or added to sauces and soups to enrich them.

- *Soured cream* – this does not whip. Used in both sweet and savoury dishes such as dips and as a topping for jacket potatoes. It has quite a sharp taste.

Activity 4.16

Practical opportunity

Make a dish using a cream of your choice.

Calculate the saturated fat content of your dish.

Assess whether it can be part of a healthy balanced diet.

Cheese

Figure 4.12

Cheese is made from milk protein coagulated by the addition of an enzyme such as rennet, which produces milk solids (casein curd) and liquid (whey), which is drained off. The different kinds of cheese result from different methods of production and raw ingredients.

Nutritional value of cheese

Cheese is a highly concentrated food. It contains protein of a high biological value, fat and carbohydrate in the form of sugars, particularly lactose. It is a good source of calcium, potassium, phosphorus, sodium and chloride, and also contains vitamins A and D.

The table at the foot of the page shows the nutrient content per 100 g of three types of cheese.

Choice of cheese

Cheese is classified according to its country of origin, and the place in which it was made. Some common types of cheese are shown below.

- *British cheeses* – Cheddar, Cheshire, double Gloucester, Caerphilly, Wensleydale and stilton
- *French cheeses* – Brie, Camembert, Port Salut, Emmental and Roquefort.
- *Italian cheeses* – gorgonzola, mascarpone, mozarella, parmesan and ricotta.

Cheese is also classified according to the methods used to make it:

- *Soft* – Brie, Camembert
- *Semi hard* – Caerphilly, Port Salut
- *Hard* – Cheddar, Cheshire, double Gloucester
- *Soft curd cheeses* – made from pasteurised milk and soured by the addition of milk souring culture and rennet to produce a soft low-fat cheese
- *Cottage cheese* – a low-fat, high protein cheese
- *Quark* – a salt-free and fat-free soft cheese.

There is now a range of low-fat cheeses with half the fat of traditional cheese.

Cream cheeses are not true cheeses because they are made from cream rather than curd.

Use of cheese

There are many uses for cheese. Some examples are given below.

- *Sauces* – hard cheeses, for example, Cheddar, are useful in dishes such as cauliflower cheese or pasta bake.
- *Fillings* – many cheeses can be used as fillings for sandwiches, paninis and jacket potatoes.
- *Toppings* – many cheeses can be used in au gratin dishes; mozzarella is a good cheese to use as a pizza topping.
- *Dips and spreads* – cottage cheese and cream cheese make a good base for dips and spreads.
- *Baked products* – hard cheeses can be grated into products such as cheese twists or Quiche Lorraine.
- *Soufflés* – savoury soufflés are often flavoured with cheese.
- *Desserts* – cream cheese and mascarpone cheese are used in dishes such as cheesecake and tiramisu.
- *Fondues* – semi hard cheeses such as Emmental can be melted to make a fondue.

Yoghurt

Yoghurt is made by heat-treating homogenised milk that has been treated with two cultures – Streptococcus thermophilus and lactobacillus bulgaricus bacteria. The introduction of these bacteria converts the lactose present in the milk to lactic acid.

Milk and milk products must be stored in a refrigerator because they are high-risk foods. Care should be taken to check the use by dates specified on the packaging. Once opened, the same also applies to UHT milks and ambient (longlife) yogurts.

Cheese	Energy kj	Protein g	Fat g	Carbohydrate g	Calcium mg	Vitamin A µg	Vitamin D µg
Cheddar	1680	26	34	0	800	363	0.3
Stilton	1930	26	40	0	350	450	0.3
Cream cheese	1840	3	47	0	100	450	0.3

Source: Michael E. J. Lean, Food Science, Nutrition and Health, *7th ed. (Hodder Arnold, 2006)*

Figure 4.13

Nutritional value of yoghurt

Yoghurt is a rich source of calcium – a 250 g serving of most types of yoghurt provides 450 mg of calcium. The live cultures in yoghurt increase the absorption of calcium. Yoghurt is an excellent source of protein, with plain (unflavoured) yoghurt containing around 10–14 g of protein per 250 g. Besides being a rich source of protein, the culturing of the milk proteins during fermentation (when milk is curdled by bacteria) makes the proteins easier to digest. Potassium and phosphorus are present in yoghurt in useful amounts, and it contains small amounts of thiamin, riboflavin and niacin.

Choice of yoghurt

There are many varieties of yoghurt available, but the main types are:

● stirred yoghurt – which has a smooth, fluid consistency

● set yoghurt – which has a solid, firmer texture.

In addition, there are low fat yoghurts and whole-milk creamy yoghurts, both of which are available plain and flavoured.

Yoghurt drinks are increasing in popularity and some contain additional bacteria to aid the digestive system.

Use of yoghurt

● *Drinks* – smoothies and milk shakes can be made with yoghurt and fruit.

● *Desserts* – yoghurt can be used when making cheesecake or mousse.

● *Salad dressings* – low fat yoghurt is particularly useful when making salad dressings and dips.

● *Cream alternative* – yoghurt is a low fat alternative to cream or cream fillings.

● *Toppings* – yoghurt can be combined with herbs or other ingredients as a topping for jacket potato.

A recent development in the range of dairy products available is the milk-based functional foods that can help lower blood cholesterol. Milk, yoghurt and cheese are now available enriched with plant-derived sterols or stanols, which can lower LDL-cholesterol.

Activity 4.17

Review

Write a report on the role of dairy products in the UK diet, and their usefulness in the preparation of meals (maximum 500 words).

Alternative protein sources

People choose not to eat meat for a number of different reasons and instead obtain their protein from other sources. Manufacturers have responded to this need and have produced meat-like products called **meat analogues** or protein alternatives. Such products are designed to imitate the sensory properties of meat, i.e. the taste and texture of meat.

CHECK YOUR UNDERSTANDING

Check you understand the meaning of the following key terms. Write a sentence using each word.

caseinogen	**lactalbumin**	**lactoglobulin**
pasteurised milk	**sterilised milk**	**homogenised milk**

Nutritional value of alternative protein sources

Meat analogues are a useful source of high biological value (HBV) protein, particularly for vegetarians. They also contain some fibre and are low in fat, particularly saturated fat.

Consuming 25 g of soya protein per day can help to lower blood cholesterol levels. The soya bean used to make some of the meat analogues is an excellent source of HBV protein. It is low in saturated fats and is cholesterol free. It also contains high levels of anti-carcinogenic properties.

Tofu, tempeh, miso and soya sauces contain HBV protein, calcium, iron, thiamin, riboflavin and niacin.

Textured vegetable protein (TVP) contains HBV protein. It is usually fortified with vitamin B12 – a vital vitamin for vegans because B12 is naturally only found in animal sources.

Soya milk and soya dairy products have a lower fat content than cows milk, and lower saturated fat content. They are usually fortified with vitamins D and B12 and calcium. Soya oil and margarine are high in polyunsaturates.

Myco-protein, known as quorn, is naturally low in fat, contains very few calories, no cholesterol and is a source of essential dietary fibre. Quorn is a source of protein, biotin, fibre, iron and zinc and is low in saturated fat.

Choice of alternative protein sources

A wide choice of alternative protein sources is available in the UK. They are very versatile and can be used in many different ways.

- *Miso* is a fermented condiment made from soya beans, rice or barley grains, salt and water. Miso is produced by steaming polished rice, which is then inoculated with the fungus *Aspergillus oryzae* and left to ferment; this product is then called koji. Koji is then mixed with soya beans, which have been heated and extruded to form strands, together with salt and water. This is then left to ferment in large vats.

- *Myco-protein* is produced by fermentation of the organism *Fusarium graminearum* to produce fine fibres, which are formed together to produce a meat

Figure 4.14 *Quorn*

alternative. It has a similar texture to meat and contains a small amount of fibre. The myco-protein undergoes forming, cutting and texturising according to the nature of the product to be made. Myco-protein should be kept in a refrigerator or freezer until needed.

- *Soya dairy alternatives* – soya milk is made from soaking soya beans in water.

- *Tempeh* is fermented soya bean paste. It is solid and has a white fluffy outer layer and can be sliced. Tempeh should be kept in a refrigerator or freezer until needed.

- *Textured vegetable protein* is basically defatted soya flour which has been processed and dried to give a substance with a sponge-like texture, which may be flavoured to resemble meat. Soya beans are dehulled and their oil extracted before being ground into flour. This flour is then mixed with water to remove soluble carbohydrate and the residue is textured by either spinning or extrusion. It is then dehydrated and may be either cut into small chunks or ground into granules. Different varieties of flavoured TVP are available either unflavoured or flavoured to resemble meat. It is usually bought dried and needs to be kept cool in an airtight container, away from direct sunlight.

- *Tofu* is soya bean curd made from coagulated soya milk. Soya beans are soaked, crushed and heated to produce soya milk. A coagulating agent such as calcium sulphate or calcium chloride is added to produce soya curd, which is then pressed to form tofu. Tofu is sold as blocks packaged in water. It can be bought as silken tofu, which is soft and creamy in texture, or as a denser, firmer version. The firmer kind may also be purchased smoked or marinated.

- *Wheat protein* comes from gluten which is extracted and processed to resemble meat. Its trade name is Wheatpro.

Uses of alternative protein sources

Meat analogues may be used to 'bulk' or extend food products. Some ingredients, such as TVP, are used to reduce the cost of a product, for example, economy cottage pie.

- *Dehydrated TVP* can be bought either unflavoured or flavoured. It is prepared simply by mixing with water or stock and leaving to stand for a few minutes, after which it may be incorporated into recipes as a meat substitute. Because it resembles meat, it can be incorporated into dishes such as shepherd's pie and Bolognese sauce and is used in sausages, burgers and pasta dishes. Soya protein is also available incorporated into various vegetarian burgers, sausages, canned foods, etc.

- *Miso* varies in colour and flavour and is used in stews, soups and sauces.

- *Myco-protein* (quorn) is available in many different formats and is made into pies, mince, burgers and sausages. It is used to make ready meals such as curries and casseroles. Quorn is sold as chunks, minced or as deli slices. It absorbs flavours well and may be grilled, stir fried, baked or casseroled.

  Soya dairy alternatives – soya milk is used to make a variety of deserts and yoghurts. Soya milk can be used in recipes in place of cows milk.

- *Tempeh* may be flavoured and cooked in a variety of ways. It has a chewy texture and distinctive flavour. It is used as a meat substitute and can be deep fried, shallow fried, baked or steamed.

- *Tofu* can be very bland in taste and absorbs other flavours well, so is best used in recipes where flavour is provided by other ingredients. It is soft and does not have a meaty texture, yet is often used as a substitute for meat in stir-fries and steamed dishes. It is sold in blocks, packaged in water, and can be bought smoked or marinated. It can be deep fried, sautéed or diced and added to salads or casseroles.

- *Wheat protein* is very similar to meat and can be bought in some health food shops.

Activity 4.18

Review and practical opportunity

Investigate the current meat alternatives on the market.

How can meat alternatives be incorporated into family meals – suggest some suitable recipe ideas.

How economical are meat alternatives compared to meat and fish?

Write a report outlining your findings (maximum 500 words).

In your next practical lesson, make one of your recipe ideas.

CHECK YOUR UNDERSTANDING

Check you understand the meaning of the following key term.

meat analogue

Cereals

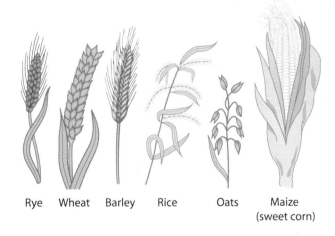

Rye   Wheat   Barley   Rice   Oats   Maize (sweet corn)

Figure 4.15 *Some varieties of cereal*

Source: J. Campbell et al, Practical Cookery, *11th ed. (Hodder Education, 2008)*

Cereals are cultivated grasses, where the grains are used as a food source. There are many different types of cereal grains and each cereal has its own individual properties. The most important cereals are wheat, maize, rice, oats, rye and barley. Most cereals are processed to form other foods or ingredients. Cereals are also known as 'staple foods' because they make up the bulk of the diet.

Nutritional value of cereals

This section gives an overview of the nutritional value of cereals. The nutritional value of each cereal is covered in more depth in the sections below on choice and use. In an average British diet, cereals and cereal products provide 30 per cent of the energy content, so they are an important source of energy and carbohydrate.

Cereals contain a significant amount of protein and because we eat a substantial amount of cereals, they can constitute a large proportion of the protein content of the diet. However, it is important to note that the proteins in cereals are low in the essential amino acid lysine. However, if cereals are eaten with other foods such as bread, lentil peas or beans, the balance of amino acids compensate one another.

Cereals contain fat, and within the fat is the fat-soluble vitamin E.

Cereals contain substantial amounts of the B group vitamins, although the amounts depend upon how the grain has been milled. The fibre content of cereals also depends on the milling process.

Cereals contain sodium, magnesium and zinc and because some cereal products are fortified, they also contain significant amounts of calcium and iron.

It is thought that eating cereals regularly, particularly wholegrain cereals, may have a role in the prevention of chronic diseases. Evidence suggests that people who consume wholegrain cereals have a lower incidence of coronary heart disease and Type 2 diabetes.

Choice of cereals

Each type of cereal has its own distinctive properties, which make it suitable for a variety of food products. Cereals are important in the diet because they are relatively cheap to produce, and are a good source of energy. Cereals are processed and used to produce a range of products such as flour, breakfast cereals, bread and pasta. It is useful to keep cereals in the store cupboard as they have a very long shelf life. However, cereals are prone to infestation by insects if kept for long periods of time, particularly if they are not kept in a covered container. They should be kept in a cool dry place.

- *Barley* is mainly sold as pearl barley, which is the whole grain with its husk removed.

- *Maize* (or corn) is not widely used in the UK but it is an important part of the diet in America and South Africa. Maize is a good source of energy.

- *Oats* are richer in fats and minerals than other cereals and contain a high level of protein. Oats are ground to produce oatmeal. Coarse, medium and fine grades of oatmeal are available and have a variety of uses. Oats are rolled into flakes after being partly cooked by steam, which makes them easier to cook.

- *Pasta* is the name given to a wide variety of wheat flour products. It is a simple mixture of flour, salt and water although sometimes egg is added to make a richer pasta. Most **pasta** is made with a special type of wheat flour called **durum wheat flour** (also known as dopio zero flour or 00 flour). It is suitable for making pasta because durum wheat makes a stretchy dough that is rich in protein and holds its shape during cooking. Pasta provides mainly carbohydrates in the form of starch and is low in protein and fat. Pasta contains some B vitamins and minerals. Pasta is used by many athletes as an energy source, because it is rich in carbohydrates. Starchy carbohydrates are ideal for fuelling the body for training and racing, as they provide slow-release energy. Pasta can also form part of a low fat diet. Cooked pasta, without sauce, contains very little fat and is reasonably low in calories.

- *Rice* is one of the world's most important food crops. It contains the lowest amounts of protein, fat and minerals of all cereals. When rice is harvested the grains of rice are milled. Brown rice has its outer husk removed; white rice is milled and polished further to remove the **bran** and **germ**.

- *Rye* is grown in areas where the climate is too severe for wheat, such as Russia, northern Europe and the northern parts of America. The nutrients in rye are present in roughly the same amounts as wheat.

- *Wheat* consists of three layers. The bran accounts for 13 per cent of the grain and is a tough outer skin that contains most of the dietary fibre and minerals such as iron, calcium and phosphorus. The germ, which is the seed part of the grain, accounts for 2 per cent of the grain and contains most of the

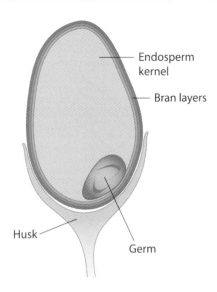

Figure 4.16 *Structure of a rice grain*
Source: J. Campbell et al, Practical Cookery, 11th ed. *(Hodder Education, 2008)*

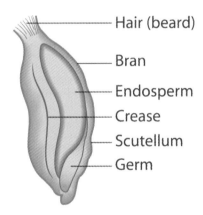

Figure 4.17 *Structure of a wheat grain*
Source: J. Campbell et al, Practical Cookery, 11th ed. *(Hodder Education, 2008)*

fat, protein and B vitamins. The scutellum is rich in thiamin. The largest part of the wheat grain is the **endosperm,** which accounts for 85 per cent of the grain. It is the starchy part consisting of mainly carbohydrate and protein.

Use of cereals

Barley

Pearl barley, which is the whole grain with its husk removed, is used to thicken soups, stews and casseroles, as the swollen barley grains remain and contribute to the texture of the casserole.

Figure 4.18 *Different varieties of flour*

Barley is also used in the production of barley water. Malt extract and malt flour is made from barley and
is used to make malt loaf. Beer is also made from barley.

Maize

Maize (corn) is mainly used as cattle feed in the UK. Maize is the main constituent in the popular breakfast cereal, corn flakes, and can be converted to glucose syrup or corn syrup. Maize is eaten as sweetcorn and corn on the cob. Maize is used to produce cornflour, which is used as a thickening agent in many food products such as custard powder. Its germ is rich in oil and can be refined to produce corn oil.

Oats

Rolled oats are used for porridge, which is simple and quick to make and provides a cheap, filling breakfast. Rolled oats are also used to make muesli and flapjacks. Ground oatmeal is used to make biscuits such as oat cakes and digestive biscuits. The soluble fibre content of oats helps to lower cholesterol levels and so prevent heart disease.

Pasta

There are so many types of pasta to choose from.

Pasta is available fresh or dried. Dried pasta has a firmer, more solid texture when cooked. It is excellent for chunky vegetable and meat sauces. Fresh pasta has a softer texture and will absorb the flavours of the

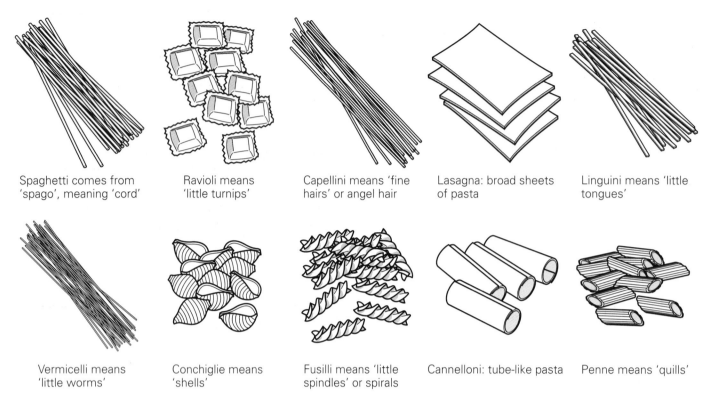

Spaghetti comes from 'spago', meaning 'cord'

Ravioli means 'little turnips'

Capellini means 'fine hairs' or angel hair

Lasagna: broad sheets of pasta

Linguini means 'little tongues'

Vermicelli means 'little worms'

Conchiglie means 'shells'

Fusilli means 'little spindles' or spirals

Cannelloni: tube-like pasta

Penne means 'quills'

Figure 4.19 *Types of pasta*

sauce it is served with. Fresh pasta suits delicate flavours and creamy sauces.

Ravioli and tortellini are types of stuffed pasta, filled with meat, cheese or vegetables. Pasta sauces coat different pasta shapes in different ways:

- long, thin pasta shapes require a runny sauce

- wide pasta such as tagliatelle and curved or hollow tube shapes such as penne are better with thicker, chunkier sauces

- very small pasta shapes like vermicelli are best for soup.

Rice

There are many different types of rice available. Rice varies according to the size and shape of the grain and the region where it is grown. Rice can be ground to make rice flour, which is used to give shortbread a short texture. Rice flour is used to make Japanese rice wine (saké).

Rice paper is made from the rice-paper plant and not from rice. It is used as an edible base to biscuits and confectionery, for example, macaroons and nougat.

Figure 4.20 *Rice grains*

Activity 4.19

Review

Copy and complete the table.

Type of rice	Characteristics and uses
Short grain rice	Rounded grains, which tend to stick together. Used for sweet dishes such as rice pudding.
Long grain rice	
Basmati rice	
Arborio rice	
Brown rice	
Easy cook rice	

Rye

Rye is made into rye flour, which is darker in colour than white flour. It is used to make bread and crisp breads such as Ryvita. Rye flour and bread contain very little **gluten**, so the bread produced is darker in colour and has a lower protein content. It also has a dense heavy texture. Rye is also used to produce alcohol.

Wheat

Wheat is usually ground into flour, which is used in many aspects of food production. The type of flour produced from wheat varies according to the rate of extraction. The **extraction rate** determines the percentage of wheat grain found in the flour:

- 100 per cent extraction flour is whole-grain flour such as wholewheat or wholemeal

- 85–90 per cent extraction flour is wheatmeal or brown flour

- 70–72 per cent extraction flour is white flour.

Couscous and cracked wheat (bulgur) is also made from wheat. Wheat can be fermented to make beer.

Activity 4.20

Research

Explain the difference in the nutrient content of wholewheat flour, brown flour and white flour.

Activity 4.21

Practical opportunity

Make a dish of pasta and sauce.
Calculate the carbohydrate content of your dish.

Activity 4.22

Review

Write a report (maximum 500 words) on the role of cereals in the UK diet, and their role in the preparation of meals.

CHECK YOUR UNDERSTANDING

Check you understand the meaning of the following key terms. Write a sentence using each word.

cereals	bran	germ
scutellum	endosperm	pasta
durum wheat flour	extraction rate	

Pulses

Figure 4.21

Pulses are the seeds of plants belonging to the leguminosae family, also known as legumes. Peas, beans and lentils all belong to this family. Pulses should be stored in clean dry containers.

Nutritional value of pulses

Pulses are a source of low biological value protein and are a useful source of protein for vegetarians because about 20 per cent of the weight of dried pulses is protein. The exception to this is the soya bean, which is of a high biological value and contains about 36 per cent of its weight as protein.

Pulses are a useful source of carbohydrate, which accounts for 50 per cent of the weight of dried pulses. Pulses are considered very healthy because they only contain small amounts of fat and are a good source of fibre.

Different pulses contain different amounts of minerals:

- soya beans and chick peas are a rich source of calcium

- green lentils, soya beans and red kidney beans are a rich source of iron

- aduki beans, soya beans and green lentils are a rich source of zinc.

Note however that the presence of phytic acid and tannins in pulses reduce the bioavailability of these minerals. Pulses also contain a number of vitamins, namely vitamin E, riboflavin, thiamin and niacin.

Choice of pulses

A wide variety of pulses are available in fresh, frozen, canned or dried form.

- *Aduki beans* – small round deep red shiny beans.

- *Black eyed beans* – white beans which have a black mark on them.

- *Borlotti beans* – pink beans with a mottled colour.

- *Broad beans* – strongly flavoured green beans.

- *Chick peas* – these look like hazelnuts.

- *Lentils* – available as red or green lentils. Puy lentils do not need soaking and hold their shape when cooking.

- *Red kidney beans* – kidney-shaped beans.

- *Soya beans* – small and round and can be black or yellow in colour. Used in the production of textured vegetable protein.

- *Split peas* – yellow in colour and similar to lentils in appearance.

Uses of pulses

Pulses have different uses in food preparation.

- Aduki beans, black eyed beans and borlotti beans can be used in stews and casseroles.

- Broad beans are used as a vegetable accompaniment to a main meal.

- Chick peas are the main ingredient in hummus.

- Lentils are used in soups, bakes, cutlets and loaves.

- Red kidney beans are used in chilli con carne.

- Soya beans are used in the production of textured vegetable protein.

- Split peas are often added to soups to provide extra protein.

Activity 4.23

Review

Explain the value of using pulses in the diet.

Activity 4.24

Practical opportunity

Prepare a main meal suitable for a lacto vegetarian, which uses a pulse as its main ingredient.

Fats and oils

Figure 4.22

Fats are obtained from animal and plant sources. In the UK, about two-thirds of dietary fat is of animal origin. At room temperature, oils are liquid and fats are solid. Fats and oils have different flavours, textures, tastes, odours and uses.

Fats and oils are mixtures of **triglycerides**, which are formed from molecules of fatty acids joined to one molecule of glycerol. A fatty acid is made up of a chain of carbon atoms with hydrogen atoms attached (see Figure 4.23).

There are two types of fatty acid that make up fats and oils:

1 **Saturated fatty acids** (SFAs), where all of the carbon atoms are saturated with hydrogen atoms.

2 Unsaturated fatty acids, which are subdivided into two groups:

a Mono-unsaturated fatty acids are fatty acids where two of the carbon atoms are joined by a double

bond, meaning that there are two missing hydrogen atoms.

b **Polyunsaturated fatty acids** (PUFAs) are fatty acids in which there are more double bonds and therefore more than two missing hydrogen atoms. They can be subdivided into *n-3* (omega 3) and *n-6* (omega 6).

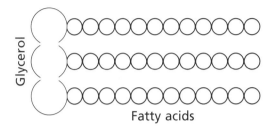

Figure 4.23 *Fatty acids*

Nutritional value of fats and oils

Fat is a concentrated source of energy – 1 g of fat provides 37 kJ (9 kcal) – more than double that provided by either protein or carbohydrate, which provide 17 kJ/g (4 kcal) and 16 kJ/g (3.75 kcal), respectively.

Fats contain the fat-soluble vitamins A, D, E and K. Only a small amount of fat is needed in the diet. Less than one-third of energy intake should come from fat. There are dangers associated with high intakes of fat, particularly saturated fats, which are associated with a raised blood cholesterol level – one of the risk factors for coronary heart disease. In addition, excessive intakes of fat result in obesity.

There are, however, fats that are beneficial to health such as omega 3 (*n-3*) fatty acids, found in oily fish, walnuts and linseeds. Omega 3 fats are thought to reduce inflammation, slow ageing, reduce the severity of respiratory disease, prevent blood clots and reduce the risk of heart attacks. It is possible to buy omega 3 supplements.

Some oils are rich in omega 6 (*n-6*) fatty acids, for example, sunflower and corn oils; others provide *n-3* fatty acids, for example, rapeseed oil and soya oil. Other oils are rich in mono-unsaturated fatty acids, for example, olive oil, rape seed oil and groundnut oil.

Margarines and spreads are important sources of vitamin E. They contribute 14 per cent of total vitamin E intake in adults. Margarines are fortified with vitamins A and D by law and low fat spreads are usually fortified with vitamins A and D too.

Choice of fats and oils

Fats and oils have different physical characteristics, so have different roles in food production. It is therefore important to choose the correct fat for the type of food to be produced.

Animal fats

Animal-derived fats tend to be solid at room temperature. Animal fats consist of 50–65 per cent saturated fatty acids, but are also a source of mono-unsaturated fatty acids and provide small amounts of polyunsaturates.

- *Butter* is not pure fat, but an emulsion of water in oil; it provides about 80 g fat/100 g.

- *Ghee* is made by heating and clarifying butter.

- *Lard* comes from pigs' fat and provides about 99 g of fat/100 g.

- *Dripping* is the fat that 'drips' from meat being roasted and has a meaty flavour; it contains 99 g fat/100 g.

- *Suet* is obtained from the shredded fat of cattle or sheep. It is solid at room temperature.

- *Fish oils* contain a high proportion of unsaturated fatty acids. Fish oils are rich in *n-3* fatty acids, vitamins A and D, and are used for vitamin supplements.

Vegetable oils

Nuts, pulses, seeds and cereals are used to make oil. Vegetable oils are often a rich source of unsaturated fatty acids, and usually contain natural antioxidants such as vitamin E, which helps the oils resist **rancidity**. Sometimes a blend of oils is used in a product to take advantage of the best characteristics of each of the different types of oils. Oils are liquid at room temperature. Some of the most common oils used in food production are:

- palm oil

- olive oil

- hazelnut oil

- walnut oil

- sunflower oil

- corn oil.

Also available are oils containing added herbs, such as tarragon, basil and thyme.

The type of oil chosen depends on what it is to be used for – olive oils are ideal for adding flavour to a salad dressing, for instance. The temperature at which an oil breaks down is an important consideration if it is being used to deep fat fry. Some oils such as sunflower oil are rich in polyunsaturates, so are a healthier choice than palm oil, for example.

Vegetable fats

Margarine

Margarine is made from a mixture of highly unsaturated oils such as rapeseed and sunflower oils. It contains less saturated fatty acids and more polyunsaturated fatty acids than butter. Margarine is defined in law as the product obtained from vegetable and/or animal fats with a fat content of more than 80 per cent, but less than 90 per cent. It is a solid emulsion of water in oil. Margarine must be produced in accordance with the Spreadable Fats (Marketing Standards) Regulations 1995.

Margarine must contain certain ingredients in certain quantities:

- Fat content – minimum 80 per cent, but less than 90 per cent

- Milk fat content – maximum 3 per cent of total fat

- Vitamin A – 800–1000 µg per 100 g

- Vitamin D – 7.05–8.82 µg per 100 g.

Source: www.nutrition.org.uk (accessed December 2008)

Margarine is available in two formats – block and soft. It is a popular alternative to butter and because it has the same fat content as butter, it can be used in cooking in the same way. Margarine is made by the process of **hydrogenation**, where hydrogen is added to unsaturated fatty acid molecules. This process changes the liquid oil into a solid fat. However, during this process trans fatty acids may be produced. This is because during the hydrogenation process hydrogen is added, which saturates some or all of the double bonds of the unsaturated fatty acid molecules. Some of the cis double bonds in the oils are changed (isomerised) to trans double bonds. Trans fatty acids can accumulate in our body and high intakes of trans fatty acids have been associated with raised blood cholesterol levels – one of the risk factors associated with coronary heart disease.

Buttery blends and spreads

There are many of these products on the market and they vary considerably in terms of their fat content, in the type of oil from which they have been made, and whether butterfat or milk solids have been added.

Figure 4.24

Buttery blends and spreads are designed to offer a healthier alternative to the product they mimic. For instance, buttery spreads mimic butter in taste but are lower in saturated fatty acids. *Utterly Butterly* is an example of such a product – it contains buttermilk and 75 per cent vegetable fat and has less than a quarter of the saturated fat content of butter.

Cholesterol-lowering spreads

Cholesterol-lowering products such as *Benecol* contain plant sterols or plant stanol esters. These have a similar structure to cholesterol and so can inhibit the absorption of cholesterol by the body.

Figure 4.25

Activity 4.25

Research

Carry out a paired comparison test (see page 145) to find out whether it is possible to tell the difference between butter and a buttery taste alternative.

Provide your testers with a sample of butter and another of a buttery taste alternative and ask them which they prefer.

Copy the table below and use it to record your results.

Discuss your results – can you tell the difference?

Paired comparison (preference) test
Which sample do you prefer – sample X or sample Y?

Results
Record each person's preferred choice with a '1' and enter a '0' against the sample they did not like.

Sample	Panellist									
	1	2	3	4	5	6	7	8	9	10
X										
Y										

Activity 4.26

Research

Visit the Benecol website (www.benecol.co.uk). Investigate the products available and word process a report on your findings (maximum 500 words). Your report should refer to types of products available, costs and health and nutritional benefits.

Low fat spreads

A huge number of low fat spreads are available. They vary in terms of fat content, the type of oil from which they have been made, and whether butterfat or milk solids have been added. They all have a very high water content, as water is added to bulk out the product. An example of a low fat spread is *Gold*. Spreads have a similar composition to margarine but are usually lower in fat. Low fat spreads contain 40 g fat/100 g. Some spreads contain as much as 75 per cent fat but they cannot be called margarine because they do not meet the minimum fat level requirement of 80 per cent. Spreads may also be fortified with vitamins A and D at levels similar to margarine; this is not required by law, but is often carried out voluntarily.

Storage of fats and oils

Butter, margarine and spreads should be stored in a refrigerator. They should be covered to prevent **oxidation** and kept away from foods with strong odours. Oils should be stored at room temperature, preferably in their original container (glass or plastic bottle). After deep fat frying the oil should be strained to remove any impurities that could lead to the oil going rancid. Oils that have been used frequently for deep frying should be thrown away because rancid oil tastes unpleasant.

Uses of fats and oils

- *Aeration* – creamed cakes such as a Victoria sandwich need air incorporated into the mixture in order to give a well risen texture. This is achieved by **creaming** the fat with caster sugar, using either a wooden spoon or an electric mixer. A fat that has been creamed contains tiny bubbles of air and form a stable foam. The result is a well-risen product with a light texture. Both butter and margarine are used to aerate products.

- *Flavour* – margarine contributes to the flavour of many foods. However, it can easily absorb strong odours from other ingredients. Butter is often used in cakes, biscuits and sauces because it gives a richer and more distinctive flavour. Butter can help retain a bakery product's moisture; this in turn can increase its shelf life.

- *Flakiness* – flaky and puff pastry use fat to produce separate layers of gluten and starch formed in the dough. The fat melts during cooking, leaving minute air pockets. The liquid present produces steam that evaporates and causes the layers to rise and prevents them from joining. Margarine and butter are used in flaky and puff pastry; low fat spreads contain too much water to make successful flaky or puff pastry. In addition, butter gives a richer flavour.

- *Retention of moisture* – in bakery items, margarine can help retain a product's moisture and therefore increase its shelf life. Fats such as dripping, butter and oil are used to baste foods cooked by dry heat, for example, barbecuing meat may be brushed with oil and a roast chicken may be basted with butter.

- *Shortening* – fats give food such as shortcrust pastry, biscuits and shortbread their characteristic short crumbly texture. The fat acts as a **shortening** agent by coating the flour particles and preventing them from absorbing water. This prevents gluten formation and therefore stops the mixture from being chewy or tough. Margarine can also be used for this purpose. Margarine produces a distinctive golden colour, while lard produces a pale yellow colour. A mixture of margarine and lard may be used to produce the desired flavour and texture combination, because lard adds shortness in baked products, making for a crumbly texture.

- *Flavour* – all fats and oils have unique flavours and odours. Some are more suited for particular purposes than others, for instance olive oil is used for salad dressings. Sesame seed oil is used to make tahini; ghee is used in curries; and butter is used in shortbread.

- *Plasticity* – fats do not melt immediately and instead soften over a range of temperatures. This property is called **plasticity**, and because it is determined by the nature of the individual fat, gives each fat its unique character. The plasticity is due to the mixture of triglycerides, each with its own melting point. Some fats are formulated so that their melting point is low and they can be spread straight from the fridge – soft margarine and 'spreadable butter', for example.

- *Cooking* – block margarine is used for cooking, and is particularly recommended for making pastry. Soft margarine is useful for cakes made by the all-in-one method. Fats that are free from water, salt and non-fat solids and which have a high smoke point are recommended for frying.

- *Spreading* – low and reduced fat spreads are not suitable for frying or baking because of their high water content. Their main use is to help reduce fat intake in the diet. Butter substitutes are formulated with a low melting point, which means they can be spread straight from the fridge.

- *Sauce making* – fat is used in the preparation of roux and all-in-one sauces. The fat prevents the flour particles from clumping together.

- *Colour* – the colour of some foods depends upon the fat used. Margarine and butter provide a rich golden brown colour.

- *Glazing* – butter is sometimes used to glaze foods, particularly vegetables such as carrots, peas and potatoes, to make them shiny in appearance.

Activity 4.27

Review

Copy and complete the table below to show the different types of fat available and their specific uses.

Type of fat	Specific uses

Activity 4.28

Research and practical opportunity

In your next practical lesson make some flaky pastry.

Recipe for flaky pastry

200 g plain flour
75 g butter
75 g white fat
Pinch of salt
5 ml lemon juice
Cold water to mix.

Method

1 Sieve the flour and salt into a bowl.
2 Divide the fat into four portions.
3 Rub in a quarter of the fat.
4 Add the lemon juice and enough water to make a soft elastic dough
5 Turn out onto a lightly floured table and knead lightly until smooth.
6 Roll dough into an oblong and mark into three.
7 Dot one quarter of the fat over the top two-thirds of the pastry.
8 Fold up the bottom third and bring down the top third, and quarter turn the pastry.
9 Repeat this twice with the remaining fat, and once more.
10 Allow the pastry to relax in the fridge before rolling and folding.

Identify the function of each of the ingredients.

Explain the changes that occur during preparation and cooking.

List some products made using flaky pastry and use your pastry to make one of them in your next practical lesson.

Activity 4.29

Review

Compare the uses of butter, margarine and oil in cooking.

Activity 4.30

Practical opportunity

Explain why butter is the choice of fat in this recipe for sweet shortcrust pastry.

In your next practical lesson, make this dish to show the use of butter in the preparation of shortcrust pastry.

Sweet shortcrust pastry dough

150 g plain flour

pinch salt

65 g butter

1 tablespoon caster sugar

2 teaspoons ground almonds (optional)

1 egg yolk

2–3 tablespoons cold water

Method

Sieve the flour and salt into a large mixing bowl. Rub the butter into the flour until it resembles fine breadcrumbs.

Stir in the sugar and almonds.

Add the egg yolk and water to make a stiff dough. Knead lightly until smooth.

Wrap in foil and chill (for 30 minutes if possible) before use.

Fruit tarts

A quantity of sweet shortcrust pastry dough (see left)

A selection of fruit such as grapes, tinned apricots or mandarin oranges

2–3 tablespoons of apricot jam for glazing

Method

Roll out the dough, cut into rounds and use to line patty tins.

Place a small round of greaseproof paper on top of each round of pastry and fill with some baking beans. Bake the cases in the oven for 15–20 minutes until golden brown.

Meanwhile prepare the fruit: Halve and seed the grapes, drain the tinned fruit.

Heat the apricot jam in a saucepan with 2 teaspoons of water. Stir until blended and sieve if it is a little lumpy.

Fill the cooked pastry cases with fruit.

Brush with the apricot glaze.

CHECK YOUR UNDERSTANDING

Check you understand the meaning of the following key terms. Write a sentence using each word.

triglyceride	saturated fatty acid	unsaturated fatty acids
polyunsaturated fatty acids	hydrogenation	aeration
shortening	plasticity	

Fruits and vegetables

Figure 4.26

Although fruit and vegetables look different, the edible parts of fruit and vegetables consist of similar types of cells (see Figure 4.27). The cell has an outer wall, which is mostly made of **cellulose**. Inside the cell there is a jelly-like substance called **cytoplasm**, which contains fat droplets and fat-soluble pigments. About 90 per cent of the cell is the vacuole containing cell sap – a watery substance containing sugars, salts, acids and pigments.

In between the cells there are small pockets called intercellular air spaces; this gives raw fruit and vegetables their opaqueness.

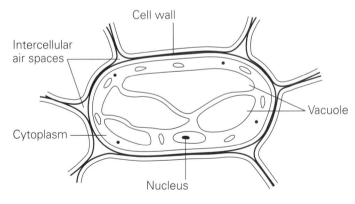

Figure 4.27 *A cell*
Source: Jill Davies, Cooking Explained, *Pearson Education Limited,* © Jill Davies 1997

Nutritional value of fruit and vegetables

Fruit and vegetables are rich sources of a number of nutrients, most notably vitamin C, folates, and non-starch polysaccharides. They also contain a number of other nutrients:

- *Carbohydrate and sugars* – roots and tubers provide much of the starch and sugar content.

- *Vitamin C* – the richest sources are in Brussels sprouts, green peppers and citrus fruits. Potatoes are also a source of vitamin C and because they are eaten in larger quantities, they do contribute quite significantly to the diet.

- *Dietary fibre* – stems are an important source of water and dietary fibre, for example, asparagus, fennel and celery.

- *Vitamin A* – the richest sources are in dark green vegetables, apricots and carrots.

- *Potassium* – bananas are a rich source of potassium.

- *Vitamin E* – avocados are a rich source of vitamin E. Most vegetables contain vitamin E, but spinach, watercress and broccoli contain the most.

- *Vitamin B group (especially folic acid or folate)* – found in spinach, broccoli and sprouts.

- *Iron* – found in peas, spinach, broccoli and prunes.

- *Calcium* – found in spinach, watercress, blackcurrants, oranges and figs.

- *Fat* – with one or two exceptions such as avocado pear, most fruit and vegetables are low in fat.

- *Protein* – protein is present in vegetables in small amounts.

The government recommends we eat at least five portions of fruit and vegetables daily – a portion is approximately 80 g. It is important to note that a portion can be fresh, frozen, canned or dried fruits and vegetables. Potatoes do not count as a portion because they are classed as a carbohydrate food. A diet rich in fruits and vegetables may lessen the risk of cardiovascular disease and some cancers.

Activity 4.31

Discussion

The table below shows the average nutrient content of fruit per 100 g of edible portion.

What observations can you make about the nutrient content of fruit?

Type of fruit	Protein g	Sugar and starch g	Calcium mg	Iron mg	Vitamin A µg	Thiamin mg	Riboflavin mg	Vitamin C mg
Apples	0.3	11.9	4	0.3	5	0.04	0.02	5
Bananas	1.1	19.2	7	0.4	33	0.04	0.07	10
Blackcurrants	0.9	6.6	60	1.3	33	0.03	0.06	200
Grapes	0.6	16.1	19	0.3	0	0.04	0.02	4
Oranges	0.8	8.5	41	0.3	8	0.10	0.03	50
Plums	0.6	7.9	12	0.3	37	0.05	0.03	3
Prunes	2.4	40.3	38	2.9	160	0.10	0.20	0
Strawberries	0.6	6.2	22	0.7	5	0.02	0.03	60

Source: Michael E. J. Lean, Food Science, Nutrition and Health, *7th ed. (Hodder Arnold, 2006)*

Note that food processing and preparation techniques can lead to the loss of some nutrients in fruit and vegetables, especially sensitive nutrients such as vitamin C and folic acid. Storing fruit and vegetables for long periods will also reduce their vitamin C and folic acid content. Fruit and vegetables should be stored in a cool, dark place for a minimum time to prevent the loss of nutrients, and to prevent sprouting, mould growth and rotting.

Activity 4.32

Discussion

The table below shows the average nutrient content of vegetables per 100 g of edible portion.

What observations can you make about the nutrient content of vegetables?

Can you make any comparisons with fruit?

Type of fruit	Protein g	Sugar and starch g	Calcium mg	Iron mg	Vitamin A µg	Thiamin mg	Riboflavin mg	Vitamin C mg
Baked beans	4.8	15.1	48	1.4	12	0.08	0.06	0
Beetroot, boiled	1.8	9.9	30	0.4	0	0.02	0.04	5
Cooked lentils	7.6	17	13	2.4	3	0.11	0.04	0
Potatoes, boiled	1.8	18	4	0.4	0	0.2	0.02	5–9
Spinach, boiled	5.1	1.4	136	4	1000	0.07	0.15	25
Tomatoes	0.9	2.8	13	0.4	100	0.06	0.04	20
Runner beans, boiled	1.9	2.7	22	0.7	67	0.03	0.07	5
Cooked cabbage, boiled	1.7	2.3	38	0.4	50	0.03	0.03	20

Source: Michael E. J. Lean, Food Science, Nutrition and Health, *7th ed. (Hodder Arnold, 2006)*

Choice of fruit and vegetables

There are many different varieties of fruit and vegetables available to us. Because of modern growing techniques and transport systems, it is easy to obtain fruit and vegetables all year round, from countries around the world. Today choice is no longer restricted to the seasons.

In recent years, the market for fruit and vegetables has become segmented, with different ranges designed to appeal to different customers. Customers can choose from value/basic range, luxury range, organic, and Fairtrade products. Ready prepared and washed products are available to suit people with busy lifestyles. Taking an example of just one product – tomatoes – a visit to a supermarket will show the huge range available today.

Activity 4.33

Starter
Name as many varieties of tomatoes and tomato-based products as you can.

Fruit and vegetables are classified into groups:

- *Soft fruits* – raspberry, blackberry, redcurrant, strawberry and bilberry.

- *Citrus fruits* – orange, lime, lemon, kumquat and grapefruit.

- *Stone fruits* – plum, apricot, peach, lychee, cherry and mango.

- *Fleshy fruits* – apple, papaya, pineapple, pear and banana.

- *Vine fruits* – grape, watermelon and cantaloupe.

- *Fruit vegetables* – aubergine, marrow, plantain, tomato and cucumber.

- *Legumes* – pea, bean and lentil.

- *Flower vegetables* – broccoli, cauliflower and calabrese.

- *Leafy vegetables* – spinach, cabbage, parsley, endive, lettuce and watercress.

- *Stem vegetables* – asparagus, fennel and celery.

- *Fungi* – oyster and button mushroom.

- *Bulbs* – onion, garlic, shallot and leek.

- *Roots* – beetroot, swede, carrot, parsnip, radish and turnips.

Chopping and preparing fruit and vegetables a short time before they are needed for cooking helps retain vitamins, as does cooking them for the minimum amount of time in as little water as possible. Dietary fibre, vitamins and minerals can be retained if fruit and vegetables are eaten with their skin on. Some fruit and vegetables go brown when cut and exposed to the air, for example, apples and potatoes. This is because of **oxidation** and is called **enzymic browning**. Enzymic browning may be slowed down by the use of an antioxidant, by adding an acidic or sugary solution to the surface, or by placing in water. Storing fruit and vegetables at low temperatures will slow down the enzymic browning process.

Activity 4.34

Research and practical opportunity
Fruit and vegetables can be eaten raw or cooked.
List all the methods of cooking fruit and vegetables, and include examples of fruit and vegetables that could be cooked by each method.
List three different recipes that use cooked fruit and three different recipes that use cooked vegetables. In your next practical session, make one of your chosen fruit recipes and one of your vegetable recipes.

Uses of fruit and vegetables

- *Addition of colour* – fruit and vegetables contribute colour to the diet. The colour pigments **chlorophyll** (green), **carotenoids** (orange) and **anthocyanins** (purples) can make dishes look attractive, for example, fruit salad.

- *Addition of flavour* – fruit and vegetables contribute flavour to the diet. Strong flavours such as garlic or orange can contribute to the appeal of a dish. Flavours can also add contrasts, for example, sweet and sour, pork and apple sauce.

- *Addition of texture* – fruit and vegetables contribute texture to the diet. They contain varying amounts of water and fibre, which accounts for the difference in their texture.

- *Setting* – fruit contains pectin which, when mixed with an acid and sugar, helps mixtures to set, for example, jam.

- *Eaten raw* – some fruit and vegetables can be eaten raw because they are appetising and doing so will ensure they retain maximum colour, flavour and texture. Raw fruit and vegetables are often eaten as snack foods or used in drinks such as smoothies.

- *Cooking* – during cooking, the cell structure of fruit and vegetables starts to break down. This is why raw fruits and vegetables become softer when cooked. Some nutrients are also lost because of the loss of water. Fruit and vegetables can be cooked by a variety of methods – stewing, boiling, steaming, baking, grilling, stir frying, and microwaving. Cooking also reduces bulk, enabling more to be eaten.

- *Processing* – fruit and vegetables can be successfully processed in a number of different ways, for example:

  - *Drying* – some fruit can be successfully dried, for example, bananas, figs and grapes (raisins).

  - *Canning* – almost all fruits and vegetables can be canned

  - *Freezing* – in preparation for freezing, vegetables must first be blanched to destroy their enzymes. This can result in the loss of some water-soluble and heat-sensitive vitamins and minerals.

- *Pickling* – some vegetables such as beetroot, cabbage and onions may be pickled successfully. The preservation process may alter physical, nutritional and sensory characteristics but it does increase the range available to the consumer.

Activity 4.35

Review and research

There are a number of strategies used to encourage everyone to eat more fruit and vegetables.

Describe the strategies that are used by the government, supermarkets, schools and parents to encourage increased consumption of fruit and vegetables.

CHECK YOUR UNDERSTANDING

Check you understand the meaning of the following key terms. Write a sentence using each word.

cellulose	cytoplasm	oxidation
enzymic browning	chlorophyll	carotenoids
anthocyanins		

Sugar

Figure 4.28

In the UK, sugar comes from sugar beet grown in the UK and Europe or sugar cane imported from tropical climates. The sugar is extracted, refined and crystallised into a variety of brown and white forms.

The consumption of sugar and preserves (such as jam) has decreased over time. However, consumption of other foods and drinks containing sugar (such as soft drinks and ice cream) has increased. Intake of non-milk extrinsic sugars should only provide an average of 10 per cent of total energy. Consuming too much sugar can increase the risk of dental decay and obesity.

Sugar, honey and syrup should be stored in airtight containers to prevent moisture entering, or moisture loss and caking in the case of brown sugars.

Activity 4.36

Research and ICT opportunity

Write a report on the dangers of too much sugar in the diet.

The nutritional value of sugar

Sugar is 99.9 per cent pure sugar so it is valuable for providing energy. All varieties of sugar provide around the same amount of energy – 394 kcal per 100 g.

Activity 4.37

Review

Copy and complete the table – use recipe books to help you.

Type of sugar	Use
Caster sugar	
Granulated sugar	
Icing sugar	
Sugar cubes	
Demerara sugar	
Soft brown sugar	
Golden syrup	
Treacle	

Choice of sugar

Refined white sugars

- *Caster sugar* – has a very fine crystal structure and is commonly used in baking and for meringues.

- *Granulated sugar* – does not have as fine a crystal structure as caster sugar. Traditionally used to sweeten drinks.

- *Icing sugar* – a very fine, powdery sugar used to make icings such as glace, royal, fondant and butter icing.

- *Sugar cubes* – lumps of sugar 'glued' together with sugar syrup. Used in hot drinks.

Partially refined sugars

- *Demerara sugar* – a type of brown sugar produced as large crystals to provide texture and crunch to baked products.

Unrefined sugars

- *Soft brown sugar* – available in both a light and dark form. Used in fudge and a range of bakery items such as Dundee cake.

Syrup and treacle

- *Golden syrup* – partially inverted syrup made from sugar liquors from the refining process. Used in a range of products such as treacle tart, flapjacks and gingerbread.

- *Treacle* – strongly flavoured, black syrup produced from molasses, which is formed during sugar production. It is used in rich fruit cakes and spicy sauces.

Uses of sugar

Sugar is not only a sweetener; it has a variety of specific characteristics, making it suitable for use in baking, food processing, preservation and cooking.

- *Aeration* – when fat and sugar are beaten together during the creaming stage of cake production, air is incorporated into the mix. Caster sugar is most suitable for this because of its fine structure and because it inhibits gluten development in flour, giving the cake a lighter texture.

- *Bulking* – sugar is used to increase a product's size, volume or weight; it gives the characteristic texture to foods such as ice cream, jam and cakes.

- *Coating* – sugar can be used to make a fondant icing to cover or decorate cake products.

  Colour – sugar has a browning effect on the surface of many bakery products.

- *Gelling* – sugar plays a crucial role in jam making. The setting of jam depends on the presence of pectin, acid and sugar in the correct amounts, which then form a gel.

- *Moisture retention*: Sugar has water-attracting properties, so the addition of sugar improves shelf life and maintains texture and mouth feel.

- *Preservation* – high concentrations of sugar help stop the growth of microorganisms and therefore prevent food spoilage. Jam is a good example of this.

- *Stabilising* – sugar stabilises egg white foam without destroying its structure. It also lowers the freezing temperature, so prevents ice crystals forming in ice-cream production.

Activity 4.38

Practical opportunity
Make a cake to illustrate the use of sugar in cake production.

Sugar substitutes

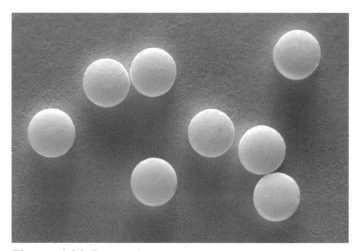

Figure 4.29 *Sugar substitutes*

Sweetening agents or sweeteners are divided into two categories:

1 **Intense sweeteners** – these are many times sweeter than sucrose and are used in small quantities.

2 **Bulk sweeteners** – these contain a similar level of sweetness as sucrose, so are used in similar quantities.

Sweeteners are available in as tablets, liquids and powders.

Sugar substitutes have no nutritional value – they are simply designed to provide sweetness without the high energy value.

Choice of sugar substitutes

Intense sweeteners

There are six permitted intense sweeteners used in manufacturing:

1 E950 – Acesulfame potassium

2 E951 – Aspartame

3 E954 – Saccharin

4 E957 – Thaumatin

5 E959 – Neohesperidine Dihydrochalcone (NHDC)

6 E952 – Cyclamic acid.

Bulk sweeteners

Sorbitol – this is found naturally in fruits such as apples, berries, pears and plums. It is approximately half as sweet as sucrose.

Aspartame – this is available under various trade names, for example, *Canderel*.

Sucralose – this is a relatively new sugar substitute made from sucralose; *Splenda* is an example of sucralose.

Uses of sweeteners

● Sweeteners allow diabetics to enjoy an alternative to sugar without affecting their blood glucose levels.

● Intense sweeteners are useful for those who wish to reduce their energy intake.

● Tablet sweeteners are added to hot drinks.

● Powder sweeteners are sprinkled onto food and are also used to make confectionary, sweets, soft drinks, diabetic foods and jams.

● Trademark products such as *Canderel* and *Splenda* can be used successfully in cooking.

Activity 4.39

Practical opportunity
Make a baked product using a sugar substitute.
Carry out some sensory analysis to establish whether it is acceptable in terms of appearance, flavour and texture.

CHECK YOUR UNDERSTANDING

Check you understand the meaning of the following key terms. Write a sentence using each word.

bulk sweetener   **intense sweetener**

Activity 4.40

Revision

Summarise the information in this chapter on commodities by copying and completing this table.

Commodity	Types	Use	Nutritional significance
Meat			
Fish			
Eggs			
Dairy products			
Alternative protein sources			
Cereals			
Pulses			
Fats and oils			
Fruit and vegetables			
Sugar and sugar substitutes			

Section 2 — Performance characteristics of eggs and flour

Introduction

Eggs and flour offer many useful performance characteristics or properties that can be incorporated into food products.

The unique chemical structure of eggs provides many valuable properties that can be used in food preparation. In this section, we will explore the key performance characteristics of eggs and the properties of flour or starch in food preparation.

Performance characteristics of eggs

Both the egg white and yolk contain protein. The main protein found in egg white is ovalbumin, but globulin and albumin are also present in smaller amounts. Egg yolk contains proteins in the form of lipoproteins, which are a combination of proteins and lipids (complex fatty substances). The most important complex lipid in egg yolk is **lecithin**. Lecithin gives the egg yolk the properties of a stable **emulsion**. The fat

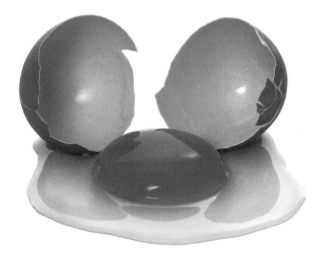

Figure 4.30

molecules in the egg yolk are held in an emulsion by lecithin.

Eggs have three main performance characteristics:

1 they **coagulate**, which includes setting, binding, coating, thickening, enriching and glazing

2 they can be whisked to create foams and aerate mixtures

3 they are emulsifiers.

The proteins found in eggs are responsible for the important performance characteristics that we will now explore in detail.

Coagulation

Coagulation is the process in which proteins change from their natural liquid state into a **gel** or a solid. This happens because each protein molecule is constructed from long chains of amino acids joined by peptide bonds. These bonds are weak and when heat, acid, or mechanical action is applied they start to break. This is a permanent change to the protein structure. Other bonds form and a three-dimensional network is created within which water is trapped. At this stage the food has a solid appearance and has coagulated. Because the protein changes its physical structure when it coagulates, it is sometimes referred to as **denaturation**.

The proteins in an egg coagulate during the cooking process. The egg white will coagulate at temperatures between 60°C and 65°C. This results in the egg white losing its transparency and when the egg reaches 70°C it becomes firm. The egg-yolk proteins coagulate at a slightly higher temperature than egg white proteins. Coagulation begins at 65°C and finishes at 70°C. This difference in coagulation temperatures explains why, with careful cooking, the egg white can be cooked until set but the yolk can remain runny.

Activity 4.41

Experiment
Preparation of a baked egg custard

The preparation of a perfect egg custard demonstrates clearly the ability of eggs to coagulate. In this experiment you will vary the cooking process and ingredients to find the optimum conditions for coagulation.

Egg custard – standard recipe

An egg custard is made from eggs, sugar, milk and usually flavourings. You will need the following ingredients for these experiments:

1 medium egg
15 g caster sugar
250 ml milk

1 Warm the milk but DO NOT ALLOW TO BOIL, as this will curdle the eggs. The milk is warmed at the beginning of the process to shorten the cooking time.
2 Beat the eggs with a fork, add the sugar and warmed milk.
3 Pour into a greased pie dish or basin.
4 Bake the custard using a bain-marie or a water bath. The bain-marie or water bath should be slightly larger than the pie dish and half filled with cold water. Stand the pie dish in the bath.
5 Bake for about 40 minutes in the centre of a slow oven 150°C or gas mark 2, until firm.

Egg custard variation of ingredients – eggs

Use the standard recipe and method above but add an extra egg.

Egg custard variation of ingredients – sugar

Use the standard recipe and method above but add an additional 15 g of sugar.

Egg custard variation of temperature and equipment

Use the standard recipe and method above but bake at 220°C with no water bath.

Egg custard variation of baking time

Use the standard recipe and method above but bake for 1 hour.

Egg custard variation of equipment

Use the standard recipe and method above but do not use a water bath.

Analysis

Describe the colour and texture of the skin on each sample.

Did any custard show signs of shrinkage?

Use a knife to cut each egg custard. Describe the texture; look at the firmness of the set, size of bubbles and for any evidence of weeping.

Conclusions

Which custard gave the best results?

How does the addition of an extra egg and sugar affect the outcome? Can you explain this?

What could cause the development of air bubbles?

Why is it suggested a water bath is used in the cooking process?

Which conditions are most likely to produce syneresis or weeping?

Figure 4.31 *Cooked eggs are coagulated*

Figure 4.32 *Meringue*

It is important to avoid overcooking baked dishes containing eggs. If egg is overcooked the process of **syneresis** may occur. The texture becomes porous as the protein shrinks and pockets of water are left in the baked product. When the baked product is cut with a sharp knife, water leaches out if syneresis has occurred. A water bath or a bain-marie is sometimes used to protect a baked egg product from overheating because of the direct heat of the oven and this reduces the risk of syneresis.

Factors affecting coagulation

Other ingredients in the mixture can affect the coagulation process. A firmer set can be achieved at a lower temperature if an acid such as lemon juice is added. A looser set and higher coagulation temperature is achieved by the addition of sugar to the mixture.

The concentration of egg yolk and whites will affect the coagulation process. One medium egg will set 250 ml of milk. The quantity of egg yolk determines the strength of the set mixture. A higher proportion of egg yolks or whole eggs will produce firmer or thicker custard. A low heat achieves a gentle heat transference, which produces perfect conditions for coagulation.

Foam formation

Foam is the dispersal of a gas in a liquid. A foam is formed when air is dispersed through the liquid egg white. Egg whites can be aerated due to the ability of the ovalbumin to stretch and hold air. This is useful when preparing meringues and mousses.

When egg white is whisked the proteins are denatured and uncoil. This forms a 3D air/liquid structure that can hold air when folded into food mixtures. The foam is stable but its properties can be affected by the use of additional ingredients or conditions.

Factors affecting foam formation

- *Salt* will decrease the pH of the egg white and this increases the resistance to foam, so the time taken to foam is increased. This makes the foam more stable and gives a better flavour.

- *Sugar* will interfere with the bonds that form as the egg whites uncoil. Therefore, the whisking time is increased and the resulting foam is denser. However, the foam is much more stable. This property is used in the production of meringues.

- *Fat* including egg yolk interferes with the development of the foam structure. It prevents new bonds being formed in the structure. Often a full foam will not develop.

- *Alkalis* will increase the pH of the foam, decreasing the foaming time but making the foam produced more unstable.

- *Acids* like tartaric and acetic (vinegar) will soften the foam.

Whole egg yolk foams

Whole eggs do not easily foam due the presence of fat, which interferes with the foam formation. Whole eggs are usually whisked with the addition of sugar.

In a whisked sponge mixture the maximum volume can be obtained if the eggs are whisked over steam; this is achieved by placing the bowl over a pan of hot water. The protein will denature due to whisking and coagulate slightly, increasing its stability. The ability to trap air is used in both the creaming and whisking cake making methods, for example, Swiss roll.

Emulsification

Figure 4.33 *Mayonnaise is an emulsion*

An emulsion is formed when one liquid is dispersed in small droplets into a second liquid with which it will not normally mix. The most common emulsion is oil in water, for example, milk, salad dressings and egg yolks. Emulsions usually cannot exist without an emulsifying agent.

Egg yolk has emulsification properties, which means it has the ability to hold large quantities of fat in an emulsion. The yolk contains lecithin, which has a hydrophobic (water hating) component and hydrophilic (water loving) component. When fat or oil is whisked into the yolk the lecithin can hold it in suspension and prevent it from separating out. This property is used in mayonnaise and other salad dressings.

Eggs can also act as emulsifiers to assist in the formation of a stable emulsion in a creamed cake mixture containing fat and sugar.

Figure 4.34 shows the action of an emulsifying agent on an unstable emulsion of water in oil.

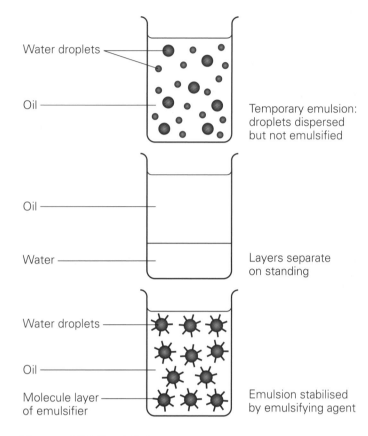

Figure 4.34 *Emulsification*

Other functions in food production

The ability of the egg to coagulate is exploited in many baked products such as cakes, quiches, meringues and egg custards. In these products the egg contributes to the finished structure. Eggs have many other functions, some of which are associated with the ability to coagulate, as described below.

- *Thickening of sauces* – an egg can give additional thickness to sauces. Eggs can be used to thicken custards, sauces and soups with coagulation. In a lemon meringue pie or a hollandaise sauce, the egg coagulation thickens the sauce.

- *Binding agent* – eggs are useful binding agents as they are very viscous and will moisten and bind foods such as rissoles and meat loaves. This helps to hold food together during cooking as the egg proteins coagulate.

- *Coating agent* – eggs can be used to coat foods. The sticky nature of the egg helps to hold breadcrumbs on the outside of foods such as fish cakes, both before and during cooking. The coating will set due to coagulation on the surface of the food.

- *Glazing* – eggs can be used to glaze the top of pastries or breads before cooking to give an attractive golden brown appearance. The proteins will brown with dry heat in the baking process.

- *Add colour and enrichment* – due to their important nutrient profile, eggs can be used to enrich food products and add colour. The yellowy orange colour of an egg yolk is due to the presence of carotene or vitamin A.

- *Contribute to flavour* – egg yolk adds a rich flavour to baked products as it is a concentrated source of fat.

Performance characteristics of flour

Flour can be made from any finely ground cereal including wheat, barley, oats, rye, rice and maize (cornflour). In the UK, most of the flour products we consume are produced from wheat flour.

The combination of protein and starch in flour give two important performance characteristics:

1 Starch gives the ability to thicken liquids, a process called **gelatinisation**.

2 Protein helps with the formation of **gluten**, giving baked products a structure.

Gelatinisation

Starches are polysaccharides made up of many units of glucose. Starch consists of two different types of molecules – **amylose** and **amylopectin**. Different starches contain different amounts of these molecules. Cornflour is made from the cereal maize and is particularly high in amylose; this enhances the ability of cornflour to gelatinise. The type of starch and quantity used will affect gelatinisation. Temperature and the affects of other ingredients are also important in the process of gelatinisation.

Amylose

Amylose molecules are long and straight (see Figure 4.35). Most starches used for cooking contain 17–28 per cent amylose. Amylose causes sauces and fillings to thicken, turn cloudy when cooked, get thicker as they

cool and weep when frozen. Freezing a pie thickened with amylose may result in it developing cracks in the middle when it is thawed. Amylose masks flavours and thickens foods to the point that they can be cut with a knife.

Amylopectin

Amylopectin molecules are short and branched like a tree (see Figure 4.35). Amylopectin produces a clear gel when it thickens and has the same thickness when hot or cold. It can be frozen without weeping, has a clean taste and does not thicken enough to cut with a knife.

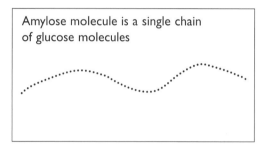

Amylose molecule is a single chain of glucose molecules

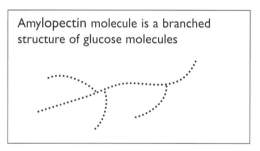

Amylopectin molecule is a branched structure of glucose molecules

Figure 4.35 *Amylose and amylopectin molecules*

Process of gelatinisation

Gels are systems where large volumes of liquids are held by a small amount of solid. The development of a gel is called gelatinisation. Gelatinisation occurs when starch (flour) is added to a liquid and heated, for example, sauce making using the blended method. This method is used to produce sauces made from cornflour and custard powder (flavoured cornflour). The cornflour is blended with a small quantity of cold liquid before being added to the remaining liquid and heated. When starch is added to a cold liquid it does not dissolve because the starch granules are suspended in the liquid. When the mixture is heated slowly and stirred the starch granules start to soften – heating starts the process of gelatinisation. The starch granules fill with water and with further heating they start to move more rapidly and the molecule bonds weaken. As more liquid enters the granules it becomes trapped, and so the

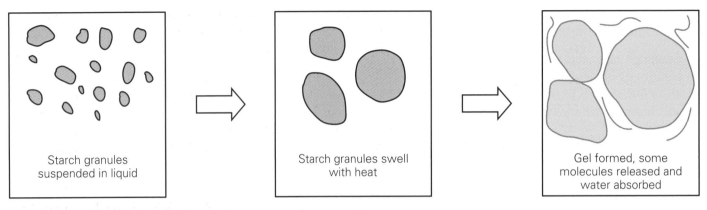

Figure 4.36 *Formation of gel*

Activity 4.42

Experiment

Gelatinisation of starch

There are several interesting experiments you can complete to demonstrate the theory of gelatinisation.

To investigate the ability of different starches to produce a gel

The basic method of making a blended sauce is outlined below and should be followed when making the gels.

The gels can be made using different starches, e.g. 25 g cornflour, 25 g arrowroot and 25 g plain flour.

1 Measure 250 ml of water.
2 Blend starch sample with a small quantity of water from the 250 ml until a paste is achieved. Add the remaining water.
3 Place the mixture in a small saucepan and stir until it boils for 2–3 minutes.
4 Pour the sauce into a ramekin dish or a small plastic carton.
5 Leave to cool and when completely cold turn out onto a plate.

Conclusions

Which starch produced the best gel? Can you offer an explanation for this finding?

What is arrowroot? How is it used?

To investigate the effect of temperature, acid and sugar on a cornflour gel

For each of the following experiments use 25 g cornflour and 250 ml water.

Temperature

Sample 1: Make the sauce using the method above but heat to a temperature of 85°C then cool.

Sample 2: Make the sauce using the method above but heat to a temperature of 95°C then cool.

Acid

Sample 1: Make the sauce using the method above but add 30 ml of lemon juice before boiling. Boil for a few minutes. Remove from the heat and cool.

Sample 2: Make the sauce using the method above but add 30 ml of lemon juice after boiling. Remove from the heat and cool.

Sugar

Sample 1: Make the sauce using the method above but add 50 g of sugar before boiling. Boil the sauce for 2–3 minutes. Cool the gel.

Sample 2: Make the sauce using the method above but add 50 g of sugar after boiling. Cool the gel.

Conclusions

Inspect each of the gels closely. Look at the strength, clarity and consistency of the gel.

How does temperature affect the gel?

What is the effect of adding sugar and acid to the thickness of the sauce?

Lemon meringue pie involves the creation of an acidic, sweet gel. What advice would you give to help ensure a firm set to the filling?

filling begins to thicken. The starch granules can swell to about five times their normal size, almost touching each other. Gelatinisation occurs at between 75°C and 87°C. The mixture must be boiled for two minutes to ensure all the starch is fully gelatinised.

The amylose molecules are involved in the process of gelatinisation as they will seep from the starch grains and stay in the liquid as long as it remains hot. But as the filling cools, the movement of the molecules slows down and the amylose molecules begin to bond with one another and with the branches of the amylopectin molecules. The swollen starch grains and molecules unite into a fairly solid mass.

Figure 4.36 shows the formation of gel.

Any ungelatinised starch will give a raw taste to the sauce. However, the sauce can be over cooked and start to thin. This is likely to occur if an acid such as lemon juice, tomatoes or vinegar are added. The acid will prevent the starch granules from thickening because it hydrolyses or breaks the starch down into smaller molecules. To avoid this reaction acidic ingredients should only be added at the end of the cooking process. Adding sugar will soften and reduce the thickness of a starch gel, so always add sugar after gelatinisation for a firmer filling.

Retrogradation

The process of staling (going stale) in starch-baked goods is called **retrogradation**. Over time, baked starch will start to shrink; sometimes this can be apparent by the weeping or syneresis in starch-based creams and fillings. Retrogradation can be seen in baked starch fillings that have been refrigerated or frozen. To prevent retrogradation, always cover baked goods to prevent moisture loss and store at room temperature if possible. Sugar, protein, fats and emulsifiers will slow down the process in pastries. Bread and rolls will stale faster and develop a hard, dry, crumbly texture if exposed to air. Flavour can also be lost with the moisture.

Characteristics of flour

The three basic flour types are:

1 Wholemeal – 100 per cent extraction; made from the whole wheat grain with nothing added or removed.

2 Brown – usually contains about 85 per cent of the original grain; some bran and germ have been removed during milling

3 White – usually contains 75 per cent of the wheat grain. Most of the bran and wheat germ have been removed during milling

This section looks at the characteristics of plain white flour. Wholemeal and brown flour absorb more water than white flour and the finished product has a coarser and distinctive nutty flavour, but the interactions and chemical processes in all other respects are similar to white flour.

When flour is used in baked products, the starch gelatinises. The presence of protein and carbohydrate together in a baked product produce an additional chemical reaction called the **Maillard reaction**. This is a form of **non-enzymic browning** that occurs on the crust of a baked product. During dry cooking methods such as baking, carbohydrate is converted into dextrin which gives a golden brown colour to the surface of the baked product.

However, it is the behaviour of the proteins in the flour that give it the qualities that are particularly suitable to the production of bread, cakes, biscuits and pastries.

Types of protein

There are as many as 30 types of protein in wheat flour. Two of these proteins make an important contribution to the performance characteristics of flour: **gliadin** and **glutenin**. When both these proteins are exposed to moisture (water, milk) and are kneaded, they produce gluten which gives elasticity, strength and shape to baked products.

Different types of flour contain different amounts of protein. Strong flour is produced from wheat that has a high protein content. Strong flour is used for making bread and yeast-based mixtures. Bread requires a stronger structure that can trap the gases created by yeast, allowing the bread to rise. Soft flour is produced from a different variety of wheat. Soft flour has a low protein content and is used for making cakes, some pastries and biscuits. The low protein content gives a less rigid structure.

Gluten formation

The development of gluten is very important in the production of yeast dough such as bread, and the wheat proteins gliadin and glutenin are crucial in this process. Gluten is formed by gliadin and glutenin combining. Gluten is stretchy and elastic and this allows it to provide a network within the dough that can trap carbon dioxide.

During the bread-making process both gliadin and glutenin are mixed with water. This creates a sticky, tangled mass of protein molecules. During **kneading** the gluten molecules are physically rearranged into a straight and untangled structure. This gives well-kneaded dough a smooth, satin-like surface. The ability of this dough to stretch enables the gas and steam produced during the rising and baking of bread to remain trapped in the structure. This protein-rich structure eventually coagulates or sets during baking, producing a well-risen baked product.

Factors affecting gluten formation

Fat coats the flour in a mixture and this prevents the absorption of water. This action reduces the amount of gluten that develops in the baked product. Sugar also reduces the amount of gluten in a product because it competes for water with the protein.

Activity 4.43

Practical opportunity
Making gluten balls

Equipment

You will need mixing bowls, strong flour, plain flour and self raising flour.

1 Measure 100 g of each flour into separate bowls. Label each bowl.
2 Slowly add approximately 50 ml water to each type of flour and knead each mixture until a soft ball of dough forms. Cover and leave the dough balls for about 10 minutes.
3 In the sink, run cold water over each dough ball in turn. Be careful not to let the dough disintegrate as the starch runs out. Wash until all the starch is released and a chewy mass of gluten is left.

Analysis

How does the texture of each dough ball feel as you wash away the starch?

Does it take the same amount of time to wash the starch away for each dough ball?

Are the gluten balls all the same size, or are some larger than others?

4 Place each gluten ball on a baking tray in a hot oven 220°C or gas 7 for 15–30 minutes.

Conclusion

What has happened to each dough ball?

Describe the texture and appearance of each cooked gluten ball.

Comment on the performance of each flour.

Which would you recommend for bread making or cake making?

CHECK YOUR UNDERSTANDING

Check you understand the meaning of the following key terms. Write a sentence using each word.

glutenin	gluten
amylopectin	non-enzymic browning
amylose	coagulate
denaturation	gliadin
syneresis	gelatinisation
foam	gel
emulsion	lecithin
blended method	retrogradation

Section 3 — Behaviour changes in food

Introduction

In this section, we explore some of the common behaviour changes that can occur when food products are prepared and cooked. Some of the principles involved have been investigated in detail in the sections on the performance characteristics of eggs and flour and you may find it useful in developing your understanding to reread these earlier sections.

You will develop an understanding of the following terms:

- beating
- whisking
- shortening
- kneading
- heating.

You will also learn how each of these behaviour changes can be applied to the production of different food products, including bread, cakes, sauces and, pastry.

Causes of behaviour changes

Behaviour changes in food products are caused by a combination of mechanical and chemical reactions. These processes and reactions occur when following a method for a recipe. To try to simplify the explanations, we will explore each behaviour change as a process applied to food. The preparation of some food products can involve many different processes but we will concentrate on beating, whisking, shortening, kneading and heating.

Beating

Beating is a method used to incorporate air into a mixture – for example, cake mixtures and batters.

Cake making: the creaming method

A creamed cake contains self raising flour, fat, sugar and eggs. Initially the sugar and fat are beaten

Figure 4.37 *A sandwich cake*

together. This process is sometimes called creaming and can be completed by hand or with an electric mixer. Air is beaten into the mixture of fat and sugar to form an air-in-fat foam. The abrasive action of the sugar crystals separates the fat, and air becomes trapped in the mixture. The addition of eggs allows some of the sugar to dissolve and with further beating to hold some air in the stretchy protein network. The gentle folding in of the flour will displace some air but give the mixture a smooth dropping consistency. When placed in the oven the fat melts and is absorbed by the starch. The self raising flour contains the raising agent baking powder, which releases carbon dioxide. The liquid from the eggs is released as steam. Air, steam and carbon dioxide expand, causing the cake to rise. The starch gelatinises and protein coagulates inside the mixture to make a light, sponge cake. The surface of the cake browns due to the non-enzymic browning reaction between carbohydrates and proteins.

Whisking

Whisking adds air to a mixture. Egg white can be whisked to produce a fairly stable foam. This principle is used in the production of meringues and mousses. Egg yolks will hold some air and can be whisked in the preparation of mayonnaise. Whole eggs can also be whisked to incorporate air, but this structure is less stable and needs to be baked shortly after preparation to reduce the loss of air. The whisking method is used for preparation of a fatless sponge or a Swiss roll mixture. The trapped air in the egg structure is an important raising agent.

Cake making: the whisking method

Figure 4.38 *Swiss roll*

In the whisking method, the egg proteins are stretched and **denatured** by the mechanical action of whisking. This new protein structure traps small air bubbles into a fairly stable foam. The mixture will become thick and creamy coloured as more air is whisked in. The heat generated from the whisking process may also allow some coagulation of the proteins into a more stable structure. Plain flour is then gently folded into the mixture. The flour sticks to the protein and produces a fine honeycomb structure. Next, the cake is baked in the oven. On heating, the water from the egg becomes steam and the combination of trapped air and steam expands, causing the cake to rise. The protein molecules in the egg and flour stretch. The protein coagulates and the starch gelatinises, producing a firm structure. The surface of the cake browns due to the reaction of protein and starches with dry heat producing non-enzymic browning.

Shortening

Shortening is when fat is used in baked goods to produce a crumbly texture. Shortening gives important features to shortcrust pastry and a rubbed-in cake mixture. Fat contributes to the tenderness, flakiness, flavour and colour of the baked product and reduces the formation of gluten so the pastry or rubbed in cake is not chewy or tough. The choice of fat used is important to the process of shortening. Fats with a high water content should be avoided due to their poor shortening ability. Butter, vegetable fats (with a high fat content) and oils coat flour so thoroughly that gluten formation is minimised.

Pastry making: shortcrust pastry

Figure 4.39 *Pie crust*

The basic ingredients in pastry are flour, fat, water and salt. The flour and solid fat are rubbed together to produce a mixture which resembles breadcrumbs.

During the rubbing in stage, many of the flour particles are coated with fat, forming a waterproof barrier. Air is also incorporated as the mixture is rubbed together. Cold water is added and uncoated flour particles absorb the water. The water allows the dough to stick together and provides water vapour (steam) when the pastry is cooked. Some gluten strands are formed at this stage.

Rolling the pastry out causes the gluten strands to stretch and allows the pastry to be rolled very thinly. If the pastry is overstretched at this stage it will shrink back during baking. It will also be tough if re-rolled as too much gluten will have formed.

On heating, the fat melts and is absorbed by the starch granules, which then gelatinise. The air and steam expand and create crumbly layers, which give the cooked pastry its distinctive flakiness. In pastry with a high fat and water content more blistering between layers of gluten and starch occurs, to produce a distinctly crumbly pastry. The layers set due to the coagulation of the gluten in the flour.

Kneading

Kneading is a process used to mix together ingredients and add strength to dough. It is used in bread making.

Bread making

Figure 4.40

The basic ingredients for bread are strong plain flour, yeast and water. During the initial stages of bread making the ingredients are mixed together and the yeast is dispersed. A small quantity of sugar may be added to the mixture to speed up the fermentation stage later on. Salt can also be added to give the finished bread an acceptable flavour. During the mixing stage, the water hydrates the flour particles and starts the process of gluten development.

Next, the process of **kneading** is applied to the mixture of flour, sugar, yeast, salt and water. The flour contains gliadin and glutenin proteins which, when they are kneaded, form strands of gluten. Gluten is important to the structure of bread. If the dough is not sufficiently kneaded, it will not be able to hold the tiny pockets of carbon dioxide created by the yeast. Kneading warms and stretches the gluten strands, eventually creating a springy, elastic dough. It can be completed by hand on a lightly floured surface or in a food mixer using a dough hook. The mechanical process of kneading involves pushing, pulling and folding the dough until it becomes smooth and silky.

After kneading, the dough is left in a warm place for the process of **fermentation** to begin. This process is sometimes called rising or fermentation. Fermentation is the process in which starch is broken down by the yeast to produce alcohol and carbon dioxide; it is used in the brewing and bread making process. Flour contains an enzyme called **diastase**, which changes the starch into **maltose**, a type of sugar. The yeast contains many different enzymes, including **maltase**, which changes maltose into the simplest form of sugar glucose. The yeast also contains the enzyme **zymase**, which turns the glucose into carbon dioxide and a little alcohol. Carbon dioxide allows the dough to rise. The fermented dough should double in size and to achieve this control of temperature is vital. In a warm environment (25°C) the rising will be fast and in a cooler environment (5°C) it may take many hours. An over fermented dough will cause the gluten strands to stretch too much and lose some of their elasticity; the subsequent rising may be poor.

The next stage of bread making involves more kneading. This is sometimes called **knocking back** the dough. The large bubbles of carbon dioxide produced from the action of zymase during the first rising need to be evenly distributed throughout the dough. Similar to kneading, the process of knocking back the dough produces smaller bubbles, giving the bread an even texture. This process continues until the dough is elastic and smooth again. It redistributes the nutrients for the yeast and allows fermentation to continue. The dough can then be shaped and allowed to prove or rise again. The proving or second rising should be conducted at 27°C; this is the optimum temperature for the yeast to function. During this stage, the dough will rise again evenly and have an improved texture.

The final stage is the baking of the bread where the dough is placed into a hot oven. At first it will rise rapidly as more carbon dioxide is produced by the yeast. This causes the dough to expand in size. At about 54°C the yeast is killed and all enzymic reactions stop. As the temperature continues to rise, the starch gelatinises and gluten coagulates at 80°C. The water in the dough turns into steam and contributes to the volume and texture of the bread. The action of dry heat on the surface is called the Maillard reaction, a form of non-enzymic browning. The combination of protein and starch causes the development of **dextrin** – a type of sugar that gives the crust a golden brown colour.

Activity 4.44

Revision

Complete the following exercise using the key words and phrases shown below.

Yeast cells feed on _____ and the gas _____ _____ is produced. This process is called _____ and is used to make bread rise.

The process starts with the enzyme _____ found in the flour. It converts starch into _____.

Maltose is a food source for yeast and an enzyme in the yeast _____ breaks maltose into _____. Yeast also contains another enzyme _____. This enzyme breaks the glucose into _____ and carbon dioxide.

Enzymes are very sensitive to heat. They are active at _____ but are destroyed at temperatures above _____.

60°C	maltase	maltose	glucose
carbon dioxide	30°C	diastase	alcohol
zymase	sugar	fermentation	

Heating

The term 'heating' describes the process of cooking food. The effect of heat on food brings about chemical and physical changes. The cake making method known as 'the melting method' uses gentle heat in a saucepan to prepare the mixture, before baking the cake in the oven.

Cake making: the melting method

Figure 4.41 *Gingerbread*

The melting method is used to produce gingerbread and some types of biscuit. A melting-method mixture usually contains sugar, golden syrup, treacle, eggs and a strong flavoured spice. The sugars and fat are melted together in a saucepan, with other ingredients including eggs, plain flour, spices and bicarbonate of soda added after melting. The mixture is then baked in the oven and during this stage the bicarbonate of soda releases carbon dioxide gas. The liquid fat and sugar is absorbed into the flour. The carbon dioxide gas and steam expand, giving the cake a risen appearance. The proteins in the eggs coagulate and starch in the flour gelatinises to give a firm structure. The soapy taste of the bicarbonate of soda is masked by the spices.

Effect of heat on food

The type of heat applied to food can be dry or moist, depending upon the cooking method chosen. In an attempt to simplify the explanation of heat on food we will explore the effect of heat on the main nutrients found in food. These principles can then be applied to many different foods.

Moist heat and carbohydrates

The effect of moist heat on carbohydrates causes the starch granules to soften and absorb water. This process can be used to thicken liquids and is known as gelatinisation. By referring back to the section on gelatinisation you can revisit the blended method of sauce making. Here, we will examine the roux and all-in-one sauce making methods, which are both practical applications of the effect of moist heat on starches.

Sauce making: the roux method

In the roux method, the fat is melted in a saucepan and the flour is stirred into the mixture using a wooden or plastic spoon. The starch granules become coated with fat and as the mixture is heated, some gelatinisation occurs. Most of the starch does not gelatinise due to a lack of liquid. The roux is then removed from the heat and the liquid is added slowly to stop lumps from forming. The fat coating on the starch granules also stops lumps forming when the liquid is added. As the liquid is added, the starch forms a suspension in the cold liquid. The sauce is then returned to the heat and brought to a gentle boil. The fat melts as the temperature rises and is absorbed by the starch, and the process of gelatinisation occurs. This process produces a thick, smooth and glossy sauce.

Sauce making: the all-in-one method

In the all-in-one method, all the ingredients are placed in a saucepan and heated and whisked continuously. The starch granules are released into the liquid and with constant stirring should not clump together. As the sauce heats, the fat melts and is absorbed into the starch. The starch gelatinises and the sauce thickens. The sauce needs to boil for a few minutes to ensure all the starch is cooked.

The consistency of a white sauce will depend upon the quantities of each ingredient used. The table below shows the proportions of the main ingredients:

Consistency of sauce	Flour	Liquid
Pouring sauce served as an accompaniment	15 g	250 ml
Coating sauce used to cover foods	25 g	250 ml
Binding sauce used to combine ingredients	50 g	250 ml

Dry heat and carbohydrates

The effect of dry heat on starch and sugar produces two different reactions, both of which are types of non-enzymatic browning. These reactions are different because they do not involve enzyme actions. (The browning in fruit and vegetables is caused by enzymes and is called enzymic browning.) In baked products, non-enzymic reactions by melanoidins and other chemicals are responsible for the brown colours created.

The two main types of non-enzymatic browning are the Maillard reaction and caramelisation.

1 The Maillard reaction is a chemical reaction between proteins (amino acids) and starch (maltose) to produce a brown colour. The starch is converted into dextrin and is called dextrinisation. This process produces the brown crust on baked products.

2 The effect of dry heat on sugar produces **caramelisation**, which is the oxidation of sugar. Sucrose (table sugar) and dry heat produce a nutty, caramel flavour and brown colour. When sugars are heated above their melting point, they produce a range of brown substances collectively known as caramel. This process occurs in toffee making and meringues. Eventually the caramel burns or carbonises if heating continues.

Effect of heat on proteins

When proteins are heated, they change shape or denature and this change is permanent. The application of heat to proteins produces coagulation, which is the change from a liquid to a solid structure, and is an example of proteins denaturing. When heated, many protein-rich foods demonstrate coagulation – for instance, the skin on heated milk. The process of coagulation in both egg and wheat proteins in the production of cakes and bread has already been explored in this chapter.

Effect of heat on fats

Solid fats melt when heat is applied. In baked products melted fat can assist with gelatinisation. Overheating produces a breakdown in fats and they will decompose into their basic components of glycerol and fatty acids.

CHECK YOUR UNDERSTANDING

Extract the words which are associated with bread making and use them to create a description of the process.

beating	denature
caramelisation	knocking back
dextrinisation	zymase
fermentation	kneading
Maillard reaction	maltose
maltase	diastase
shortening	whisking
heating	proving
rising	gluten
gliadin	glutenin
carbon dioxide	shaping
yeast	optimum temperature
coagulation	mixing
folding in	

Section 4 Food additives

Introduction

Additives are added to food during processing to achieve a specific technological function, for instance to preserve, colour or improve the texture of a food product. Food additives are not new; for many hundreds of years people have improved their food with naturally occurring **preservatives**, flavourings and dyes. Some food additives are still taken from natural sources, while others are made by the food industry. Preservatives, colours and flavours are the most familiar food additives but **antioxidants**, **emulsifiers**, **stabilisers**, gelling agents, thickeners and sweeteners are frequently used. Consumers are demanding more choice and convenience, together with higher standards of food safety and affordable prices, and food additives are vital in meeting this consumer expectation.

We begin this section by examining the basic grouping used to classify food additives and the regulations associated with the use of food additives. The final part of the section provides a detailed analysis of the different types of food additives and their use in the food industry.

Groups of food additives

Food additives may be described as natural, nature identical or artificial.

- *Natural additives* – these are obtained from natural sources. For example, the purple colour extracted from beetroot is used to colour sweets, ice-cream and yoghurts.

- *Nature identical additives* – these are synthetic copies of substances that occur naturally. The natural source may be expensive, so an identical additive is manufactured in the laboratory. Vanillin is extracted from vanilla pods but the flavour can be produced chemically from a plant material called lignin.

- *Artificial additives* – these do not occur in nature and are made synthetically. Some sweeteners such as saccharin are artificial food additives.

Regulation of food additives

Food additives are thoroughly tested for safety before they are allowed for use within the European Union. The range of products that they can be used in is limited. Once approved by the European Food Safety Authority, the food additive is given an 'E' number. The E number shows the additive has been accepted as safe for use within the European Union. When an additive has been approved, regular testing is completed to maintain its status as 'EU approved'.

The current EU approved additives and their E Numbers can be found on the Food Standards Agency website (www.food.gov.uk). The E numbers system is used to classify food additives into different groups.

Functions of food additives

- Prevent food spoilage and preserve food products, for example, bread that remains fresh for seven days.

- Produce a wide range of food products to meet consumer demand for greater choice, for example, ice creams, baked products, chilled ready meals and confectionery.

- Improve or enhance the flavour and appearance of a food product, for example, to ensure a strawberry yoghurt is pink and tastes like strawberries.

- Restore a nutrient to a food product after processing, for example, adding B vitamins to breakfast cereals.

- Maintain the consistency and texture of food products by using emulsifiers, stabilisers, gelling agents and raising agents.

- Keep the price of the food competitive and reduce wastage for the manufacturer.

Types of food additives

Preservatives (E200–E299)

Preservatives help to keep food safe for longer by slowing down or preventing the reactions of decay. Preservatives have benefits to both the consumer and manufacturer, because they minimise food waste, make food safe and offer convenience.

Figure 4.42 *Processed meats*

Preservatives are present in nature but only in very small quantities, making it difficult to extract large quantities. To obtain commercially useful amounts of a preservative, synthetic versions of the natural products are produced. There are over 80 substances that are allowed to be used as preservatives.

Microorganisms contaminate every environment. Microorganisms include bacteria, fungi, moulds and yeasts. If the conditions are suitable, some microorganisms will cause food to spoil and decay. Microorganisms will grow quickly if provided with warmth, moisture, the correct pH and a supply of food to grow on. Preservatives prevent the growth of fungi, moulds and yeasts. They have some effect on bacteria, and using a combination of preservatives and antibacterial properties can give some protection against bacteria. Preservatives attack the enzymes inside the microorganisms and stop them from functioning; they also damage the cell wall so that substances cannot enter or leave the cell. These processes destroy or slow the growth of food spoilage microorganisms.

Food with a long shelf life is likely to contain preservatives. Sometimes a method of preservation such as freezing, canning or drying is used alongside a food additive. For example, to stop mould growing in dried fruit, it is often treated with sulphur dioxide. Cured meats including bacon, ham and corned beef are often treated with nitrates during the curing process. Preservatives are commonly used in low fat spreads, cheeses, salad dressings, fruit juices, preserves, bakery products and dried fruit preparations.

Arguably the most important use of preservatives is in processed meats such as ham, bacon, salami and sausages. The bacteria *clostridium botulinum* can produce deadly toxins and the use of preservatives in these products is very important to reduce this risk. Most cured and cooked meats contain the preservative potassium or sodium nitrate.

Antioxidants (E300–E399)

Antioxidants make food last longer by stopping those chemical reactions responsible for food going off or going rancid by coming into contact with oxygen in the air. **Rancidity** is the process in which fats exposed to the air oxidise and deteriorate, and it occurs due to a process called **oxidation**. Oxidation is a chemical reaction which involves an increase in oxygen or the loss of hydrogen. Vitamin C, also called ascorbic acid, is one of the most widely used antioxidants. Vitamin C is able to slow down oxidation in fruit and vegetables and is used in fruit juices to extend shelf life.

Some food such as fats and oils are more susceptible to oxidation and the addition of antioxidants extends their shelf life and reduces wastage. Antioxidants are used to prevent rancidity in many products that contain a small quantity of fat – for example, stock cubes, dried soups and cheese spreads.

Food colouring (E100–E199)

Food colouring is added to food to make it look more attractive to the consumer. The colour may be used to replace the natural colour lost during food processing or storage, or to make different batches of the same food product a consistent colour. Food colouring can also reinforce or strengthen an existing pale colour, making a product more aesthetically acceptable to the consumer.

Natural sources are used for some food colourings. These are obtained from grasses, leafy vegetables, fruit skins, roots and seeds of plants. Animals can also be a source of food colourings. Cochineal is a red colour that is obtained from the bodies of a species of scale insects. Caramel is the most popular colouring used in soft drinks, biscuits, gravies and confectionery.

European law allows 43 colours to be used in foods. The law lists the foods that may be coloured and maximum levels of colour that may be added. The amount of colouring allowed in food is very low.

Food colouring and health

The Food Standards Agency monitors food colourings to make sure their presence in food products does not compromise food safety. Certain combinations of some artificial food colours have been linked to a negative effect on children's behaviour. The following food colourings have been linked to allergic reactions, hyperactivity, impulsive and inattentive behaviour in children.

- Sunset yellow (E110) found in orange squash, cheese sauce and ice cream.

- Quinoline yellow (E104) found in smoked haddock and scotch eggs.

- Carmoisine (E122) found in yoghurts, jellies and jams.

- Allura red (E129) used in sweets.

- Tartrazine (E102) used in fruit squash, fruit cordial, coloured fizzy drinks.

The European Food Safety Authority funded research by Southampton University into artificial additives commonly found in sweets and drinks and their links with hyperactive behaviour in children. The findings of the report published in March 2008 were inconclusive and did not provide sufficient evidence to justify a policy change and a ban on the food colourings.

The Food Standards Agency suggests that parents concerned about artificial food colourings and children's behaviour should avoid products containing these additives.

Flavour enhancers and flavourings (E600–E699)

Flavour enhancers improve the taste of food. They achieve this by enhancing the flavour of a food product, for example, a strawberry yoghurt may require a distinctive strawberry flavour to gain consumer acceptance. A flavour enhancer can achieve this outcome.

Monosodium glutamate (MSG) is a flavour enhancer that is added to many processed foods, especially ready meals, soups, sauces and sausages. MSG brings out the flavour in a wide range of savoury foods without adding a flavour of its own.

Flavourings are added to a wide range of foods, usually in very small amounts, to give a particular taste. Flavourings can also restore a flavour or smell that may have been lost during processing.

Flavourings and flavour enhancers are controlled by different food-safety laws. By law, the ingredients list on a food product must say if it contains flavourings, but individual flavourings might not be named.

Emulsifiers and stabilisers (E400–E499)

Emulsifiers and stabilisers help to improve the consistency of food during storage and processing.

Natural emulsifiers such as lecithin found in eggs, helps mix ingredients together that would normally separate, such as oil and water emulsions. Lecithin is used in salad dressings, low fat spreads and mayonnaise. Emulsifiers give foods a smooth, consistent texture and thicken sauces.

Nutritional additives

Nutritional additives improve the nutrient content of certain foods and may be added to restore nutrients lost during food processing. For example, the process of milling cereal grains to produce white flour removes many nutrients, so UK law requires that iron, thiamin and niacin are added back to white and brown flour after processing. In addition, calcium carbonate is added to all brown and white flour products. This is done to ensure that vulnerable groups receive enough calcium in their diet. Research suggests that on average 20 per cent of the UK dietary calcium intake is provided by bread and flour products. Wholemeal flour does not require this restoration of nutrients because it is made from the whole wheat grain.

Fortification is the process of adding nutrients to foods, irrespective of whether or not the nutrients are originally present in the food. Nutrients are added to some substitute products so they have a similar nutritive value to the original product. For example, margarine has vitamins A and D added to levels similar to butter. In the UK, this is compulsory by law.

Other foods are fortified on a voluntary basis (breakfast cereals, for example). Fortification of most food and drink (with the exception of alcoholic drinks) is permitted, provided such an addition does not make the food 'injurious to health'. The food product must be clearly labelled as fortified. Some food products have compositional standards which are controlled by law and they cannot be fortified, for example, powdered baby milks.

Activity 4.45

Data response

The table below compares the nutritional composition of white, brown and wholemeal bread.

Using the data in the table, answer the following questions.

1 Which bread contains the most calcium? Explain why it is a good source of calcium.

2 Which bread contains the most dietary fibre? Explain why it is a good source of dietary fibre.

3 How much iron is found in a kilogram of wholemeal flour?

4 List the nutrients added to brown and white flour.

5 Give one reason why flour is fortified.

	White	Brown	Wholemeal
Carbohydrate %	49.3	44.3	41.6
(of which sugars) %	2.6	3.0	1.8
Protein %	8.4	8.5	9.2
Fat %	1.9	2.0	2.5
Dietary fibre %	2.3	4.7	7.1
Calcium mg/kg	1100.0	1000.0	540.0
Iron mg/kg	16.0	22.0	27.0
Thiamin mg/kg	2.1	2.7	3.4

Other food additives

Gelling agents are used to change the consistency of food and produce a firmer texture. An example of a gelling agent is pectin, which is used to make jam.

Sweeteners are often used instead of sugar in products such as fizzy drinks and yoghurt as they are lower in calories and do not damage teeth. Intense sweeteners such as aspartame and saccharin are many times sweeter than sugar, and so only very small amounts are used. Bulk sweeteners, such as sorbitol, have a similar level of sweetness to sugar but are used to improve the texture of food. They are particularly important in sugar-free confectionary and preserves required by diabetics.

Figure 4.43

Anti-caking agents are added to allow powders to flow and mix evenly. They are necessary because many processed foods contain ingredients that are mixed as powders. Magnesium carbonate is used in table salt to improve its flow. Many other food products will absorb moisture from the air and require anti-caking agents to be added – for instance, icing sugar, baking powder, drinking chocolate and cake mixes.

Glazing agents are used to create a protective coating or sheen on the surface of a food such as confectionery or citrus fruit.

Activity 4.46

Discussion

Evaluate the snacks in school vending machines by looking at the food additives in the list of ingredients.

Identify the functions of the food additives.

Discuss whether school vending machines could operate without the use of food additives.

CHECK YOUR UNDERSTANDING

Check you understand the meaning of the following key terms. Write a sentence using each word.

glazing agents	nutritional additives
anti-caking agents	flavour enhancers
bulk sweeteners	food additives
intense sweeteners	nature identical additives
gelling agents	natural additives
fortification	artificial additives
emulsifiers and stabilisers	European Food Safety Authority
oxidation	antioxidants
rancidity	preservatives

Exam-style questions

1 Discuss the choice and use of fats and oils in the UK diet.   (25 marks)

2 Explain the uses of sugar in the production of food products.   (8 marks)

3 List three sugar substitutes.   (3 marks)

4 Describe the performance characteristics of eggs.   (25 marks)

5 Describe the behaviour changes in shortcrust pastry.   (8 marks)

6 Explain the benefits to the consumer of food additives.   (6 marks)

(Total of 75 marks)

DESIGN, DEVELOPMENT AND PRODUCTION OF NEW PRODUCTS

Learning objectives

By the end of this chapter you will be able to:

- describe the process of design, development and production of new food products
- explain in detail the methods used to promote new food products.
- explain the costs involved in the design, development and production of food products
- investigate the pricing of a food product and the strategies used to price a product
- explain why sensory analysis is important in food production and describe the different types of sensory analysis tests used in food production
- explain how to carry out a fair test
- investigate in detail the importance of risk assessment, including Hazard Analysis and Critical Control Point (HACCP) in the food industry, and explain the terminology used
- outline the range of materials used to package food and explore their advantages and disadvantages for the manufacturer, retailer and consumer
- explain why food labelling is important, and describe current legislation associated with it
- outline the current approaches to nutritional labelling.

Introduction

This chapter looks at the procedures a food manufacturer may follow when producing a new food product. You will explore the costs involved in the process of food production and will investigate in depth sensory testing, food packaging and labelling.

Food product design, development and production

Product development is crucial in the food industry, and can range from the development of a completely new product to refining an established product range. However, it is a process fraught with risk that often ends in failure, since around 90 per cent of all new food products fail in the first year.

The process of design, development and production of food outlined in this chapter is a linear sequence of events that has a beginning and end. However, in the food industry, the whole process involves regular feedback and therefore stages may be revisited to allow further refinement and improvement of the product.

Step 1: Concept generation

Identifying a need

Everyone needs to eat food to remain healthy. Once this basic need has been fulfilled, people want different foods and more choice. Within the food industry, it is the role of the product development team to find out what people want and produce solutions to their problems. The process of identifying a consumer need for a product is called **concept generation**.

Concept generation is important as it involves developing ideas for new food products. Ideas for new food products can come from a variety of sources:

● changes in the food industry and society

● consumer demand

● developments in technology.

The purpose of the initial research is to identify a gap in the market and a potential market for a new product.

Understanding changing consumer needs

In recent years, growing consumer interest and demand for more convenient food has influenced the development of new food products in the following areas:

● partly prepared meals, for instance, cook–chill products, both single portions and for families

● functional foods, for example, foods with health-promoting benefits

● ethically sourced food, including products that specifically concern themselves with animal welfare or environmental issues and Fair-trade products

● exotic foods and indulgent foods.

Identifying the intended target market

A food product is usually aimed at a specific group of people. To ensure the food product meets their needs, the group must be clearly identified. The product development team call this group of people a target market. A **target market** may include working parents, people with wheat allergies, people following low fat diets or families on a low income, for example.

Activity 5.1

Discussion

Identify a food product that is aimed at a specific target group. What are the features of this product that suggest it is aimed at this particular group?

Media and consumer attention on the subject of food additives, farming practices and healthy eating have led to changes in the choice of food available. Discuss how food manufacturers are responding to this in their development of new food products.

Investigating the market

The purpose of **market research** is to gather, organise and analyse information that will be used to identify the market for a product and can anticipate the customers' future needs and wants.

Market research is a valuable source of information to food manufacturers to help identify new ideas. It reduces the uncertainty when launching a new food product or making changes to existing products. Market research ensures that informed decisions are made about planning and managing a product.

Market research is a continuous and circular process. It begins at the concept generation stage and continues after the final launch. The feedback received may lead to further refinements or developments of the product.

Once a product is launched, market research can be used to monitor its performance in the market place. Market research can focus on consumer buying behaviour or sales data, which is likely to fluctuate over time. New trends may emerge and manufacturers need to be aware of them for further product development. Information received from market research may be used to select a new brand image,

Activity 5.2

Research

There are many methods of market research available to food manufacturers.

For each of the methods shown below, write a brief statement indicating how it could be used to supply information to a food manufacturer about to begin the development of a new product.

● questionnaire
● face-to-face interview
● postal, electronic or telephone surveys
● government reports and publications
● business publications and statistical data
● observations of purchasing habits by scanning technology
● pilot trials
● sensory testing
● focus groups and expert panels
● recipe books, and using the internet for recipe ideas
● evaluating existing products
● visiting restaurants
● visiting other countries.

invest money in advertising, widen distribution or select an idea to be developed.

Once a gap in the market and a target group are identified then a design brief can be written. A **design brief** is a statement that identifies a problem that needs to be addressed.

There are two main types of market research:

1 **Quantitative research** involves the study of factual data of consumption patterns and market size. It focuses on what food we buy and where and when we buy it.

2 **Qualitative research** could be in-depth interviews or questionnaires with consumers. It focuses on the why and how of decision making associated with food shopping.

Analysis of consumer behaviour in the food market using either of these methods can suggest trends and changes in consumer behaviour that a food manufacturer can respond to.

Other factors can contribute to the generation of new food products. There may be a genuine gap in the market, or changes in government legislation can lead to the generation of new food products. For example, the Department for Education and Skills (DfES) has established nutritional guidelines for products sold in school vending machines. New products have emerged to meet this requirement.

The success of a competitor can inspire a food manufacturer to develop a new product. Manufacturers do not want to copy existing products but they may investigate a popular existing product, look at its features, and then aim to produce something similar yet with subtle modifications. A disassembly of an existing food product may be used to achieve this goal.

Disassembly of a food product

To disassemble means to take something apart. A **disassembly** of a food product involves taking it apart to find out more information about it, for example, its main ingredients and the role of the food additives. Disassembly is achieved by carefully weighing or measuring each separate component. This will give a food manufacturer an idea of why the product is successful or how it could be improved. One purpose of disassembly is to see if an existing product can be improved by adding new features, either to boost flagging sales or to produce a 'new and improved'

Activity 5.3

Research opportunity

Figure 5.01

Disassemble a sandwich or snack product

Examine two different versions of one type of sandwich or snack product, for example, a reduced calorie sandwich and a standard sandwich.

Copy the table below to record your comparisons. The headings in the table are only suggestions; you may wish to add further headings.

Features to be compared	Product 1	Product 2
Ingredients		
Cost		
Overall product weight		
Shelf life		
Nutritional profile (100 g)		
Energy		
Total fat		
Saturated fat		
Fibre		
Sodium		
Weight of filling		

Weighing and measuring the different components of the products will allow you to make further comparisons and these can be added to the table accordingly.

Write a conclusion summarising your findings.

Explain why this information is valuable to a food manufacturer.

version. Food manufacturers invest considerable time and money into asking consumers about their own and competitors' products. Consumers are attracted to newly developed food products with a marketing strategy focusing on the refinements, for example, a product that now contains extra fruit. Disassembly also helps a manufacturer understand how a competitors' product works by enabling them to evaluate ingredients, manufacturing process and packaging.

Step 2: Concept screening

Once the initial ideas have been formalised, they are then refined. During this stage, some ideas are rejected but this is an important stage because it moves the process along from initial thoughts to the actual development of ideas. The best ideas are taken forward and a **design specification** is written. A general design specification is a list of criteria that initial design ideas are evaluated against. Design specifications are usually written after the initial research has been conducted and may contain generalised statements, for example, the product will be low fat. Sometimes a design specification will categorise the criteria as 'essential' or 'desirable'.

A design specification for a food product may contain references to the following:

- type of product – sweet or savoury

- appeal to particular consumer group(s)

- storage conditions required.

The general criteria included in the design specification are developed from potential users and their identified needs.

Design ideas are based upon the initial research and the general design specification. All the design ideas should meet the design brief. The costing and feasibility of some ideas is explored. Ideas may be rejected because the supply of the ingredients and price is too unpredictable. From this initial stage of development, the ideas may be reduced to one or two feasible products. These products will then enter the next stage of development – the production of the prototype.

Step 3: Development and testing

This stage allows the range of possible solutions to be refined further. The most appropriate and feasible food product will eventually be developed further. A **product specification** is developed containing the most vital aspects of the design specification with greater clarity, for example:

- The product will be a savoury snack.

- It will be a single serving.

- The retail price will be less than £1.20.

- Storage conditions will be dry and cool.

A product specification contains specific details that enable the development of a prototype.

Prototype production

Next, the design idea is developed into a working **prototype** of the food product – an example or model of what the food product will be like. It allows designers to evaluate in more detail the characteristics of the product. One or two prototypes could be developed and compared against the product specification.

Further modifications or a rejection can still occur at this stage. A successful prototype can attract more financial investment from a food manufacturer or other interested parties.

Product testing

Product testing is an important stage in the development of new food products. Expert sensory (organoleptic) testers within the food manufacturing company will conduct sensory testing to refine the food product further, if necessary.

Once the development work is completed, a **manufacturing specification** is written. Now the final prototype is ready for manufacturing in large quantities. The manufacturing specification will provide the manufacturer with accurate information on proportions, ratios and tolerances within the product. It will include the name of the product, the production process, a list of raw ingredients and the quantities, cooking temperatures and the net weight of the product.

Here is an example of a manufacturing specification:

- specific details on the type, size and quantity of each ingredient

- microbiological tolerance of the product

- cooking methods, time and temperature

- critical control points to be adhered to during production

- details of the packaging materials to be used

- photographic and written statement on the presentation of the product.

Step 4: Production methods

Production systems

Figure 5.02 *Batch produced products*

There are three types of production system – **job production**, **batch production** and **mass production** – and the system chosen will depend upon the quantity of food to be produced.

- *Job production system* – this is used for the production of a prototype or an individual food product and involves making a one-off food product for a specific customer. The product made by this method will meet a unique design specification and often requires specialist skill to produce. The product can take time to make and may be expensive.

- *Batch production system* – this is a system where small numbers of identical products are produced. A small bakery may produce a specified number of floured, white loaves each day using batch production. Slight adaptations can be made to the production system, for example, a seed topping can be used on the bread loaves. Because each set of loaves is batch produced, lower production costs are maintained and the consumer is offered more choice of food product.

- *Mass production* – this is used to make large quantities of identical food products. Many well-known brands are produced by this method, as it

enables food manufacturers to meet the high demand for their products. For example, every day thousands of potato crisps, biscuits and frozen chips are manufactured using mass production techniques. One leading food manufacturing company produces 1.5 million tins of baked beans every day!

Activity 5.4

Discussion
Can you identify some food products that may be produced by job production?

Small-scale factory trial

Before a food product is manufactured by batch or mass production, a small-scale factory trial will be conducted. Initially, several small production runs are completed. The food product is continually assessed during this stage, and small changes and refinements may be made to the process. Careful monitoring of the trial helps to eliminate any problems and ensures all aspects of the production are checked. Refinements may still occur to ensure that the product can be produced within a costing set down in the development. Once the production run is established, the recipe will be scaled up for a large-scale production.

Safety and quality control

During production the food manufacturing system is controlled by a variety of checks. These vary depending upon the product being manufactured and could include shelf-life analysis and microbiological testing.

The **HACCP (Hazard Analysis and Critical Control Point)** system of risk assessment and safety checks is widely used in the food industry. It is a systematic way of identifying food safety hazards and making sure they are controlled on a daily basis. The implementation of HACCP will be explored later in this chapter.

Quality control and quality assurance systems are used to ensure the maintenance of a good-quality end product. Uniformity of the end product will also be monitored and controlled during the manufacturing process. Quality testing is usually completed off-line, with samples taken at the beginning, middle and end of each batch. Quality control reduces the wastage of the product because errors are identified during the manufacturing process. Many different attributes or characteristics are monitored, including colour, flavour and texture. Quality control is important to reassure the consumer they are purchasing a high quality food product.

Sensory testing may also be completed to ensure quality is maintained. There may be photos of the food product and a series of tasting notes, for instance, initial flavours, mouth feel and flavours that linger on the palate. Individuals who are trained organoleptically may complete daily random tastings.

Distribution system

A distribution system is required for the food product. Refrigerated storage and transportation will be required for a fresh, chilled food product. Distribution systems may involve not just road transport but also transportation of food by air, sea or rail.

Step 5: Packaging and labelling

Statutory guidelines exist on the type of information found on food packaging and the following are required by law:

- name of the product
- name of the manufacturer
- list of ingredients
- shelf life
- storage requirements
- instructions for use.

Legal and advertising teams may have to work together to ensure the packaging and labelling of a product meets all the necessary requirements.

Food manufacturers can include additional information on a food package to help sell their product. This information is not statutory and may include logos or quality marks – for example, the 'Red Tractor' logo (an independent mark that guarantees the food that features the mark comes from farms and food companies that meet high standards of food safety and hygiene, animal welfare and environmental protection). A statement about the environmental impact of the packaging may also be included, which can help to market the food product.

If a specific nutritional claim is made on a product, then nutritional information must be included on its packaging. In the development and production of a new food product, a detailed list of ingredients may be produced so that accurate nutritional information can be added to the product label.

The type of packaging chosen by a manufacturer will be investigated and tested and must be suitable for the food product. The packaging may have to withstand freezing or refrigerated storage. The food product may be microwaved or baked in a conventional oven straight from storage. The packaging must remain intact to protect the product from contamination, damage and tampering.

Step 6: Advertising

Marketing plan

A marketing plan is developed to focus on a marketing strategy for the food product. The focus of the strategy will be to balance the four elements of the **marketing mix** – price, place, product and promotion.

- *Price* – correct pricing of a product is crucial to its success. The initial price is decided by the product's potential market or target group. Some food products are launched with a special introductory price to attract interest. Alternatively, a food product may be priced and marketed at a high price to denote quality in order to attract a particular target group. (The costs involved in food production and methods of pricing new food products will be explored in detail later in this chapter.)

- *Place* – where a product is sold is important to its success. A food product may be sold in a particular region to see how well it performs and who it appeals to, before a national launch. Supermarkets decide where the product will be situated to attract most consumers, including the shelf, aisle or checkout position.

- Product – this aspect of the marketing mix explores how the product meets the customers' needs. If this is exploited fully during marketing, then the product has a greater chance of success.

- *Promotion* – this involves the development of a range of activities to promote the food product in order to ensure maximum sales. This may include some of the methods outlined below.

Promoting a new food product

There are two types of marketing technique: **above the line advertising** and **below the line advertising**. We will now explore the methods used to promote goods using each of these techniques.

Above the line

Above the line techniques involve purchasing time and space in the media – television, cinema, radio, advertising hoardings and search engines – to promote a company brand or product. These techniques are considered to be impersonal methods of advertising to consumers. The following techniques are all above the line methods of advertising.

- *Television advertising* is an effective method due to the popularity of television as a form of entertainment. Advertisements that feature a memorable jingle or a famous celebrity appeal to the public. The timing of adverts are scheduled to suit particular target groups, although significant restrictions now exist to limit children's exposure to the broadcast advertising of food and drink products that are high in fat, salt and sugar.

- *National newspaper and magazine articles* may contain advertisements for new food products and coupons to encourage a purchase. Advertising space in magazines that have a specialist readership, for example, *BBC Good Food* magazine may be used to a launch a new food product.

- *Food manufacturer and retailer websites* can provide the consumer with information on the development of new products. Money-off coupons may be available from the website to encourage consumers to purchase.

- *Advertising hoardings* can have a huge visual impact, particularly if a celebrity is used to attract consumer attention to a product.

- *Supermarkets' own magazines* can be used to promote own brands or new food products. They may contain coupons, recipe ideas or features on new products.

Below the line

Below the line advertising is more personal and uses brand-building strategies, such as direct mail, price promotions and printed media. Some examples of below the line methods are shown below.

- *Price promotions* can be used to market a new food product. Strategies include offering a percentage extra of the product included in the normal retail

Figure 5.03 *Example of below the line advertising*

price, for example, 'buy one get one free' (BOGOF), '3 for 2' offers or a discounted introductory price.

- *Money off coupons* can encourage consumers to try a new food product. Coupons are found in a number of sources including food packaging, newspapers, till receipts, magazines, in-store leaflets and flyers.

- *Gift with purchase* can be used to entice the consumer into making a purchase. Often products aimed at children use this strategy, since children will pester their parents to purchase the product. Novelty packaging and brand collectables can also appeal to some consumers.

- *Competitions and prizes* can be used to focus on specific consumers. The prizes offered, for example, days out at a theme park, will appeal to families with children.

- *Link promotions* can be used to increase sales, for example a 'Dine in for £10' deal, where the consumer selects from any three products. This can drive up the total basket spend as instead of purchasing just one product there is an increased likelihood of spending £10 if the items are linked together in a deal.

- *Frequent user/loyalty incentives* can provide the retailer with information about the consumer. The use of loyalty cards with personalised mail shots may help to promote a new food product. Loyalty to a product can also be encouraged if purchases are associated with a good cause, for example, 'Computers for schools'.

- *Point-of-sale displays* near the check out and queuing area in many supermarkets are often used to market products to consumers. Small, inexpensive snack products are often displayed, with the aim of tempting an impulse purchase as the consumer waits to pay. However, Co-op supermarkets have voluntarily chosen not to sell unhealthy snack food at their check outs.

- *Product placement* in the store is used to market a new product. The entrance to the store can be used to promote a special offer, as the consumer has to walk past this area to shop. End of aisles displays or eye level shelving are effective areas for marketing new products or special offers. The movement of offers around the store will encourage more impulse purchases on the route to retrieve essentials. A promotional area linking food products or a 'theme' display may also be used. Some retailers also use in-store televisions with a touch screen to display offers, ideas and information to the consumer. This aspect of marketing is currently unregulated with only voluntary steps taken by some retailers to control it.

- *Exhibitions and trade shows* are used as a platform for a food manufacturer or producer to launch a new food product. Exhibitions and trade shows, for example, the Good Food Show, can also be used to launch a new product to the public, although participation in these events can be expensive for manufacturers. At these events a product may be offered as an exclusive or at an introductory price before a national launch.

- *Displays and in-store signage* is an important method of promoting a new product or directing the consumer to a product. The floor, ceiling, doors and shelving can all be used to promote goods. In large supermarkets, even the shopping trolley can carry information about deals available in store. The latest developments in shopping trolley design incorporate a small screen that can display special offers for products that are near the location of the trolley. The screen can also display a map showing the layout of the supermarket and the location of special offers so they can be easily reached.

- *In-store demonstrations and taste sessions* are a valuable method of promoting a new food product, because consumers can sample the product while they are shopping. Giving the consumer an opportunity to taste before buying and issuing money-off coupons with the tasting may generate more sales. Consumers may also switch to a higher priced product.

- *Free recipe leaflets* may be available in store or recipes can be included on the food packaging to give further ideas for use.

- *Charity endorsement and quality assurance schemes* are included on some food packaging. Endorsements from charitable organisations such as the British Heart Foundation or British Dental Association may encourage consumers to make a purchase. The use of logos and symbols such as the 'Red Tractor' logo or RSPCA 'Freedom Food' symbol can also influence purchasing.

Activity 5.5

Handling data

The graph shows the methods influencing purchase of new food products.

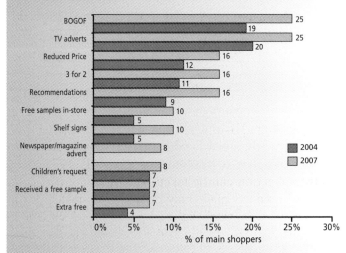

Figure 5.04 *Methods influencing purchase*
Source: IGD Consumer Research, www.igd.com

Use the data in the graph to answer the following questions.

1 In 2007, which two methods were the most effective for promoting new products?

2 Which two methods were the least effective in both 2004 and 2007?

3 Besides the use of newspapers and magazine adverts, which method has seen the greatest increase since 2004?

4 Which methods may become more popular in times of economic recession? Give a reason for your answer.

5 What other methods of promoting new products are not mentioned in this data?

Step 7: Launch

The final stage of the design and development process is the launch. As outlined earlier, the food product may be launched initially in just one region. Once the food item is on sale, the process does not end – a small-scale launch may suggest that the marketing strategies need to be adjusted.

The full-scale national launch is monitored closely. Initially, sales figures are checked very carefully and this information is fed back to the manufacturer so that appropriate action can be taken. For example, the volume of products made may need to be adjusted or the food product may need slight adaptations, which can be completed economically and effectively shortly after launch. However, at this stage, it is too late to make major changes and so the lifecycle of the food product may be short if sales are lower than anticipated.

Design, development and production costs

In this section we will examine the cost of the design and development process, which is met by the organisation commissioning the new food product. This cost may be added to the retail price of the finished product.

Design and development

A product development team may be employed to complete the whole process of design and development. They will make key decisions relating to the product's ingredients, packaging materials and manufacturing process.

Market research

The methods used to analyse a need for a new food product and identify a gap in the market will incur costs. Market research is expensive and time consuming. Research of the existing market (including the use of questionnaires, in-depth interviews, and the disassembly of existing products) requires staff who may need to be expertly trained, and it takes time to complete.

Food manufacturers need reliable and accurate information about sale patterns and future consumption trends. Quantitative research collected from large-scale studies produced by companies specialising in market research is expensive to purchase. Yet the analysis and interpretation of this type of data will assist in the development of ideas and give the company confidence to invest money in its new product.

Information technology

Design possibilities and ideas are explored with the development of a product specification and prototype. **Computer Aided Design** (CAD) may be used extensively to support the design process and development of new food products.

A CAD graphics package is often used for modelling and communicating product ideas, packaging and labelling designs. Information technology can be used to produce spreadsheets with costing, nutritional analysis and a HACCP plan. There is a statutory requirement for food manufacturers to have a food safety plan in place for the production of food products, based on the HACCP principles. Email can be used to communicate with companies and suppliers. The purchase of hardware and software will contribute to the production costs.

Product testing

The development and evaluation of prototypes, including sensory testing and piloting small trials, are expensive to manage. Detailed testing and modifications may be made to the recipe. Trained organoleptic testers will be required to refine the sensory characteristics of the food product. This will provide the manufacturer with accurate information on proportions, ratios and tolerances within the new food product.

Trials

Consumer trials may be required and the production of samples for trials will contribute to costs. The results of consumer trials will need to be analysed and reported.

Packaging

Ideas for packaging will be explored and the legal requirements for food labelling implemented. There must be consideration of the target market, storage conditions and cost of the packaging designs. Packaging must be appropriate for the food product. The consumer will link the quality and design of the packaging with the quality of the product itself. Packaging may add further costs to the product selling price.

Raw materials and labour

A buyer will seek out the best possible quality raw materials for maximum profitability. The raw materials in food production are the ingredients. Bulk purchases of ingredients may enable the company to negotiate a discount. The cost of raw materials and the reliability of supplies is considered. Importing ingredients is expensive, particularly if they require air transport into the UK. International and domestic producers may have to follow regulations and implement European legislation to meet the requirements of the food manufacturer. These costs may be incorporated into the sourcing price of raw materials.

Figure 5.05

Activity 5.6

Research

The cost of raw materials can be affected by a number of factors that are beyond the control of food manufacturers.

Research how the weather, price of oil and food scares such as BSE can affect the sourcing of ingredients.

The cost of labour is very important to overall production costs. Staff may require training; specialist skills may be needed for production. Unskilled or semi skilled labour may be required to work on a production line. Staff may be required to work shifts, which could mean that labour costs increase. **Continuous flow production** is often used in the mass production of a food product. This method usually involves the production of one product 24 hours a day, seven days a week. The system is usually automated but staff are required for maintenance during production, so shift payments will add to production costs.

Factory and machinery

A production team will be required to organise the large-scale manufacture of the product. Production may involve the purchase of new machinery or adaption of existing machinery to perform a particular task. Equipment may have to be rented, thus incurring a charge. Land may need to be purchased or rented if a new factory needs to be constructed.

Fixed costs are maintenance, staff salaries, fuel and insurance costs. Variable costs are affected by output and include the cost of ingredients, packaging materials and running costs of machinery. As the number of food products manufactured increases, fixed costs become less important and variable costs become more significant.

The food manufacturing system will be controlled by the HACCP system of risk assessment and safety checks. High-risk products will require stringent safety tests and this will add to production costs. A product safety team or manager will be employed to manage a range of tasks including:

- *approval issues* to ensure the raw materials, production processes and preparation methods are appropriate and safe

- *surveillance issues* to monitor the process and complete microbacterial checks

- *emergency issues* to assess how any changes in production or supplier affect the quality of the product.

Quality control and quality assurance systems are used to ensure the maintenance of a good quality food product.

The production of the food product may be large scale and controlled by a **Computer Aided Manufacturing (CAM) system**. A CAM system can complete a number of tasks in the automated mass production of food products. Many food products are produced on conveyer systems feeding into ovens, chillers or freezers. The tasks completed on the conveyor system are standardised procedures, which are repeated with accuracy on each food product. CAM monitors this system and checks many aspects of the food product including the temperature, weight, thickness and colour. CAM benefits the manufacturer because it reduces human error, increases production speed and can give the retailer greater confidence in the reliability of the end product. However, the establishment and maintenance of a computer controlled manufacturing system is expensive.

Distribution

Establishing a distribution system for a food product will incur costs. Refrigerated storage and transportation is required for some perishable food products, so specialist vehicles are needed, which generates further costs for the distributor. According to DEFRA (Department for Environment, Food and Rural Affairs), haulage vehicles completed 5.5 million food miles in 2004 and road haulage remains the main method used to transport food to retailers. The price of diesel and aviation fuel also affects the cost of the food product.

Marketing

A marketing team assesses the market and is involved in the development of food packaging and advertising campaigns. Legal advice is sought to ensure compliance with legalisation relating to the manufacture and sale of food. Information provided to the consumer must not be misleading.

Retailers and food manufacturers may use a variety of marketing techniques to launch the product. Staff may be employed to conduct personal selling in retail outlets. This may encourage a consumer to try a new product and provide feedback for the retailer but is expensive to maintain.

The quality of the packaging can give the consumer an indication of the quality of the product and is designed to appeal to the target group. The type of packaging chosen, particularly if it is modified atmospheric packaging (MAP), will affect the selling price of the product, as the cost of the additional processing to produce MAP will be added to the retail price.

Advertising

A new or modified product may be advertised on television, internet, magazines, newspapers, flyers, radio and cinema. Each year over £600 million is spent on food advertising in the UK. Before producing an advert, the needs and wants of the product's target audience will be researched.

In-store advertising such as free samples, money-off coupons, loss leaders, competitions and extra loyalty card points has a cost implementation for retailers.

Merchandising is an attempt at the point of sale to influence the consumer to make a purchase. The display material, positioning and design layout of the product is structured to encourage the consumer to make a purchase. Free publicity is achieved if the food product is used as part of a recipe in a magazine or is endorsed by a celebrity.

Pricing a product

Pricing the product accurately for the competitive marketplace is critical for its success and is not difficult if the product has a sales history. However, it can be more challenging to set the selling price of a completely new product.

The final selling price aims to maximise profit, encourage sales, achieve a market share and produce a return for the financial investment made by the company.

Influences on price

Many factors influence the final selling price of a product. When pricing a product, consideration must be given to the costs of production and manufacture. The minimum cost of the product must cover all the production costs. The media can affect the demand for a product, for example, if a product is heavily advertised then it is likely to create more demand for it than one that is only advertised in a few places.

The cost of any competitive food products will be considered, since there is direct competition between retailers and pricing policies have to remain competitive in order for a product to succeed.

Manufacturers that establish a strong brand identity can control their pricing more closely. Products with a strong brand identity can be differentiated from others and may command a higher price. Demand for a product and market trends can also influence its selling price – if demand is great and the product in short supply the price may increase.

Consumer expectations and perceptions of a product are important, so a product must be priced to meet consumer expectations. If the price is too low then the consumer may not purchase it because they fear it is inferior quality.

The market segment or target market the product is aimed at is also significant. Marketing a product as a luxury item may enable a higher price to be set, since consumers will be prepared to pay more for what they perceive as a quality item.

The most successful pricing falls between a minimum price, which will cover all costs and a maximum price, which will lead to a decline in demand.

Pricing strategies

There are three main strategies used for pricing products – **cost based pricing**, **market based pricing** and **competition based pricing**. We will explore each strategy in turn.

Cost based pricing

This method of pricing products is based on production costs. The price is set by calculating the average cost of manufacturing the food product and adding a fixed mark up for the profit. The market requirements are not a priority with this method. The disadvantage of this method is that if costs increase, the price of the product must also increase.

Market based pricing

This method is based on an analysis of the conditions in the market at which the product is aimed and of consumer requirements. The following are examples of market based pricing methods.

- *Penetration pricing* – used to gain a foothold in the market with a new product. Prices are usually set at a low level to encourage the consumer to make a purchase.

- *Market skimming* – involves selling a new product at a high price for a limited period. The aim is to gain maximum profit for the product while it remains unique in the market.

CHECK YOUR UNDERSTANDING

Check you understand the meaning of the following key terms. Write a sentence using each word.

competition based pricing
Computer Aided Manufacturing (CAM)
cost based pricing
fixed costs
variable costs

Computer Aided Design
continuous flow production
market based pricing
merchandising

- *Loss leader pricing* – frequently used by supermarkets, it involves charging below cost price to try to attract customers to the product.

- *Psychological pricing* – involves setting price points that are significant, for example, £2.99 appears to be better value than £3.00.

- *Discount pricing* – offers lower prices for a set time period to increase sales and sell off discontinued products or food reaching the date mark.

Competition based pricing

Competition based pricing is also known as rate or market pricing and involves charging the same as competitors or the market leader, in order to avoid a price war. The manufacturer examines its competitors' prices and selects a price broadly in line with them.

Importance of sensory testing

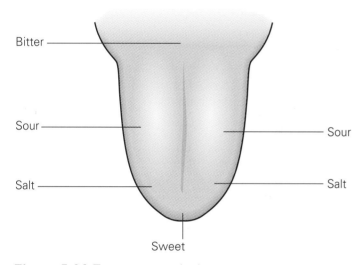

Bitter

Sour — — Sour

Salt — — Salt

Sweet

Figure 5.06 *Taste areas on the human tongue*

Introduction

The sensory analysis of foods plays an important role in the food industry. Food product-development specialists carry out a range of sensory analysis tests to produce the variety of foods that are available in the shops. Food manufacturers wish to ensure customers continue to buy existing products because they like their taste and new products because they are innovative and exciting.

Sensory analysis tests are carried out to:

- evaluate new and established food products

- analyse food products for improvements

- establish consumer response to a product

- ensure that a product meets its original specification

- conduct a product review, assess quality control and make improvements to the product

- maintain product quality

- assess shelf life.

Sensory analysis tests

British Standards issue procedures for the standard tests to be used by the food industry.

Preference tests or acceptance

Preference tests or acceptance are used to establish the acceptability of a product by finding out consumers' opinions. The information gathered is subjective and large numbers of consumers are required to complete the testing. There are a number of different types of preference tests.

- *Paired preference tests* – a tester is given two samples and asked which they prefer.

- *Hedonic ranking or descriptors* – allow the consumer to rank the product in order of preference. These tests are used to establish the best samples from a group.

- *Differences tests* – used to highlight specific changes to a product, for instance, reduced sugar. The information gathered is objective. There are a number of differences tests:

  - *Paired comparisons* – these help a manufacturer confirm what they can predict about a particular product, for example, a reduced fat content may make a biscuit harder.

  - *Triangle test* – used to demonstrate small differences between products. Three coded samples are presented, with one sample the odd one out. Used to detect small differences between products.

– *Duo-trio test* – used when a smaller sample is required. This test is used with strong flavours. The tester is presented with a control sample and two further samples are given, one identical to the control. The tester must identify the sample that is different from the control.

– *Two Out of Five test* – used to see if differences can be detected between two products. Three samples are identical and two are the same.

– *Taste threshold test* – occasionally used to find out the lowest minimum quality of an ingredient or substance that can be added to a product before a noticeable change occurs to its flavour or colour, for example.

Grading tests

Grading tests are used to produce a ranking, rating and profiling of a product. Trained testers can also assess the flavour or texture of a product to provide a sensory profile. These tests assess the intensity of specific sensory qualities. A set of sensory descriptors may be given that represent the ideal profile of the product; this may be represented as a star diagram or star profile. The presentation of the results in a diagram may help the product developer modify the product characteristics.

- *Ranking test* – used to sort a variety of foods into order of popularity by taste, for example, different flavoured crisps made by one manufacturer.

- *Ranking test with descriptor* – used to place a variety of one type of food into order, for example, flavour of tomato soups processed by different methods.

- *Rating test* – allows people to rate the extent to which they either like or dislike a variety of products, for example, when tasting the flavour of different biscuit bases in a cheesecake the sweetness could be rated on a scale 1 (far too much sugar) to 5 (far too little sugar).

- *Star profile* – used to describe the appearance, taste and texture of a food product. Can also be used to record the suitability of other aspects of the product, such as packaging.

How to carry out a sensory analysis test

1 Find a quiet area, away from any distractions, in which to hold the sensory test.

2 Place the food samples in serving containers, making sure there are as many containers as there are people taking part in the test. Code each sample with a random number, letter or symbol. Do not use 1, 2, 3, etc., because this could imply bias.

3 Supply each person with a glass of water to sip between each sample.

4 Ask each person to taste one sample at a time and record his or her responses. Allow time and a drink of water between samples so that tasters can record their opinions.

Activity 5.7

Review

Explain why the food samples should look the same in a paired comparison test.

Why should testing take place in a booth or in isolation from others?

What is the purpose of the assessor drinking water between each test?

Why are at least five assessors required for each test?

Explain why random coded samples are used.

Activity 5.8

Research

Use the testing sheet below to carry out a ranking test (see page 145) to establish the best ginger biscuit.

Use five different varieties of ginger biscuit, for example, McVities, a basic range, a premium range and two from supermarket own-brands.

Testing sheet

Samples of ginger biscuits	1 Excessive sweetness crunch ginger golden colour	2 A little too much sweetness crunch ginger golden colour	3 Right amount of sweetness crunch ginger golden colour	4 Not quite enough sweetness crunch ginger golden colour	5 Insufficient sweetness crunch ginger golden colour
Sample 139					
Sample 467					
Sample 940					
Sample 606					

Results

Assessor	Sweetness	Crunch	Ginger flavour	Golden colour
Sample 139				
Sample 467				
Sample 940				
Sample 606				

Analysis

Which were the best biscuits and why?

CHECK YOUR UNDERSTANDING

Explain the key features of each group of tests using a web diagram:

preference tests   grading tests

Risk assessment in the food industry

Introduction

Risk assessment is used by the food industry to ensure the food we eat is safe. It is a legal requirement of the Food Hygiene (England) Regulations 2006 that every food business has risk assessment documentation to demonstrate that they have exercised 'due diligence' to prevent a food safety offence from being committed.

Hazard Analysis Critical Control Point

Hazard Analysis Critical Control Point (HACCP) is a risk assessment system adopted by the food industry and is important for the reasons shown below.

● It is legal requirement for all food businesses. Since 1 January 2006, all food businesses are required to have written food-safety management systems.

● A HACCP system identifies hazards associated with food, suggests procedures to reduce risks, and ensures food is safe to eat.

- The system requires an active approach to removing risks and hazards, thus helping the business to prevent problems rather than reacting to them after they have happened.

- The HACCP system applies throughout the food chain, from the primary producer to the final consumer, making traceability of ingredients possible.

- It offers food manufacturers some measure of legal protection, since a defence counsel in a court case could demonstrate that the manufacturer had exercised diligence through arrangements being in place to prevent an offence being committed.

- It helps to ensure food is safe for customers to eat and increases customer confidence in food production.

- It results in less food waste during production and more effective use of resources.

Terms used in a HACCP plan

Below are some important terms that appear in a HACCP plan.

- A **hazard** is anything that can cause harm to the consumer. HACCP focuses on identifying where hazards could occur.

- A **control point** is a step in food preparation where control can be applied to stop a hazard occurring or reduce it to a safe level.

- When handling high risk food, **critical control points** are identified. A critical control point (CCP) is a step in food preparation where control must be applied to prevent a hazard or reduce it to an acceptable level.

- When a critical control point has been identified it is important to give it a critical limit. **Critical limits** are the accepted level of tolerance that can be applied to a situation and are usually expressed as a temperature, weight or period of time. These standards must be rigorously monitored and checked to ensure the quality and safety of the outcome remains high.

- Action must be taken to maintain critical limits and tolerances when required. If the monitoring of a critical control point indicates that critical limits have not been met, action must be taken to bring

the critical control point back within critical limits – this is called **corrective action.**

How does HACCP work?

Every single process from preparation, processing, manufacturing, transportation, distribution, handling, packaging, storage, selling and supplying food can be controlled by a HACCP system.

In large-scale food production, a team of highly trained people is required to organise a HACCP system. However, all food businesses are required to have a food-safety management system in place, no matter what the nature or size of their business.

A HACCP plan has seven stages:

1 Identify the *hazards*

2 Identifying the *critical control points*

3 Set the *critical limits*

4 *Monitor* the critical limits

5 Take *corrective action*

6 Have a *record* system

7 *Verify* the system.

We will now explore each stage in more detail.

Stage 1: Identify the hazards

The first stage in the development of a food safety plan is to identify the hazards.

The food we eat must be safe but it can be contaminated by three types of hazard:

1 physical hazard

2 chemical hazard

3 biological hazard.

Physical hazard

Physical hazards are objects that can enter the food chain at any point during production. They include insects or the droppings of pests that are living in the food production environment. Fragments of glass from broken bottles or plastic from packaging are also physical contaminants. Sometimes poor personal hygiene can become a source of contamination,

Figure 5.07

including jewellery, hair or nails which may be lost in the food production process. Soil and dust are also hazards.

Chemical hazard

The residues of chemicals can contaminate food production, for example, from the use of cleaning chemicals in a food production factory. Agricultural chemicals can also enter food.

Biological hazard

Microorganisms are biological hazards. Some microorganisms are capable of causing food poisoning and can affect the quality and safety of food products. If the conditions are favourable, pathogenic bacteria can affect the food production process. Sometimes the raw ingredients used in food production can contaminate cooked food. Poor personal hygiene, dirty

equipment and food waste can all be a source of biological hazards.

Control measures are needed at points where hazards are likely to occur in the production process. Figure 5.08 illustrates two types of hazard and the control measure required to prevent each hazard.

Activity 5.9

Review

Copy the diagram in Figure 5.09 and indicate the type of hazard represented in each of the circles (i.e. physical, biological or chemical).

Expand the diagram to show ways in which the hazard could contaminate food.

Expand it further to show some control measures that could be used to prevent the hazard from contaminating food.

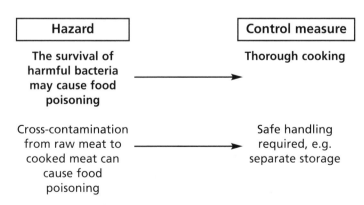

Hazard		Control measure
The survival of harmful bacteria may cause food poisoning	→	Thorough cooking
Cross-contamination from raw meat to cooked meat can cause food poisoning	→	Safe handling required, e.g. separate storage

Figure 5.08 *Examples of hazards and control measures*

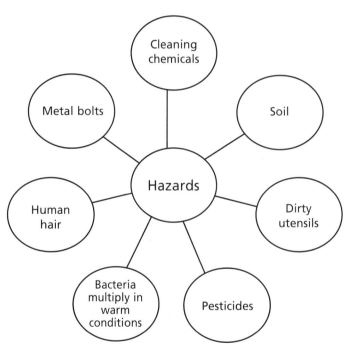

Figure 5.09 *Important hazards in food production*

Figure 5.10 shows the steps in food production from purchase of ingredients to serving the hot food. By creating a flow chart of the food production system a food business can identify the process steps and the subsequent control measures needed.

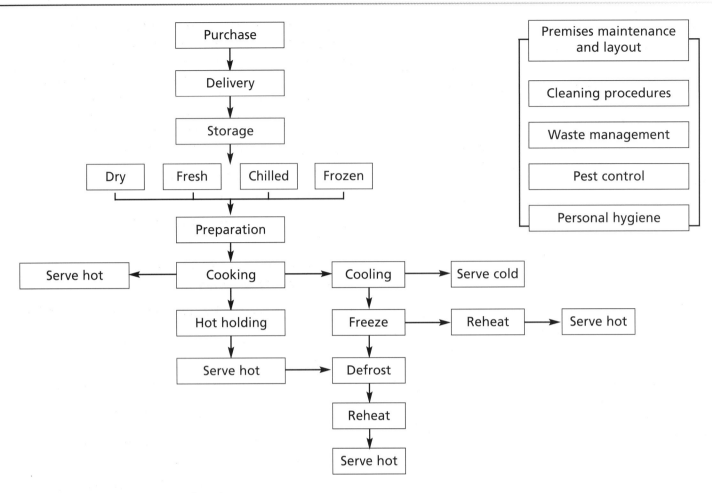

Figure 5.10 *Food production flow chart*

Activity 5.10

Review

Below is a list of control measures to produce safe food.

Copy the diagram in Figure 5.10 (but allowing more space within the boxes) and using the list below, place each control measure in the correct box under the appropriate heading.

Use reputable suppliers

Defrost frozen foods before cooking

Adequate lighting/ventilation

No pests present

Chilled food in fridge within 15 minutes of delivery

Wash hands before handling food

Display without refrigeration for 4 hours max

No food to be kept after use-by date

Report illness to supervisor

Cool quickly/4 hours maximum

Store cooked food over raw foods in fridge

Toilets do not lead into food rooms

Cook to 75°C

Keep bins clean, secure lids

Reheat only once

Store chilled food below 8°C

Remove waste regularly

Wear clean, protective clothing

Hot hold only once

Clean work surfaces before use

Store frozen food at or below 18°C

Surfaces to be in good repair

Stage 2: Identify critical control points

Some stages in food production have critical control points. A critical control point (CCP) is a step in the process at which control *must* be applied so a food safety hazard can be eliminated or reduced to an acceptable level.

Every CCP must have an effective control measure; these could be cooling to prevent microorganisms from growing or the control of weight to ensure consistency in cooking between products. A CCP could also be the control of time and temperature, for example, perishable foods can be displayed for sale for a single period of not more than four hours above a temperature of 8°C.

Stage 3: Critical limits

A critical limit is the maximum or minimum tolerance to which a physical, biological or chemical hazard must be controlled at each critical control point. This will prevent, eliminate, or reduce a hazard to an acceptable level. Some critical limits are easy to define, such as the maximum temperature a fridge should be working at to ensure food remains safe (the critical limit or tolerance would be 0°C to 8°C).

Stage 4: Monitor critical limits

A monitoring system must be set up for each critical control point to ensure that the process is under control. Figure 5.11 demonstrates a critical control point to check cross-contamination prevention.

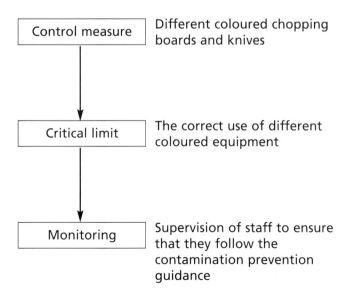

Figure 5.11 *CCP: Checking cross-contamination prevention*

Monitoring of critical control points, by observation and taking measurements, for example, ensures that any loss of control is dealt with immediately. Whatever methods are used, they should be as simple as possible. Monitoring ensures that the critical limits for each critical point are not exceeded and action can be taken before food becomes unsafe. Some examples of checking and monitoring procedures include:

- temperature and time measurements for cooking, cooling and chilling

- using a probe to check core temperatures of each batch

- using a probe for daily checking of refrigeration equipment temperatures

- observation of 'use by' date and daily stock rotation

- daily observation of equipment and work surface cleanliness

- daily inspection of packaging on incoming food

- daily visual check of storage conditions

- keeping records of deliveries, suppliers and complaints

- visual check of cleanliness of delivery vans on arrival.

Stage 5: Establish corrective actions

Corrective action is required when monitoring suggests that critical limits have not been met. Corrective action should deal with the immediate problem and prevent the problem happening again. Some examples of corrective actions are given below.

- Reheat food until thoroughly cooked if cooking temperature is inadequate.

- Adjust or repair refrigerator if temperature is greater than 8°C.

- Clean equipment again if it is dirty.

- Destroy the food concerned.

- If equipment fails and critical limits are exceeded, corrective action could include contacting a repair engineer, replacing machinery, staff training and advising staff on correct action.

Stage 6: Record system

Full details must be kept of all aspects of the food production process, including:

- temperature logs for storage
- cleaning schedules
- staff training programmes
- delivery records
- names and addresses of suppliers.

Records documenting the monitoring of critical control points, critical limits, verification and deviations must also be kept. A review of procedures and documentation may be required if the product or the controls are not satisfactory, the method of preparation changes or new equipment is introduced.

Stage 7: Verify the system

Verification is a check on the food production process and involves taking an overview of the HACCP system to ensure it is working. Verification procedures may include such activities as review of HACCP plans, CCP records, critical limits and microbial sampling and analysis. An example of verification could be a recording device to check the testing time and temperature of a cooker to ensure it is working properly.

The HACCP system is verified to ensure it is working by reviewing the plan and modifying procedures. Any verification actions undertaken must be recorded.

CHECK YOUR UNDERSTANDING

Look at the key stages shown below and rearrange them into the correct order on a HACCP plan.

Describe each stage.

Identify a critical control point
Take corrective action
Monitor critical limits
Identify the hazard
Set the critical limit
Maintain a record system
Verify the system

Importance of food packaging

Introduction

Food production methods have changed dramatically in the past forty years and the function of food packaging has responded to this development. In the past, food packaging was mainly concerned with the preservation and storage of food. Today, food packaging serves many different purposes for the retailer and the consumer. It must not only protect and keep food in a good condition but also be suitable for long distance transportation, fulfil a marketing role and meet consumer need for convenience and product information.

Reasons for food packaging

- *Physical protection* – food enclosed in a package requires protection from vibration, compression (being squashed) and temperature. The main purpose of the packaging is to preserve the original quality of the food.

- *Product containment* – packaging should contain or hold the food and keep it secure. Food products can be stored together for convenience, for example, a pack of biscuits.

- *Barrier protection* – packaging provides a barrier to oxygen, water vapour, air and dust and this reduces food spoilage and contamination. The protection of the food packaging can extend to a controlled atmosphere. Some food products are packaged in reduced-oxygen bags or trays to keep food fresh and attractive for the whole of the intended shelf life.

- *Product information* – packaging informs the consumer about the food product – it identifies the product and provides a variety of useful information about it. The food package and label communicate how to use, store and prepare the product. It may also inform the consumer how the packaging may be recycled or disposed of.

- *Convenience* – packaging can have features that add convenience for both retailer and consumer. The design can assist handling and provide greater convenience in display, storage, use and reuse of the product. Packaging that specifies the number of portions gives the consumer more convenience and can reduce wastage, since the consumer can choose between a bulk packaged or single serving of the product.

- *Marketing the food product* – packaging and labels can be used to encourage sales and reinforce brand image. The retailer can use attractive colour images of the food product effectively and the quality of the packing materials and style can contribute to consumer perception of the product.

- *Security* – packaging can ensure the product is safe, for example, tamper-proof jars and seals. Packages can also include anti-theft devices, for example, electronic article surveillance tags.

Activity 5.11

Research opportunity

Figure 5.12 *Landfill site*

Food waste is an important issue. It has been estimated that 6.7 million tonnes of household food waste is produced each year in the UK, most of which could have been eaten. Food packaging technology has a role in reducing the amount of food wasted.

Investigate how the following innovations in food packaging technology are helpful in maintaining food quality for longer for the consumer:
- breathable films
- modified atmosphere packaging
- resealable packaging.

Materials used for food packaging

Plastics

Figure 5.13

Using heat and pressure, plastics are made from oil into bottles, tubs, films, trays and caps. There are many different types of plastic and over half of all plastic packaging is used for food and drink. Plastics have a high strength to weight ratio, making them strong and lightweight. However, this can make plastics more difficult to recycle as their low weight and bulk means that vast quantities are required to make recycling economically viable.

Because so many different types of plastics are used in food packaging, recycling is a challenge. The American Society of Plastics Industry has developed a standard marking code to help consumers identify the type of plastic used in food packaging. This information can help recycling.

The most common types and some uses are shown below:

PET   *Polyethylene terephthalate*
        Drink bottles

HDPE   *High-density polyethylene*
        Milk cartons

PVC   *Polyvinyl chloride*
        Food trays, cling and packaging film

LDPE   *Low density polyethylene*
        Carrier bags

PP   *Polypropylene*
      Fat spread tubs and microwaveable meal trays

PS   *Polystyrene*
      Yoghurt pots, foam trays (used for fresh meat, for example)

OTHER   *Any other plastics* that do not fall into any of the above categories such as melamine, which is often used in picnic ware

Source: adapted from www.wasteonline.org.uk

Polythene terephthalate (PET) is rigid and tough, which makes it suitable for bottles that hold liquid. PET is one of the main plastics used in food packaging.

High-density polyethylene (HDPE) is another important plastic; it is flexible, translucent and weatherproof. HDPE can withstand low temperatures and is inexpensive to produce.

Polystyrene (PP) is widely used in food retailing because it is used to make trays on which a wide range of fresh produce such as meat and vegetables are displayed. It can be expanded and pressed into a variety of shapes and sizes, including cups. Polystyrene is a good insulator and can be used to serve hot drinks and takeaway foods.

Polypropylene is used to make containers suitable for microwave cooking.

Another widely used plastic is low-density polythene (LDPF) or packaging film. It can withstand water vapour and is strong and resistant to low temperatures. However, it cannot withstand high temperatures and does not provide a good oxygen barrier.

Plastic used to package frozen foods must withstand the temperatures required for commercial freezing. PET and low and high-density polythenes can be used in extremely cold conditions. Some plastics, including polystyrene, are only appropriate for refrigeration or chilling.

Recycling plastics is difficult. At present only two types of plastic are collected for recycling. These are polyethylene terephthalate (PET) and high-density polyethylene (HDPE).

It is possible to combine plastic with other materials. Plastics can be laminated; this means that they are coated with layers of other materials, such as card, polyester or aluminium. Using laminated materials in packaging can reduce the need for food preservatives and extend the shelf life of a product. **Aseptic** cartons made of laminated material are widely used in the food industry and this involves the use of paper, plastic and aluminium foil. The materials are laminated together to produce one material which is excellent for packaging oxygen- or moisture-sensitive foods. The foods can be heat-treated to extend their shelf life and packaged with tamper closures. Aseptic cartons can last for up to a year without the need for preservatives or refrigeration.

Aseptic cartons for long life packages are generally constructed from paperboard (usually 70–90 per cent), low-density polyethylene (usually 10–25 per cent) and aluminium foil (about 5 per cent). Figure 5.14 shows the structure of an aseptic carton.

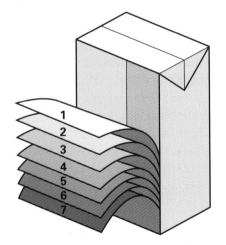

Key

1 – Polyethylene to seal in liquid
2 – Polyethylene is an adhesion layer to unite the layers
3 – Aluminium foil acts as an oxygen, aroma and light barrier
4 – Polyethylene is an adhesion layer to unite the layers
5 – Paper for stability and strength
6 – Printing inks
7 – Polyethylene to protect against external moisture
    Printing is protected on the food
    packaging by a thin coat of plastic

Figure 5.14 *Structure of an aseptic carton*
Source: Tetrapak

Advantages of plastic

For the food manufacturer, plastics provide a versatile packaging material that can be adapted to a wide range of packaging styles. Some plastics can be modified to meet different requirements and can withstand high and low temperatures.

The food retailer has many opportunities to exploit the potential of plastic packaging. Flexible plastic packaging in the form of Stand-Up Pouches (SUPs) can be used for soups and sauces. SUPs save shelf space and are attractive to consumers.

Laminating the polythene film on the package can improve a product's resistance to oxygen and extend the shelf life of foods containing fat. This allows the retailer to display products for longer periods. Some food retailers are experimenting with recycled PET (rPET). Recycled PET can be incorporated into new plastic packaging and a retailer can specify rPET content to the packaging as a requirement. This can help the retailer demonstrate to customers its commitment to environmental issues. Moulded bottles and heat-formed trays have been successfully manufactured using up to 50 per cent rPET.

Plastics offer the consumer lightweight, easy to carry and strong food storage. In 1983, a 1.5 litre PET plastic milk carton weighted 66 g; developments in the plastic industry have reduced the weight to 42 g. Some plastic packaging incorporates easy to pour spouts and re-closure devices. The consumer also finds plastic packaging more convenient to use. The introduction of squeezy formats in plastic bottles as opposed to traditional glass has improved sales of mayonnaise and tomato ketchup.

Disadvantages of plastic

The use of plastics is an area of increasing concern as they are made from non-renewable oil resources. The overuse of plastic packaging has gained considerable negative media attention. There is pressure from both the government and environmental groups to move away from the use of plastic bags. Many major food retailers have set voluntary targets to reduce the use of plastic bags in their stores.

Although biodegradable plastics are possible, they are expensive for the food retailer. Some types of plastic can be recycled but the majority are difficult to recycle

because the facilities for recycling plastic do not cover all types. Educating the consumer about recycling plastics is a challenge as there are so many types of plastic.

Paper and cardboard

Figure 5.15

Paper is a natural product manufactured from wood pulp and is the most common type of material used for food packaging. Paper is used for bags, labels, greaseproof paper, cartons and parchments. Wood pulp is also made into paperboard or 'board', as it is sometimes referred to in the food industry. Board is used for boxes, sleeves, lids and many outer food containers. A smooth coating is usually applied to the top of the pulp board to produce a good surface for printing.

Bleached pulps are used where there may be direct contact with a food product. Packaging made from paper and board is available in many weights and grades. Corrugated board has built in fluting which makes it stronger, so it is used for more robust food packaging. Paper can be coated or laminated to reduce absorption of oil or fat. Wax coatings may be applied to paper for packaging frozen food.

Paper can be recycled. The cellulose fibres used to produce paper are recovered from used paper and a variety of other materials including cotton, grasses, sugar cane or straw. Paper cannot be recycled indefinitely, however, because the cellulose fibres become shorter and weaker each time they are recycled. Some new wood pulp (virgin pulp) must be introduced into the process to maintain the strength and quality of the fibre. Recycled board may need to be made thicker to achieve the same strength and tear-resistance as 'virgin' based boards.

Advantages of paper and cardboard

The advantages of paper and board to the food manufacturer are significant. The material is relatively inexpensive, lightweight and offers good protection to food during transit. Paper and board protect food from light exposure and therefore extend the shelf life of the product. Paper and board are easily stacked.

For the food retailer, paper is available in a wide range of thickness and types. High standards of printing onto paper are possible, enabling the use of pictures, labels, logos and windows to give an excellent visual impact for the food product. This can be a powerful marketing tool as information about the product can be displayed, including price promotions, money-off coupons, competitions, recipes, etc.

The consumer also benefits from the range of packaging produced from paper and board. Card is a component of aseptic packaging, which has a longer shelf life. This type of package may be more appealing to the consumer who has no refrigeration. Paper and board are lightweight and easy to carry and tend to be easier to open than other materials. 'Ovenable' boards are coated with polypropylene and can withstand microwave temperatures, making them useful for ready prepared foods. Paper and board is easy to collapse after use, which makes disposal easier, and facilities available for recycling it are widely available in the UK.

Disadvantages of paper and cardboard

Paper and board can be damaged if stored in a damp environment. Contamination from odours or pests can occur with incorrect storage. Odours from the paper production process can taint food products so care must be taken to avoid contamination during packaging.

Metals and foils

Metals and foils are used in different ways to protect food.

Metals

Figure 5.16

Two metals – aluminium and steel – are used in the food industry to make cans, aerosols, foil containers and metal tie closures, as well as screw tops, bottle tops, trays, foil wrappings and laminates.

Some cans are made from **tinplate** – sheet steel covered with a thin layer of tin. Steel cans are often called 'tins'. These are expensive to produce but most food cans are produced by this method. Aluminium is used for packaging canned drinks. It is estimated that 75 per cent of all canned drinks in the UK are packaged in aluminium because it is lightweight and cheaper than steel.

Tinplated cans made from a thin layer of steel are protected from corrosion by a layer of tin inside the can. Coating the inside of the can with lacquers reduces costs and protects the product from discolouration. Food cans are expensive to produce but thinner walls supported by strengthening ribs have reduced the amount of aluminium required and therefore production costs.

Metal has the highest recycling rates of any packaging material in Europe, so food packaging made from steel or aluminium will contain recycled metal. According to Corus Steel Packaging Recycling, a steel can collected for recycling can be manufactured back into another steel can within a 33-day cycle. In the UK, metal recycling facilities are good; steel and aluminium are valuable resources and can be recycled many times without loss of quality.

Metal packaging has an excellent strength-to-weight ratio, which means it can protect food using a small amount of raw material. However, the extraction of metal ores and the production of metal from the raw material use large amounts of energy and produces pollution.

Foils

Figure 5.17

Foil is an inexpensive packaging material that is unaffected by extremes of temperature, so it can withstand heat and cold without deterioration. It is strong, flexible and versatile and can be manufactured into many different shaped trays and dishes, which are used to bake pies and to pack takeaway meals and ready to eat snacks.

Foil is used for food wrappings and pot lids where information can be printed or embossed onto the surface. Foil trays are used for cook–chill meals, as uncoated aluminium foil will not react with the vast majority of foods.

Aluminium foil is an excellent barrier to light and oxygen, reducing the risk of oxidation of fats and protecting the food from bacteria and moisture. Aluminium foil is also used to make long-life aseptic packaging for fruit drinks and dairy products, which enables storage without refrigeration.

Smooth wall trays are a type of aluminium packaging. The trays have a smooth rim that allows each tray to

be heat-sealed with plastic film. This is useful for fresh meat products as they can be stored in modified atmospheric packaging. This type of packaging involves the flushing and sealing of gas, usually carbon dioxide or nitrogen, into the tray. The removal of oxygen and its replacement with another gas extends shelf life of the product. This process enables fresh meats to be stored for retail sale with an extended shelf life. With the film removed, the tray is placed directly into the oven, offering the consumer greater convenience, minimal handling of raw meat and less washing up.

Advantages of metal

Cans are available in different sizes, shapes and with direct surface decorations. The product is secure inside and contents protected from damage. Coatings applied to the inside of tinplate ensure that virtually any food can be canned, including foods that have a strong acidic content such as tomatoes. Canned food does not need the addition of preservatives because the canning process preserves the contents until opening.

The food retailer is reassured that the product is protected by a shock resistant and robust material. There is also a reduced need for secondary packaging. Food products stored in metal cans are easily stacked in supermarkets. The food products stored inside have a long shelf life.

Food purchased in cans is already prepared and cooked, giving convenience to the consumer because the food can be eaten straight from the can or reheated quickly. Canned food will last for many months or even years, provided it is stored in cool, dry conditions. The consumer can feel confident that canned food is protected from contamination by dirt and bacteria, and the metal is a barrier to moisture, oxygen and odours.

The development of ring pull technology enables metal cans to be opened easily and reduces littering because the ring pulls do not separate from the can. Self-heating metal cans offer the consumer a choice of hot beverages 'on the go' and the development of widget technology allows alcoholic beverages such as beer to be served from a can and still retain a characteristic 'head'. Any beverage that requires a foam topping, including milk, yoghurt or coffee-based drinks, can benefit from widget technology: once the can is opened, the decrease in pressure causes the widget to release nitrogen and foam is produced.

Metals can be easily recycled. Many local authorities have kerbside collection services and consumers are encouraged to be actively involved in the recycling process.

Disadvantages of metal

There are very few disadvantages of metal packaging. However, once a metal can has been opened it cannot be resealed, so shelf life is limited.

Glass

Figure 5.18

Glass bottles are used to package milk, wines, salad dressings and olive oils. Glass jars are used for packaging sauces, fruits, preserves and jams.

Glass provides a hard but brittle barrier to protect food. It is impervious, which means that food stored in glass containers cannot be contaminated by environmental conditions.

Silica from sand is used to produce glass bottles and containers. According to WRAP (Waste and Resources Action Programme), around 2.5 million tonnes of glass containers are used each year in the UK. A substantial amount of glass packaging (over 1.2 million tonnes) is recycled.

Cullet is broken or waste glass returned for recycling and its use in glass production is increasingly important to the commercial glass industry. Glass packaging usually contains some cullet. Glass can be recycled many times and will remain strong. However, recycling glass requires the consumption of energy (although a reduction in the thickness and weight of glass containers is helping to ensure less material is used from the outset).

Glass is normally colourless but the addition of chemicals can produce different colours including green, blue or amber. Some food products are light sensitive and require coloured glass packaging, for example, beer requires brown or amber glass to reduce damage by light. Green glass is imported in large quantities into the UK but very little is used in the recycling industry.

Advantages of glass

Food manufacturers find glass useful because it is inert, meaning it will not transfer any microbiological or chemical contamination. Glass can be moulded into a wide variety of shapes and is easily and successfully sterilised by a food manufacturer. The consumer can also sterilise glass at home and reuse it for food storage. Glass provides an excellent moisture and gas barrier and does not affect the taste of the food inside. Food processed at high temperatures can be hot-filled directly into glass containers, saving manufacturing time and ensuring a high quality product is produced.

Glass offers some advantages to the retailer, as the consumer can see the product and it is a cheap form of packaging to produce, allowing food products stored in glass to remain competitive in price. Some premium products are associated with heavy glass packaging by consumers, for example, spirits and champagne. Research is currently being undertaken on consumer perceptions of lighter weight glass packaging for wine, food, beer and spirits.

The consumer can recycle glass easily. In the UK there is an extensive recycling infrastructure, with many local councils offering kerbside collections and large food retailers having bottle banks.

The consumer can reuse glass in the home for making chutneys, jams and wines. Glass bottles and jars can be opened and resealed easily.

Glass packaging offers the consumer more choice of food products. Some luxury food products are sold in heat-resistant borosilicate glass or Pyrex. These products may be cooked or reheated in their packaging at home, for example, individual crème brulée.

Disadvantages of glass

Glass is relatively strong and durable but it is vulnerable to breakage. Retailers may suffer some profit loss due to breakages on the shop floor. However, polystyrene sleeves can protect glass bottles from breakage and provide the consumer with more printed information about the product.

Although a significant amount of glass is produced from cullet or recycled glass, mixed and dark coloured glass is currently difficult to recycle.

Glass is heavier for the consumer to carry than other packaging materials

Biodegradable and compostable packaging materials

Biodegradable and **compostable packaging** is made from agricultural waste products or special crops grown for packaging production. After use, they will decompose back into their basic elements. However, many compostable materials will only decompose properly in commercial composting systems; the conditions required to break down the material are not usually present in domestic composters.

In the right circumstances, biodegradable materials are broken down by microorganisms into carbon dioxide, water and inorganic compounds.

In the UK, the Composting Association sets the requirements for packaging recoverable through composting and biodegradation for both home and commercial composting systems. The EN13432 seedling logo and the wording 'compostable' is used on packaging that meets the European guidelines (see Figure 5.19). Commercial and home composting conditions are very different. Therefore, it is important to label packaging clearly to inform the consumer whether the packaging is home compostable or not. Starch and sugar-cane based materials are currently being introduced to meet the need for home-compostable materials.

Figure 5.19

Food and nutritional labelling

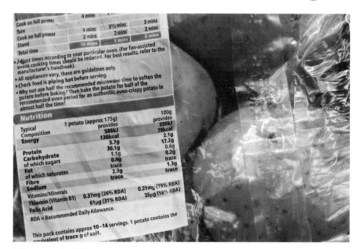

Figure 5.20

Introduction

This section looks at the importance of food labelling, legislation and current approaches to nutritional labelling. Food labels are a useful source of information and their role is to inform and protect consumers. The information provided on the packaging of food products helps consumers choose between different foods. There is also a legal requirement for much of the information provided; laws regarding food labelling are based on EU legislation. Falsely describing, advertising or presenting food is an offence, and there are a number of laws that help protect consumers against dishonest labelling and misdescription.

Food Labelling Regulations 1996

The following information must appear on a food label by law.

Name of the food

The name of the food must be clearly stated. The description of the food must be not be ambiguous nor misleading. If the food has been processed, the process must be included in the title, for example, dried apricots.

Weight or volume

The weight or volume of the food must be shown on the label. This enables customers to compare weight and price of different products. The actual weight of the product must be within a few grams of the weight stated on the label. The symbol ℮ is used to show that the weight complies with the EU requirement for weight under the average system.

Ingredients

Ingredients are listed in order of weight, with the highest proportion ingredient listed first and the lowest proportion ingredient listed last. A new EU labelling rule came into force in November 2004 which requires the following 14 food ingredients to always be clearly labelled:

- milk
- eggs
- peanuts
- nuts from trees (including Brazil nuts, hazelnuts, almonds and walnuts)
- fish
- crustaceans (including crab and shrimps)
- soya
- wheat
- celery
- mustard
- sesame
- lupins
- molluscs
- sulphur dioxide.

This information is particularly helpful for people with food allergies and intolerances who need to avoid specific food ingredients.

GM ingredients

Any genetically modified organisms (GMOs) or ingredients produced from GMOs must be indicated on the label.

Date and storage conditions

Information must be provided on how long a product will keep once it has been bought and/or opened. Information on how the product should be stored to keep it fresh or how it could be eaten must also be given. High risk or perishable foods that spoil quickly, such as cooked meat and fish, have a 'use by' date. If kept for too long, these foods may cause food poisoning even though they may not taste any different. Other foods have a 'best before' date, after which foods may not be at their best, with regard to flavour, colour and texture, even though they will probably be safe to eat.

Preparation instructions

Where necessary, instructions on how to prepare and cook the food must be given on the label. If the food must be cooked, the oven temperature and cooking time is stated. Instructions for reheating in a microwave oven must also be given.

Name and address of manufacturer, packer or seller

The name and address of the manufacturer, packer or seller must be stated on the label so that they can be contacted if there is a problem or a query.

Place of origin

The label must display clearly where the food has come from.

Lot or batch number

The lot or batch number is a code that can identify batches of food in the event that they have to be recalled by the manufacturer, packers or producers.

Nutrition information

Manufacturers do not have to provide nutrition information by law unless they make a nutrition claim. Any nutritional information provided must follow specific rules:

- energy value of the food in kilojoules (kJ) and kilocalories (kcal) must be provided

- amount of protein, carbohydrate and fat in grams (g) must be provided

- amounts of sugars, saturates, fibre and sodium must be provided if a specific claim is made about the nutrient.

Optional further information can be given on the amounts of other nutrients such as polyunsaturated fatty acids, monounsaturated fatty acids or cholesterol, and some specified vitamins and minerals. Information must always be given as values per 100 g or per 100 ml of food. Values for a portion or serving can be given as well, provided the number or size of portions/servings is quantified on the label.

Guideline Daily Amounts (GDAs)

Guideline Daily Amounts (GDAs) are designed to help consumers understand the nutrition information provided on food labels. GDAs are guidelines for healthy adults and children on the approximate amount of calories (energy), fat, saturated fat, carbohydrate, total sugars, protein, fibre, salt and sodium required for a healthy diet.

Because people vary in their size and activity levels, GDAs cannot be used as targets for individuals. They simply provide a benchmark against which the contribution from macronutrients, fibre, salt and sodium per serving of a food product can be roughly assessed. It is acknowledged that it is very difficult for an individual to achieve the GDAs for all nutrients in any one day, but this is not the purpose of providing such information. Instead, the aim is to provide a guide for consumers to assist them in making appropriate dietary choices.

Guideline Daily Amounts are based on population average figures, i.e., an average adult with a healthy weight and a normal level of activity. However, individual requirements vary depending on age, growth rate, weight and level of activity. A very tall male with an active lifestyle may need more energy (calories), while a less active, small male may need fewer. The GDAs do not consider these variations.

In addition, because there is limited space on food labels a set of 'Adult' GDAs have been developed which use the same figures as the healthy woman GDAs. Guideline daily amounts for children aged 5–10 years are given, but the GDA values for teenagers are similar to adults, so the adult figures should be used. The table below shows the GDAs used by the food industry.

Some organisations including the UK's National Heart Forum believe that presenting the GDA as percentages on the front of food packaging suggests to the consumer that the figures are daily targets. The consumer may not be aware that the figures represent limits rather than targets.

	Women	Men	Adults	Children (5–10 years)
Energy – Kcal (Calories)	2000	2500	2000	1800
Protein	45 g	55 g	45 g	65 g
Carbohydrates	230 g	300 g	230 g	220 g
of which sugars	90 g	120 g	90 g	85 g
Fat	70 g	95 g	70 g	70 g
of which saturates	20 g	30 g	20 g	20 g
Fibre	24 g	24 g	24 g	15 g
Sodium	2.4 g	2.4 g	2.4 g	1.4 g
Equivalent as salt	6 g	6 g	6 g	4 g

GDAs used by the food industry
Source: Institute of Grocery Distribution, www.igd.com

Traffic light labelling

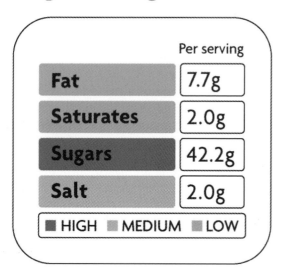

Figure 5.21
Source: Food Standards Agency

Many supermarkets and food manufacturers use traffic light colours on the labels of products to help consumers choose healthy foods. As part of a healthy diet we should be trying to cut down on fat (especially saturated fat), salt and added sugars.

Food products with traffic light labels on the front of the pack show whether the food has high, medium or low amounts of fat, saturated fat, sugars and salt. In addition to traffic light colours, the number of grams of fat, saturated fat, sugars and salt contained in what the manufacturer or retailer suggests is a serving of the food is given. Consumers can compare foods using the traffic light system and can check products to see which have the most ambers and greens.

A red light on the front of the pack means the food is high in one or more of the following: fat, saturated fat, sugars and salt. It is recommended that consumers only have the food occasionally and monitor how often they choose such foods, or try eating them in smaller amounts.

An amber light on the front of the pack means the food is neither high nor low in one or more of fat, saturated fat, sugars and salt, so this is a choice that could be made most of the time.

Green means the food is low in one or more of fat, saturated fat, sugars and salt and is a healthier choice.

Activity 5.12

Review

Almost all the food we buy is packaged.

Identify and explain four pieces of information that are legally required to be on a food product label.

Explain the importance of nutritional labelling to the consumer.

CHECK YOUR UNDERSTANDING

Collect some evidence of each type of nutritional labelling – Guideline Daily Amounts (GDAs) and traffic light labelling.

Evaluate the strengths and weaknesses of each method.

Exam-style questions

1 Explain **one** benefit to a manufacturer of the following stages in product development.

- market research

- testing a prototype

- quality control

- risk assessment (4 marks)

2 Discuss the costs involved in the design, development and production of a new food product.

(25 marks)

3 Describe the different sensory analysis tests that may be completed on a new food product.

(12 marks)

4 Describe three advantages and three disadvantages of each of the following packaging materials.

- glass (6 marks)

- paper (6 marks)

- plastics (6 marks)

- metals (6 marks)

(Total marks 70 marks)

DEVELOPMENTS IN THE FOOD INDUSTRY

Learning objectives

In this section, you will:

- describe the issues that are driving change in the UK food industry
- explain the factors affecting food production
- detail some of the developments in the range and types of food products available
- explain how environmental and moral concerns affect food production.

Introduction

The food and drink industry is the largest manufacturing sector in the UK, with a total turnover of £70bn and employing about 500,000 people. According to a 2007 Food and Drink Federation report, in 2005 consumer spending on food and drink was nearly £153.8bn – 20 per cent of total UK consumer expenditure. Over the years, the food industry has been affected by huge social, economic and demographic changes. These changes have influenced our eating habits, needs and lifestyles and the food industry has had to respond to these issues. In this chapter we examine the current issues affecting the food industry, look at how a range of factors have affected food production, and explore the reasons for changes in availability and supply of food in the UK.

Current issues in the UK food industry

This section provides an overview and explanation of the most important issues relevant to the UK food industry today. Note, however, that over time the significance of some issues will change and new concerns will emerge which must be considered alongside the points raised here.

Supply and availability of food

The supply of food and the need to ensure the population had enough food available to remain healthy was an important issue in the past. In the UK, the population experienced a time of food scarcity and limited choice during and just after the Second World War. Many basic food products were rationed as supplies became limited. Some imported food such as tea, oranges and rice were impossible to obtain.

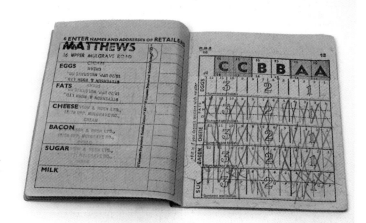

Figure 6.01 *Ration book*

During the post war period tinned fruit, fish and meat were in demand as they provided 'fast food' for working families. Over time, many new foods and products became available because of increased overseas trade and investment in British farming. The choice and diversity of food has increased considerably since this time and continues to grow today.

Large supermarkets in the UK sell a vast range of food products to meet virtually every consumer demand. The diversity and availability of food products is continuing by a widening of the supply of food and an integration of more food from overseas into the diet.

Globalisation is the term given to the wider sourcing of food within the UK and overseas. Globalisation has occurred because there have been significant improvements in the transport of perishable goods and a reduction in trade barriers between countries. Food production techniques have also become more standardised across the developed world, so the consumer can expect quality and reliability from imported food products.

The rise of the supermarket as a major food supplier is an important issue. Consumers have changed their food shopping habits and switched from frequent food shopping at a selection of local shops to weekly shopping by car at a large out-of-town supermarket. Just four supermarket chains account for an estimated two-thirds of all food retail sales. Supermarkets globally source many food products. As a result, food now travels greater distances from the producer to retailer, a distance sometimes referred to as **food miles**. The Department for Environment, Food and Rural Affairs (DEFRA) reported that since the late 1970s the amount of food moved in the UK by HGVs each year has increased by 23 per cent, and the average distance for each trip has increased by over 50 per cent.

Activity 6.2

Review and discussion

Define the term globalisation. Keep a record of the foods you eat in one day and discover where they are produced or grown.

What are the implications of consuming globally sourced foods?

Activity 6.1

Research

The pie chart in Figure 6.02 shows that the UK sources food from many different continents. Conduct some research into the type of foods imported into the UK from these continents. The UK imports 90 per cent of its fresh fruit. Why do you think this is necessary?

Rest of Europe 1%
Australasia 2%
South America 4%
North America 5%
Asia 5%
Africa 6%
United Kingdom 49%
European Free Trade Association (EFTA) 29%

Figure 6.02 *Origins of food consumed in the UK*
Source: DEFRA

Food security

Food security is a major issue for many people in the world and is of increasing significance for the industry and consumer. Food security occurs 'when all people, at all times, have physical and economic access to sufficient, safe and nutritious food to meet their dietary needs and food preferences for an active and healthy life' (Food and Agriculture Organization of the United

Figure 6.03

Nations, 1996). Food security is linked to issues of availability, access and affordability of food:

● *Availability* is about how much food is produced and the reliability of the supply.

● *Access* is concerned with the distribution of food.

● *Affordability* is about food being available at prices that people can afford to pay.

Food security is relevant in the UK as the affordability or economic access to food by individuals or households is very important. Many low-income households cannot afford to eat healthily and so the combination of poverty and **food deserts** has affected the food security for many in the UK. (A food desert is an area where access to food shops and healthy food is relatively limited, particularly for those on low incomes or without cars.)

Activity 6.3

Discussion

According to the United Nations, food security exists 'when all people, at all times, have physical and economic access to sufficient, safe and nutritious food to meet their dietary needs and food preferences for an active and healthy life'

Discuss the implications of poor food security in the UK today.

Food security can also be applied to global food supply. Failed harvests and climate change can disrupt the supply chain and push up food prices. Increased global demand for food can put a strain on the world's agricultural producers and if this demand is not met, then food shortages can occur. In recent times, a combination of droughts, floods, increased food demand from developing countries, falling global food stocks and increased production of biofuels have led to a dramatic rise in the price of wheat and other stable foods.

To combat these problems, future investment by the government into UK food producers and farming to make them more resilient in the face of change is vital. Becoming too dependent on global food supplies and food with a single source will make consumers vulnerable to price increases and shortages – for example, when oil prices surge, poor weather affects crop yields or biofuels production takes precedence over food crops.

Price of food

The price of food is a significant issue affecting both the food industry and the consumer. In the UK, food prices have fallen relative to income for a long time when compared to other goods and services. According to DEFRA, in 2007 the average household spent 9.2 per cent of its weekly expenditure on food compared to the 1960s when the figure was around 20 per cent. Improvements in efficiency across the supply chain have reduced the real cost of food.

However, recent increases in global commodity prices (cereals, sugar and meat) have brought to an end the decline in the price of food and access to cheap food can no longer be taken for granted. An increase in the price of food affects the poorest members of society the most. Those on the lowest income spend a higher proportion of their income on buying food than those who are better off.

The increasing price of food is a global issue. In 2008, world prices of rice, maize and wheat reached a record high. The most recent estimate by the Food and Agriculture Organization (FAO) suggests that 854 million people worldwide are malnourished and that in July 2008 an additional 50 million people became malnourished due to higher food prices in 2007.

Health and nutrition

Figure 6.04

Food and health is a very important issue. Research suggests that diet-related ill health may contribute an additional £6bn to the cost of the NHS each year. In addition, 70,000 premature deaths in the UK could be avoided each year if UK diets matched nutritional guidelines (Strategy Unit 2008). Since 2000, the government has developed a range of initiatives to encourage healthy eating, reduce obesity and increase consumer awareness of the nutritional content of food. These strategies include improving the standard of food served in schools, and restrictions on the broadcasting of advertisements for products high in fat, sugar and salt within programmes targeted at children. The UK food industry is considered to be a world leader for its development of clear front-of-pack food labelling. A further discussion of how the food industry has responded to concerns about food and health will be explored later in this chapter.

Food safety and quality

The points outlined below will demonstrate how the significance of food safety has risen to influence many different aspects of the food industry and inform the consumer. The issue of food safety and quality is discussed in detail later in this chapter.

In the UK the safety and quality of food is rigorously monitored. A number of agencies and organisations are involved in ensuring that the consumer is protected and has adequate information about food products.

The Food Standards Agency (FSA), established in 2000, has a primary aim to protect the public health and consumer interests in relation to food. A number of high-profile food-poisoning cases in the 1990s created the need for an independent body to investigate issues of farming and food safety objectively. The FSA is independent of any government department so is able to vigilantly monitor the safety and quality of food at a national level. The Department for Environment, Food and Rural Affairs (DEFRA) has a significant role in monitoring pesticide safety and animal health at a national level. DEFRA also provides information on the environmental impact of food choice and on issues concerning food quality.

Local authority environmental health departments monitor food hygiene and safety in business environments. The 'Scores on the Doors' is a scheme that makes information about food businesses available to consumers (see Figure 6.05). The information gathered during a food hygiene inspection is presented to consumers as a rating in or on the door of the premises.

Consumer demand for better quality food has risen, because people want to eat more healthily and to buy food that is produced with a greater sensitivity for the environment. There are many quality assurance schemes to meet consumer demand for knowledge about the origin of food and production methods used.

Food chain and the environment

The environmental impact of food production is a very important issue. It has been estimated that around 18 per cent of UK greenhouse gas (GHG) emissions are related to food production and consumption. Scientists are becoming increasingly concerned that GHG emissions are causing the global temperature to rise. A rise in global temperatures will cause the global climate to change; this may make food production more challenging in some areas of the world.

Activity 6.4

Research
Investigate the greenhouse effect.
How is it caused?
What are the possible implications for food producers?

In order to address some of the key environmental issues in food production, a move towards a **sustainable food** chain is being proposed. A sustainable food production system considers the whole process from field to fork. The aim of sustainable food is to minimise the energy used in the food chain, so food should be produced, processed and sold in ways that ensure it:

● contributes to successful local economies and sustainable livelihoods in the UK and abroad

Figure 6.05

- protects the diversity of plants and animals and avoids damaging natural resources and contributing to climate change

- provides social benefits including good quality food and safe and healthy products.

'Sustain' is a registered charity which champions better food and farming practices as well as considering the health and welfare of both people and animals. It suggests that consumers wishing to support a sustainable food system should follow seven principles:

1 Buy local and seasonal ingredients as standard to minimise energy used in food production, transport and storage.

2 Buy food from farming systems that minimise harm to the environment, for example, organic produce.

3 Reduce the amount of meat, dairy products and eggs eaten, as livestock farming is one of the most significant contributors to climate change. Alternatively eat meals rich in fruit, vegetables, pulses, whole grains and nuts. Choose meat, dairy products and eggs that are produced to high environmental and animal welfare standards.

4 Stop buying fish species identified as most 'at risk' by the Marine Conservation Society and buy fish only from sustainable sources accredited by the Marine Stewardship Council.

5 Choose **Fairtrade products** for foods and drinks imported from poorer countries, to ensure a fair deal for disadvantaged producers.

6 Avoid bottled water and instead drink plain or filtered tap water, to minimise transport and packaging waste.

7 Protect yourself and your family's health by making sure meals contain generous portions of vegetables, fruit and starchy staples, for example, whole grains. Cut down on salt, fats and oils, and avoid artificial additives.

Activity 6.5

Practical opportunity

Demonstrate in a food practical session how you can implement some of the principles suggested by Sustain to support a sustainable food system.

Major factors affecting food production

We will now explore the major factors affecting the food industry in more detail. Figure 6.06 shows how these factors can be grouped. Although many of the factors and issues raised are linked, to simplify the discussion they are addressed under the following broad headings:

- Environmental and moral concerns

- Social changes

- Technological changes

- Food safety

- Health issues.

Environmental and moral concerns

Concerns about the environment and moral issues affect the food industry and the production of food in a variety of ways. The high media profile given to some of these concerns ensures that public interest is maintained in the issues.

Sourcing food

The source of ingredients supplied to the food industry for processing and retailing is becoming more important to the consumer, possibly due to increased media coverage surrounding the issue. Consumers are becoming increasingly concerned about the distance food travels to reach the retailer, often referred to as food miles. Food products with a high number of food miles are linked to the environmental debate and are regarded negatively by some consumers. One result of this consumer concern, has been the emergence of more regional brands and the promotion of regional products in supermarkets. A product is defined as a **local source** if it is made within a 30-mile radius of where it is sold. Some supermarkets are using interest in the source of the food product as a marketing tool. For example, meat, vegetables and dairy products may feature an image or description of the local farmer who supplied the produce with the aim of reassuring the consumer that the product is local.

Non-governmental organisations (NGOs) campaign on environmental issues and animal welfare and set standards for food, for example, the RSPCA. Some supermarkets and food manufacturers have made

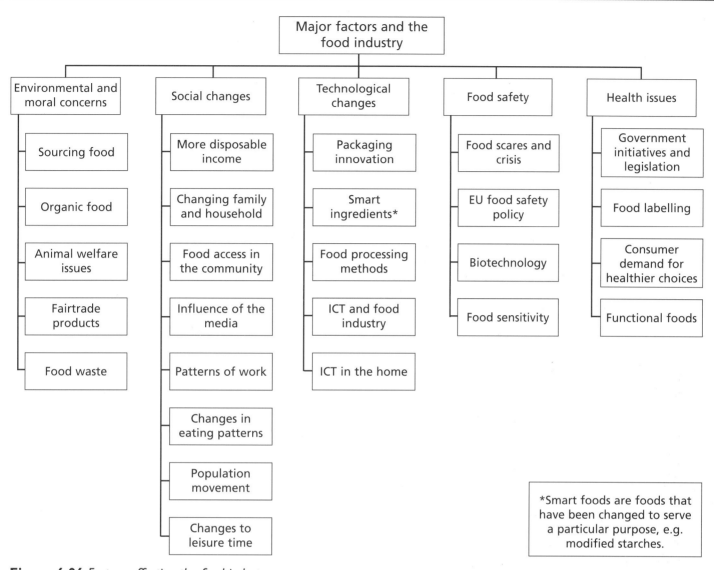

Figure 6.06 *Factors affecting the food industry*

commitments to source fish from stocks that are carefully managed, sometimes referred to as a **sustainable source.** Fish products from managed or sustainable supplies may have certification by the Marine Stewardship Council (MSC) and a blue eco-label (see Figure 6.08).

Figure 6.07 *Food sourced from overseas: tea*

Figure 6.08 *The MSC eco-label*

Organic food

Media coverage highlighting the impact of conventional farming practices on the environment has fuelled the organic debate. **Organic farming** has severe restrictions on the use of pesticides and avoids the use of artificial chemical fertilisers. The term 'organically grown' can be applied to meat, dairy products, fruit and vegetables, and means the products have been produced without the aid of artificial chemicals or hormones.

To be awarded certification, organic farmers must also operate to high standards of animal welfare. The Soil Association (see Figure 6.09) is just one of many bodies that inspects and awards farms wishing to apply for certification. The term 'organic' is defined by European law, and all certifying bodies must comply with regulations. Some certifying bodies, including the Soil Association, have standards that go beyond the minimum legal requirements and are more rigorous.

Figure 6.09 *Soil Association symbol*

A recent Food and Drink Federation report found that the organic sector is growing, with sales reaching around £1.3bn in 2005; however, this still represents only a small proportion of total grocery sales. The increase in demand for organic food can be partly attributed to the growth of farm shops and farmers' markets. These satisfy consumers' increasing demand for knowledge of the source of produce and their wish to buy food locally.

However, it is important to note that without conventional farming practices, i.e. the use of chemical fertilisers, a significant number of the world's population would starve to death. Synthetic fertilisers are possibly the most significant development in food

production of the twentieth century. A combination of conventional and organic farming practices provides the best mix of efficient production while minimising environmental damage.

LEAF (Linking Environment and Farming) is a farming charity with a membership scheme in which farmers adopt an Integrated Farm Management (IFM) system to ensure food production remains viable and has a reduced impact on the environment. The scheme covers the use of fertilisers, pesticides and soil management and combines the best of traditional farming methods with modern technology. Members of the scheme can use the LEAF Marque on their products (see Figure 6.10).

Figure 6.10 *LEAF Marque*

Animal welfare issues

Animal welfare is an area of growing public concern, with many celebrity chefs championing the cause of animal welfare on high profile television programmes. These programmes highlight instances of poor animal welfare and have contributed towards the growth in **ethical consumerism**. Ethical consumerism is buying products that are made with minimal harm to or exploitation of people, animals and/or the natural environment. Research suggests that more consumers are choosing ethical products as a conscious decision to improve standards of welfare in food-producing animals. The Royal Society for the Prevention of Cruelty to Animals (RSPCA) awards the Freedom Food logo. Food manufacturers may apply to use the logo to reassure consumers that measures are taken to ensure a good standard of animal welfare during food production.

Figure 6.11 *Free range chickens*

Vegetarianism is often regarded as an expression of concern about animal welfare. The number of vegetarians has remained static for a number of years at around 5 per cent of the population. The largest group of vegetarian consumers are women aged 17–34 years. Meat alternative such as soya and quorn have increased in popularity and can be purchased in a variety of ready meals.

Fairtrade products

Figure 6.12 *Fairtrade Mark*

Fairtrade products are concerned with fairer prices, decent working conditions and sustainability for farmers and workers in the developing world. Fairtrade products attempt to address the injustices of conventional trade, which usually discriminates against the poorest and weakest producers.

The UK Fairtrade market is one of the largest in the world and consumers in the UK have a greater choice of Fairtrade products and more awareness of Fairtrade than any other country. The Fairtrade Foundation estimates that the UK market is doubling in value every two years, and in 2007 reached an estimated retail value of £493 million. At present, around 20 per cent of roast and ground coffee and 20 per cent of bananas sold in the UK are Fairtrade. The remarkable growth of Fairtrade products in recent years is evidence of the growing concern among consumers about the impact of their purchases on the producer in the developing world.

The Fairtrade logo (see Figure 6.12) is an indicator that the producer is paid a sustainable and reasonable price for their produce.

Food waste

Food waste in the UK is an important moral concern. Waste and Resources Action Programme (WRAP) suggests that consumers throw away 6.7 million tonnes of edible food every year and this food waste is worth an average of £420 per household. When food is thrown away, it rots and produces methane gas, which is a very harmful greenhouse gas. WRAP is running a campaign 'Love Food Hate Waste' to raise consumer awareness of this issue and offer practical steps to reduce food waste.

Food processing also generates large quantities of waste food and packaging materials. It has been suggested that 18 million tonnes of carbon dioxide is unnecessarily emitted each year because of food waste.

The Courtauld Commitment is a voluntary agreement between WRAP and the major food retailers and food producers in the UK. The agreement requires signatories to support the WRAP objectives to design more efficient food packaging and to identify ways to tackle the problem of food waste. It is a powerful vehicle for change and in 2008, it led to zero growth in packaging despite increases in sales and population. The food industry is investing in new packaging technology and re-sealable packaging to keep food fresh in order to reduce waste. Some retailers also give more information to consumers on how to store and portion food to reduce wastage.

However, inadequate methods of processing, transporting and storing food in developing countries account for up to 40 per cent of food harvested being lost before it is consumed. This wastage can contribute to increased costs for the food manufacturer and consumer – costs that would be avoidable with more efficient transport and logistics systems.

Social changes

There has been a significant amount of social change in the UK since the Second World War. In this section we explore how social change – factors that influence the family and households – has affected food production and food choice in the UK.

Disposable household income and food purchase

The amount of disposable income determines the standard of living of many households and individuals. Disposable income is money left after spending on essentials of rent/mortgage, food, heat and light. Generally, disposable income has increased over the past 25 years and has been spent on a range of items, including technology in the home and leisure. On average, disposable income spent on food in the post-war years was 33 per cent but this has declined to about 10 per cent of income today.

Activity 6.6

Discussion

The graph in Figure 6.13 shows the percentage of consumer expenditure on food since 1963. The long-term decline in real food prices is shown in the decline in the proportion of household expenditure spent on food.

If food prices change, what would you expect to happen to the proportion of consumer expenditure spent on food?

Why has consumer expenditure on food declined?

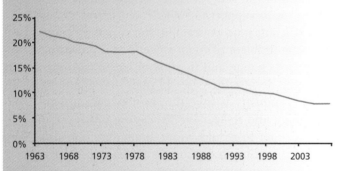

Figure 6.13 *Percentage of consumer expenditure on food since 1963*

Source: ONS Family Expenditure Survey, National Statistics website: www.statistics.gov.uk

Rises in the price of food affect family budgets. Households with the lowest income spend the greatest percentage of their household income on food. In the UK, the poorest 10 per cent of households spend 15 per cent of their income on food. Increases in the price of food therefore affect poorer households more significantly than others and, coupled with rises in energy, fuel and housing costs, this has implications for food retailers.

In times of an economic downturn, there is an increased likelihood of more consumers trading down to value ranges and seeking bargains when purchasing food. The emergence of and popularity of budget supermarkets such as Aldi and Lidl is evidence of this consumer interest. Food retailers and manufacturers try to accommodate low-income consumers on a budget and affluent consumers with greater disposable income by offering both a value range and premium branded foods.

Changing nature of the family and household

Increases in life expectancy have resulted in many more people living alone. Today a greater number of single person households exist than ever before and food manufacturers and retailers have responded to this by producing smaller portion foods, such as half loaves of bread and single portion ready meals.

Patterns of work

Work patterns and changes in lifestyle affect the consumption of food, for example, UK employees work the longest hours in Europe and the employment patterns of women have changed dramatically. Since 1992 there has been a significant increase in the number of women working 48 hours a week. The impact of this increase in working hours has led to changes in the food we eat. Many more women are working and, as stated earlier, there are greater numbers of single person households and both these factors have meant the choice of convenience foods continues to rise. A recent survey by Oxo revealed that a typical 1950s housewife would prepare a stew or hotpot with around 14 food items including a variety of vegetables, suet, milk or lard and plenty of salt, pepper and butter. The average meal today is made from only seven ingredients and is likely to have a global influence or theme, for example, curry or stir fry. The time taken to cook a meal today is less than 20 minutes; by comparison, meal preparation took, on average, about one hour in the 1950s.

Changes in eating patterns

People now eat at different times within a family/household unit, so convenience food that can be microwaved, for example, is popular. More people travel greater distances to work and food products that reflect this lifestyle have been developed, for example, snack foods and 'food to go'. According to research company Datamonitor, UK consumers are the biggest spenders on meals on the go, with an average bill of £120 per person each year.

Changes in eating patterns are highly significant to the food industry. Many people skip breakfast or eat breakfast at work and so more products have been developed to fulfil this need. Many garage forecourts offer breakfast type snacks and hot beverages. There has been a reduction in formal meals times, which has led to increased consumption of snack foods and grazing.

Changes in leisure patterns

Increased leisure time for families and individuals may also mean that less time is spent in the home preparing meals. The food industry has responded to this demand by producing part-prepared products that assist with the speedy preparation of meals, such as part-cooked meals and stir-in sauces.

By contrast, cooking for leisure or as a hobby is becoming more popular and, as a result, many exotic food products have become commonplace.

There has been significant growth in fast service restaurants, pubs, restaurants, hotels and leisure facilities. Eating out and the consumption of takeaway food have dramatically increased. The food industry has responded by manufacturing products that are easy to prepare by food caterers and easy for consumers to eat on the move. A wide variety of food catering establishments and outlets exists for every budget and palate. More disposable income is available to spend on food and a 2007 survey by DEFRA suggested that restaurants, cafés, work canteens and other food outlets provide one in six meals and account for 27 per cent of consumer expenditure on food, on average.

Population movement

Population changes including migration have increased consumer choice, as specialist food products are widely available. Migration of different cultures into the UK means people bring their food tastes and style of cooking with them into the community. Demand for

Figure 6.14

these products increases and so food retailers meet this demand.

The increase in tourism and opportunities to try foods from different cultures has widened the choices available in shops. More sophisticated consumer tastes have evolved to include Chinese, Indian, Italian, Thai and Mexican food.

Food access in the community

In 1961, only three out of ten households owned a car; today 70 per cent of households own a car. Much of our food shopping today is centred on car ownership. A British Brands Group survey in 2007 reported that there were no cars in almost half of all lone parent households with dependent children, and no car in 69 per cent of single person households where the householder was over pension age. Access to supermarkets is a particular issue for elderly people without a car, who may be unable to carry shopping great distances.

Large supermarkets are increasingly becoming the main source of good quality, affordable food. However, many households on low incomes live in parts of the country where local shopping facilities and transport networks are limited. This change in food retailing is affecting low-income families, the elderly, and those with disabilities who live in areas with limited transport and access to large supermarkets. Supermarkets selling basic goods below cost price, and changing prices according to nearby competition exacerbate the problem because smaller, local food retailers find it difficult to compete. The prices of some food products recommended for health, such as fresh fruit, may be higher in the local shops than in large supermarkets or town centre markets.

Influence of the media

Role models within popular culture influence our food choices because we aspire to their lifestyles. Cooking is a leisure activity for many people, and ingredients, equipment, recipes and new ideas are widely available. If celebrities on television use a particular product, this often creates a demand for that product.

Food has become a source of media entertainment and while consumers may follow the 'good' advice and suggestions of well respected individuals or organisations, they are also affected by negative publicity about any aspect of the food industry. More than ever before, media coverage has led to public scrutiny of production methods and accountability in the food industry.

Technological change

Developments in technology have prompted changes in the food industry, including improved food choice, production methods and food safety, all of which have resulted in more convenience for the consumer.

In 2005, microwave ownership stood at 84 per cent of all households. Most people own a refrigerator/freezer and the purchase of cook–chill products and frozen foods have increased significantly in the UK. According to Mintel, the market for frozen and chilled meals was valued at about £2.1bn in 2008. Growth has slowed in recent years but the frozen and chilled meals market sector still represents a significant amount of consumer spending. Technology has also driven the development of new products to meet changing consumer needs, including a range of products available for those with special dietary needs.

Packaging innovation

Developments in food packaging have been influenced by both the food industry and the consumer. The Food and Drink Federation is committed to a plan called Environmental Ambition, which contains pledges to:

- cut greenhouse-gas emissions during food production
- send less food waste to landfill
- reduce packaging
- cut water use
- achieve 'fewer and friendlier' food transport miles.

The Environmental Ambition pledge to send zero food and packaging waste to landfill from 2015 will undoubtedly affect the consumer, and the use of recycled, biodegradable and compostable packaging materials is becoming more evident in supermarkets. The industry has responded to the Environmental Ambition pledge with more efficient use of packaging materials, producing lighter weight glass, plastics and metals.

Aseptic packaging helps food producers and manufacturers meet the consumer demand for products with an extended shelf life. The process of aseptic packaging involves filling a sterilised pouch with a sterile food in a hygienic environment. The method gives producers, manufacturers and consumers a product with an extended shelf life without the use of preservatives or refrigeration.

In 2005, Warrick Research indicated that over 130 billion packs were aseptically filled worldwide in the previous year; this is the equivalent to around 20 packs per year per person. Aseptic packaging is used in the production of milk, fruit juices, soups, sauces, tomato products and baby foods.

Modified atmosphere packaging (MAP) has been used for a number of years by the food industry but is now extended to a much wider range of food products. MAP is important because from the point of harvest or slaughter, fruit, vegetable or animal products start to deteriorate by the action of enzymes and spoilage bacteria. This can lead to unattractive colour changes, loss of flavour and a poor texture developing in the food product.

MAP can slow this process by adjusting the normal breathable atmosphere around the food. MAP generally involves the use of three gases – carbon dioxide, nitrogen and oxygen. Food products are sealed inside packs with a single gas or a combination of all three gases, depending on the physical and chemical properties of the food.

MAP therefore offers considerable advantages to the food manufacturer and retailer, because the shelf life of the food product is extended significantly and the product looks better for longer.

Smart ingredients

Food additives are essentially smart ingredients and perform important roles in food products (see Chapter 4 for more information on additives).

Modified starch is a food additive (or smart ingredient), that has been treated physically or chemically to change one or more of its properties. The changes result in a starch that can be used as a thickening agent, stabiliser or emulsifier. Modified starches become stable in a wide range of food products and have valuable properties which are exploited by food manufacturers. They can thicken liquids without heat, for example, instant desserts, and resist lumping when boiling water is added, for example, instant gravies. Modified starch is used as a fat substitute for low fat versions of traditionally fatty foods and is added to frozen food products to prevent dripping when defrosted.

ICT in the food industry

Figure 6.15

Food production and retailing is affected by developments in information and communication technology (ICT). Some advantages of ICT are given below.

- ICT creates fast links between food retailers and suppliers so shortages in products are dealt with quickly, and increases profitability for retailers, as the computer schedules deliveries as required.

- The use of ICT in food production reduces the chances of human error, thus helping to improve quality and ensure consistency of products.

- Quality control and HACCP systems are developed and controlled by ICT.

- Accurate nutritional profiling of food products can be achieved.

- Many food retailers offer an online method of purchase.

- Rapid transportation of perishable food products in a controlled environment increases consumer choice.

Food processing methods

New processing techniques offer the consumer greater choice of food products. The process of extrusion is widely used in the food industry to produce a range of food products and food containers. Extrusion is a technique used to form shapes by forcing a material at high-temperature and/or pressure through die holes to form a desired shape. Food products manufactured by extrusion include breakfast cereals, pasta shapes and ready to eat snacks such as tortilla chips.

The need for greater convenience has lead to the development of spreadable butters and filtered milk. The New Zealand Dairy Research Institute first developed a method of fractionation to produce spreadable butter. The process involves combining liquid butterfat with solid butter to make a spreadable consistency (some manufacturers use vegetable oil to produce the spreadable product). Sales of spreadable butter have increased significantly and research suggests that consumers regard the product as convenient, 'wholesome' and an indulgence.

The special treatment of milk can give the consumer a more convenient fresh product. Filtered milk goes through an extra, fine filtration system, which prevents souring bacteria entering the milk. This can extend the shelf life of milk to up to 45 days (unopened) in a refrigerator and an average of seven days once opened.

ICT in the home

Technology has affected how we purchase food and it is estimated that almost 14 million households in the UK have an internet connection. All the major food retailers have a dot.com strategy. According to international food and grocery expert, IGD, internet food sales are currently worth £1.6bn in the UK and these sales are expected to increase significantly.

Technology has an impact on the decision-making process about the food we purchase and eat. The internet has provided another avenue of food choice because many small specialist food suppliers can be accessed by consumers using this technology.

Food safety

Concerns about food safety have had a major impact on the food industry. In reality, food is probably safer to eat today than ever before. Nevertheless, high profile food scares have affected consumer confidence and more awareness about food allergies has affected food labelling and increased demand for 'additive free' products. EU legislation is now applied throughout the entire food chain and aims to protect all European consumers.

Food scares and crises

Figure 6.16

Food scares and crises have an enormous impact on the food industry. The outbreaks of BSE (Bovine Spongiform Encephalopathy) in 1996 and Foot and Mouth disease in 2001 dramatically affected the UK meat industry and led to a significant fall in the sale of British meat. Yet in reality, the number of cases of variant CJD (a possible outcome of consuming meat affected by BSE) at present is about 15 to 25 per year and there are no human deaths associated with foot and mouth disease.

Naturally, the public is very concerned about food scares, and fears about the unknown and unfamiliar tend to cause anxiety. The reality, however, is that these events are not the most significant issues associated with food safety. Instead, by far the most important issue regarding food safety is the dietary contribution food makes to the development of obesity, heart disease and cancer. These diseases contribute to tens of thousands of deaths every year in the UK; it is estimated 30,000 deaths a year are related to obesity alone.

EU food safety policy

The 'farm to fork' approach is now considered a general principle for EU food safety policy. The European food laws that apply in the UK protect the health of people and animals. The food safety laws in many European countries have been harmonised to allow the free movement of food, animals and animal feed within Europe. Consumers are provided with safe food and accurate information. A key part of the EU legislation is the requirement for the food industry to put in place procedures based on HACCP principles. Food businesses are expected to keep scrupulous records of their HACCP plans and food safety management systems.

The **traceability** of food has become significant because of food scares like those mentioned above and recent worries about a chemical 'dioxin' contaminating food products. Traceability is a cornerstone of the EU's food safety policy and means that any food, animal feed, animal or substance used for animal and human consumption can be tracked through all the stages of production, processing and distribution in order to protect public health. Traceability allows the food industry and the FSA to withdraw or recall products that are identified as unsafe. Traceability is achieved by clear labelling and bar codes on packaging to indicate the actual source of food, and on cattle using ear tags and passports.

Biotechnology

Figure 6.17 *Genetically modified crops*

The term **biotechnology** includes the process of genetic modification of food products. All plant or animal cells contain information carried in genes. Genes affect the colour, size, shape and growth of the plant or animal and are passed on to the next generation when it reproduces. **Genetic modification** (GM) is when the genetic material is altered (or a gene is transferred from another organism) in order to produce certain characteristics. Food containing GM products and ingredients of more than 0.9 per cent must be labelled accordingly. Some imported products contain ingredients made from genetically modified soya and maize. Only a small number of genetically modified foods and food products containing genetically modified ingredients are sold in the UK.

There are consumer concerns about the environmental aspects of genetic modification and uncertainty about the impact on wildlife. Polls suggest that about 70 per cent of Europeans remain opposed to GM foods and so both the food industry and retailers have been reluctant to push GM technology. However, the UK Government is interested in reviving the debate as GM crops produce greater yields, use less chemical pesticides and can be more resistant to climate change.

The first GM field trial for four years began in the UK in 2007 by the plant science company BASF. The trial tested potato varieties that had been genetically modified to be resistant to a potato fungus. Potatoes are sprayed with fungicides about fifteen times each season to protect them against potato blight but GM potatoes required significantly less fungicide. The company responsible for the UK trial may eventually seek permission to market, grow and sell GM potatoes in Britain.

Nearly 90 per cent of hard cheese manufactured in Europe is produced using a genetically modified enzyme called chymosin instead of rennet (which is taken from calves' stomachs); this makes the cheese suitable for vegetarians. The cheese is GM free but is produced using a GM enzyme.

Food sensitivity

Food allergy and **food intolerance** are both types of food sensitivity. A food allergy is a reaction by the immune system to a particular food, which can make a person very ill. A severe food allergy can cause a life-threatening reaction called anaphylaxis which can affect the body within minutes. Anaphylaxis requires urgent medical treatment. Food intolerance is not an allergic reaction and is usually not life threatening but can make an individual feel unwell.

Figure 6.18 *Fruit cake may contain nuts, a common allergen*

European labelling laws require a detailed ingredient list to be included on all pre-packed food, making it easy for those with food allergies to identify products they should avoid. There are 14 foods commonly associated with food allergies that must be listed on all pre-packed foods, including alcoholic drinks, sold in Europe:

- peanuts

- nuts (including the main varieties; almonds, hazelnuts, walnuts)

- eggs

- milk

- shellfish (including prawns, crab and lobster)

- fish

- sesame seeds

- cereals containing gluten (including wheat, rye, barley and oats)

- soya

- celery

- lupin

- molluscs (including oysters, mussels and snails)

- mustard

- sulphites and sulphur dioxide (preservatives used in some foods and drinks) at levels above 10mg per kg or per litre.

Food businesses selling food prepared or wrapped on their premises are not required by law to indicate whether the food contains any of the 14 ingredients that consumers may be allergic to, but some do voluntarily. Food manufacturers also use the phrase 'may contain nuts' to show that there could be small amounts of nut in a food product, but this is not a legal requirement.

Health issues

Because of increasingly efficient processing methods, the food industry is able to produce great quantities of inexpensive food. Many of these food products are high in saturated fats, salt and sugar and are marketed very effectively by the industry, thus creating a high demand. A diet high in saturated fat is linked to high levels of blood cholesterol, which in turn is associated with coronary heart disease. Both consumers and the government are increasingly concerned about the potential health risks associated with a diet high in processed fatty and sugary foods. We will now explore the many different ways in which these concerns have affected the food industry.

Government initiatives and legislation

Since 2000, the government has taken a number of steps to promote healthier food choices and encourage healthy eating. Many of these initiatives have been directed at children because of concern about increasing levels of childhood obesity.

There are rigorous new standards regarding the nutrient content of school lunches, which has meant changes in the choice of food eaten inside schools. Government guidelines indicate that school lunches must include at least two portions of fruit and vegetables and deep-fried foods are restricted.

The School Fruit and Vegetable Scheme encourages fruit and vegetable consumption and ensures all children aged four to six years in LEA-maintained infant, primary and special schools are entitled to a free piece of fruit or vegetable each school day.

The government hopes that the food industry will implement a new healthy food Code of Good Practice. At present, this code is voluntary and can be summarised as a seven-point plan:

1 Simple, clear front of pack labelling.

2 Smaller portion sizes for energy-dense and salty foods.

3 Responsible promotion of food to children and increased promotion of healthy choices.

4 Support individuals and families to reduce their consumption of saturated fat, salt and sugar.

5 Increase consumption of healthier foods including fruit and vegetables.

6 Single set of key healthy eating messages delivered by the whole industry.

7 Simple and clear nutritional information available on food eaten out of the home.

Food labelling

Consumers are demanding clearer food labelling that includes information about the source, production and nutritional profile of the product. Food manufacturers have bowed to these health concerns by introducing voluntary labelling schemes, for example, the Guideline Daily Amount (GDA) and traffic light system. Nutrition labelling helps consumers both meet their dietary needs and consider the nutrient content of a product before purchase. See Chapter 5 for a more detailed explanation of the GDA and traffic light labelling system.

Consumer demand for healthier choices

Interest in healthy eating has never been greater and the food industry has responded in a variety of ways. Information about health and well-being is widely available through television, magazines and the internet. For example, the FSA's Eatwell website offers advice on healthy eating, food labelling and dietary requirements for different age groups and life stages.

Figure 6.19 *Healthy eating in schools*

For consumers aspiring to follow healthy eating guidance the choice of products available is growing. Food manufacturers constantly develop products to meet the demand for healthier lifestyles, for example, low fat ready meals and snacks, and artificial sweeteners developed for sweet products that need to be low energy.

The reduced use of hydrogenated fats by some food manufacturers is clearly stated on their food packaging, enabling consumers to make an informed choice and avoid hydrogenated fats if they wish to do so. Consumption of hydrogenated fats has been associated with increased risk of coronary heart disease.

The use of food additives in products aimed at children has decreased as public concern about the effect of additives has increased. Many food manufacturers label their products as free from artificial additives.

Functional foods

A **functional food** may be defined as a food that has health promoting benefits beyond the usual nutritional value. Functional foods include probiotic drinks and yoghurts, cholesterol reducing spreads, milk with omega-3 oils and cereals fortified with vitamins and minerals.

Sales of functional food and drink in the UK have experienced tremendous growth due to effective labelling and marketing. Institute of Grocery Distribution (IGD) research suggests an increase in sales of 523 per cent during the period 1998 to 2003. The market research organisation Mintel also forecasted an increase in demand for functional foods and estimated they would reach a market value of £1720 million by 2007.

In 2006, the European Commission published regulations on the use of nutritional and health claims requiring that all such claims made about a food product must be substantiated.

Activity 6.7

Handling data

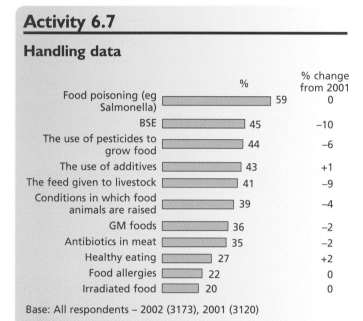

Base: All respondents – 2002 (3173), 2001 (3120)

Figure 6.20 *Concerns about specific food issues (prompted)*
Source: Food Standards Agency, Consumer Attitudes Survey 2002

The graph in Figure 6.20 shows the results of a survey conducted in 2002. The respondents were shown a list of food issues and asked which, if any, they were concerned about.

Use the data in the graph to answer the following questions.

1 Which two issues were consumers most concerned about in 2002?

2 Which two issues were consumers least concerned about in 2002?

3 Since 2001 concern has increased about which issue. Give an explanation for this increase.

4 Concern about both BSE and the feed given to livestock has decreased since 2001. Give an explanation for this decrease.

5 If this survey was carried out today, which three issues do you think would show increased consumer concern?

CHECK YOUR UNDERSTANDING

Check you understand the meaning of the following key terms. Write a sentence using each word.

aseptic packaging	ethical consumerism
food miles	Fairtrade products
modified atmosphere packaging (MAP)	genetic modification
	traceability
smart ingredients	food allergy
biotechnology	local source
functional foods	sustainable source
organic farming	

Product range developments

Introduction

The food industry is highly competitive and manufacturers are continuously developing new products or refining existing products. Globalisation has undoubtedly contributed to the supply and choice of food products for both consumers and manufacturers. The supply of ingredients from overseas and those produced in the UK is huge. In this section we examine the main developments in the type and range of products available to UK consumers.

Growth of ready meals and convenience foods

Figure 6.21 *Ready prepared food products*

The growth of ready meals and ready prepared products has increased significantly in the past decade. Social change and the need for convenience during meal preparation has been the main reason for this growth. The food industry has responded to this change with an increasing range of products, including foods that are ready to heat, ready to eat and part or ready prepared. Within the ready meal sector there are many ranges including healthy eating, organic, gourmet products, vegetarian, and value for money. The most popular ready meals sold have an ethnic style or origin, for example, an Indian or Italian influence.

The growth in the need for convenience is reflected in the growing demand for part prepared and 'value added' products. A **value added food product** is one that has been processed to make it more appealing to the consumer, for example, ready chopped carrots, pork ribs sold with a barbeque sauce. Added value food products can be sold at a much higher price, increasing the profitability of the product for the retailer. Part-prepared sauces remain popular as they give the consumer a feeling of satisfaction that the meal is 'home cooked' and can be used to accommodate a desire for healthy eating if combined with vegetables and lean meat.

The frozen ready meal market tends to see a higher than average level of new product development to maintain consumer interest. Research suggests that frozen foods are perceived as inferior to fresh foods by consumers. Changes in the population resulting in smaller households, more families with busy lifestyles and an increase in single person households have led to the development of many frozen ready meal products aimed specifically at these groups.

Supermarket own brands

Own brand groceries account for approximately 40 per cent of sales in large supermarkets (source: IGD 2004). The success of own brand goods is perhaps based upon consumer perception that they are good value for money and that the supermarket has a good reputation for quality products.

Within the retailer's own brand range, many sub brands are developed that are aimed at different consumers. Many retailers now offer value ranges, premium ranges, healthy eating ranges and children's ranges of food products.

Indulgence products

Traditionally, indulgence food products were regarded as 'treat' items that consumers purchased occasionally. Indulgent products included confectionery, cakes and products associated with festive occasions. Indulgence products are often described as premium, gourmet, fine and speciality foods and there is considerable development of new food products in this area. Many busy, stressed and tired consumers now find relaxation and reward through the purchase of luxury food and drink products. The range of products has also been expanded to include healthy, free range and organic indulgence products.

Provenance of the food product

There is growing consumer demand for local products because consumers have become more interested in food production and provenance. **Food provenance** means origin or source of product. Interest in the origins of food has lead to an increase in farmers' markets and special food markets that provide producers with direct channels to consumers. National Farmers' Retail and Markets Association (FARMA) estimated in 2006 that there were 550 farmers' markets in the UK, compared with just one in 1997. The number of farm shops has increased to around 4000 and the annual turnover from direct selling by farmers on the farm or at specialist markets is worth around £2bn a year.

The EU can award producers of regionally distinctive foods special protection (see Figure 6.22). This safeguards the names of these foods and promotes them to UK consumers, tourists and to the rest of Europe. UK products with protected food status include Whitstable oysters, Cornish Clotted cream, Jersey Royal potatoes and Newcastle Brown ale.

Figure 6.22 *EU mark of protection of origin*

Food intolerance products

The market for food products that are specially designed for consumers with food intolerance has increased and in 2005 the market was estimated to be worth £90 million. Research from Euromonitor in 2006 suggested that the UK is the third largest global market for gluten-free foods. In addition, sales of lactose-free products (dairy products, ice cream and baby foods) have increased by 29 per cent since 2002. The market research organisation Mintel forecasts that the 'free-from' food market will continue to grow by an estimated 117 per cent to reach a value of £195 million by 2010.

Specialist products tend to be more expensive than 'normal' products, and although the range is expanding, sometimes supplies are restricted to major food retailers or specialist shops.

Manufacturing wheat free products can be a problem as some food processing methods share the same production line. This contaminates many wheat free cereals with wheat during production and makes the subsequent products unsuitable for coeliacs, for example.

Healthier food products

The link between diet and health has been acknowledged for a long time and it is well known that a poor diet increases the risk of cancer, heart disease and obesity. Research indicates the rates of obesity will rise considerably in the UK so that by 2050 60 per cent of men, 50 per cent of women and 25 per cent of children will be obese (*Healthy weight, Healthy lives: A Cross Government Strategy for England*, 2008). Many premature deaths could be avoided each year if diets matched the nutritional guidelines on fruit and vegetable consumption, and saturated fat, added sugar and salt intake.

Many different products have been introduced or modified to meet growing consumer need for healthier food. Healthy eating trends are making an impact on dairy products and many traditional products now exist in a low fat version. Liquid milk is available in a range of forms with semi skimmed and skimmed milk more popular than full fat milk, with some types specifically targeted at children and parents. Functional milk sales increased dramatically in 2005 due to the successful launch of 'clever milk'. This product is liquid milk fortified with omega acids from fish oil. The availability of organic milk, goat's milk and alternative milk products such as dairy-free soya beverages have also increased.

Research from Euromonitor suggests that probiotic drinking yoghurt is the fastest growing dairy product in the last five years because it combines health benefits and convenient packaging. Low fat and low cholesterol versions of spreads, yogurts and cheeses have increased. In yoghurt products, the move is towards healthier versions using 'natural' ingredients such as fruit juices.

Since 2003, sales of meat and meat products have grown strongly because concerns about health scares such as BSE and Foot and Mouth disease have faded from public concern. There has been increasing sales of premium products, including organic, free-range and ready prepared meat products. Poultry has seen the most significant changes, with organic, free range or corn-fed birds widely available. Red meat is leaner than ever due to selective breeding programmes and feeding practices to reduce the amount of fat, and therefore saturated fat, in the product.

Consumer concern about health issues and food has lead to the introduction of fat substitutes, artificial sweeteners and a range of cholesterol lowering products. Many new food products are being developed to replace the use of fats and sugar in food. Fat substitutes such as *Olestra* can be used instead of fat in traditionally high-fat foods like ice cream, frozen desserts, cakes and biscuits. Many low-calorie and reduced-calorie food products containing artificial sweeteners are widely available and sugar substitutes are also used to produce sugar-free drinks and snacks.

Concern about fibre intake has led to the introduction of more varieties of high fibre and wholegrain crackers, cereals and breads. The sales of nuts and seeds have increased because they are a healthy snack product. Dried fruit is traditionally associated with home baking, but in recent years consumer views on healthy eating and dried fruit have changed. Now small, snack-size packages of dried fruits are available to compete with traditional savoury snacks and crisps.

Salt consumption is a health issue for those who are prone to sodium-induced high blood pressure. The low-salt market and salt-free market is growing. Many products now exist in a low-sodium format, including soups, crisps, bacon and ham. Low-sodium versions of table salt are also widely available.

Activity 6.8

Research
Survey the types and range of food products purchased by students in your class and their families. Find out which food products are purchased for different meal occasions. Analyse your results and write some conclusions (maximum 500 words).

Changes in availability and supply

Introduction
The UK has imported food products for hundreds of years. According to DEFRA, in 2006, 68 per cent of food imports into the UK were from other European Union member states. Our European trading partners ensure we have a reliable supply of high quality food entering the UK. However, changes in the availability and supply of food in the UK can occur; we will now explore this and how the price of food is affected by these changes.

Climate change
Climate change presents one of the greatest threats to agricultural production and the supply of food. Current projections estimated by the Intergovernmental Panel on Climate Change (IPCC) in 2007 suggest that global temperatures could rise by between 1.7 and 4°C by the end of this century unless international action is taken to reduce global greenhouse-gas emissions.

Climate change and agricultural production are closely linked. Small changes in global temperatures could adversely affect areas of the world where agriculture depends upon rainfall. Many developing countries would be affected and their yields reduced.

Figure 6.23 *Effects of climate change: drought*

Poor weather also affects the supply of food. In recent years successive poor harvests in countries that are major exporters of cereals has affected the amount of food available for sale on the world market. This problem has been exacerbated by the fact that many countries, including the UK, have low stores of food stocks.

Climate change means food production techniques will need to change. In some parts of the world, food production is based on extensive water use. Water is a crucial resource in the production of food, and the mismanagement of water is widespread. Research from the United Nations suggests the amount of fresh water available globally per person is falling rapidly. The quality of soil used for farming is also under pressure because of over-grazing. These issues must be addressed to ensure a secure supply of food.

Demand for biofuels

The growing demand for biofuels has meant the use of agricultural land has changed. Land that was previously used for growing cereals and staples is now used for growing crops that can be converted into biofuels. According to DEFRA, around 27 per cent of the American maize harvest in 2008/09 is expected to be used for ethanol production. This may increase the price of cereals and reduce their supply.

Price of oil

An increase in oil prices will undoubtedly affect the cost and supply of food. The production, processing and distribution of food all require the use of energy from oil and petrol. Increases in the price of oil will result in high fuel, fertiliser, transport, packaging and storage costs. Many of these costs are added to the price of food.

Common Agricultural Policy

The Common Agricultural Policy was set up following the Second World War, and had the following aims:

● To increase productivity of European agriculture

● To provide a fair standard of living for European farmers

● To ensure the European agricultural market was stable and food supplies guaranteed

● To give reasonable prices for European consumers for farm products.

The principles of CAP are to create a single market in farm products with common prices and free movement of agricultural goods within the community. The market gives preference to community members by imposing import tariffs on certain goods from outside the EU.

The Common Agricultural Policy may have kept some food prices high. Reform of the system is affecting farming practices in the UK and the choice of crops produced.

The continued expansion of the European Union to include more countries means the removal of existing trade barriers and a further opening up of markets. Europe will become the world's largest single market, with everyone working to the same rules. Food manufacturers in the UK will operate in a barrier-free market, providing access to a wider range of suppliers, as well as export opportunities. UK consumers may have access to a wider range of food products.

Over-fishing

Figure 6.24

Fish stocks continue to decline due to over-fishing. Domestic supplies of cod and haddock are so low that they are now imported into the UK. Fishing quotas have placed restrictions on the type and quantity of fish caught and this may affect the choice available to the consumer and manufacturer when developing products containing fish or purchasing fish. New exotic species will appear in many processed fish products and be available for retail sale.

Sustainable fishing policies are required across Europe to ensure the supply of fish is maintained. Under the Common Fisheries Policy in the EU, a range of measures are being undertaken which will affect the range and choice of fish available in Europe.

European legislation

Many aspects of our food chain are regulated by European legislation, thus affecting the supply and availability of food. Such legislation aims to make the food we eat safer and reduce the impact of food production on the environment. European laws on pesticides and food additives are currently being modernised and as a result, restrictions on the types and levels of pesticide approved for use on food may change. This in turn may affect the price, supply and production of some fruit and vegetables. European laws restricting the use of some artificial food colourings have already resulted in the removal of some products from the UK market.

Emerging economies

Emerging economies are those areas of the world that are currently experiencing industrialisation and rapid growth. They include countries like China, India and Brazil, and represent large potential markets for products. High income growth in emerging economies is increasing consumer demand for more meat and dairy products. Put simply, as people get wealthier they eat more meat. Global agricultural systems are using cereals and staple food to feed farm animals in order to meet the demand for meat and dairy products. This reduces the affordability of cereals and staples to the

poorest consumers across the globe and can cause shortages in the UK.

The supply of food is affected by some countries reducing their exports to build up their own food stocks. This strategy drives food prices up further. When supplies fail to meet rising demand, a division between the richer nations and the poorer nations becomes more apparent and those with limited resources often go hungry.

CHECK YOUR UNDERSTANDING

Check you understand the meaning of the following key terms.

Write a sentence using each word.

Describe how each affects the food supply and food availability.

climate change	food provenance
biofuels	value added food product
sustainable source	emerging economy

Exam-style questions

1 Describe the environmental and moral concerns that affect food production.

(10 marks)

2 Explain the term food security.

(2 marks)

3 The range and types of food available is constantly changing. Explain how manufacturers have responded to consumer need for healthier foods.

(25 marks)

4 Describe four reasons for changes in the supply and availability of food.

(8 marks)

(Total marks 45 marks)

7 INVESTIGATIVE STUDY

This chapter will focus on how to complete the investigative study as required by A2 Unit G003 in the OCR Home Economics (Food Nutrition and Health) **specification**. It is an internally assessed unit and is of an **investigative** nature. You develop the **context** and title of the study with teacher guidance as necessary.

Learning objectives

By the end of this chapter you will be able to:

- select an appropriate area of interest and develop a context and a title
- understand how to address the four **assessment criteria**
- explain what you need to do to produce an investigative study for submission for internal assessment.

Figure 7.01

Introduction

The investigative study at A2 is worth 25 per cent of your final grade and is marked out of 100. The title of the study should be developed from an area of the specification which you find interesting. Ideally the title should be worded in the form of a context that sets the scene and a question to investigate. Once you have established a title, your investigation can begin.

However, before you commence work it is a good idea to be organised and collect the resources you will need. Here is a suggested list of resources.

- An A4 hard backed ring binder so that coursework is kept separate from class work.

- Dividers –15 to start with to keep each section separate.

- Plastic wallets – there should be no punched holes in work in case the work is spirally bound; it also makes it easier to update and amend individual pages.

- A USB stick to save work and digital images.

Understanding assessment criterion 1

Analysis and aims

In this section you are required to undertake **analysis**, select an appropriate context and title, demonstrate an understanding of the opportunities for study and develop aims and objectives. This section is marked out of 15.

Assessment criteria

Analysis and aims

Criteria	0–5 marks	6–10 marks	11–15 marks
1a	Explores in a limited way possible areas of interest from the AS and A2 specification and is able to identify some issues/factors	Explores possible areas of interest from the AS and A2 specification and is able to explain a range of relevant issues/factors	Explores thoroughly possible areas of interest from the AS and A2 specification and is able to discuss a range of relevant issues/factors
1b	Selects an appropriate context and title with little justification and reasoning	Selects an appropriate context and title with justification and reasoning	Selects an appropriate context and title with clear justification and reasoning
1c	Shows limited understanding of the scope of the opportunities for practical and investigative work relevant to the area of study	Shows an understanding of the scope of the opportunities presented for practical and investigative work relevant to the area of study	Shows a clear understanding of the full scope of the opportunities for practical and investigative work relevant to the area of study giving clear reasons for the methods chosen
1d	Formulates aims and objectives for the study	Formulates detailed aims and objectives for the study	Formulates specific, detailed and realistic aims and objectives for the study

Activity 7.1

Discussion

Check you understand the assessment criteria by discussing them with your group. Looking at the high band only, explain in your own words what you think is expected from you.

Completing assessment criterion 1

Before you consider your area of interest there are some important points to remember.

- Choose an area that really interests you – you will be more inclined to work on it.

- You must choose an area from the specification – this is a requirement of the examining board.

- Try to select something original to study.

- Choose an area where you will have access to information, for example, if you choose to do

something related to pregnant women you will need access to a clinic to test ideas, collect food diaries and conduct interviews.

- Make sure your title allows you opportunity for practical work. If it does not, you will not be able to score enough marks in the implementation section.

- Make your work aesthetically pleasing wherever possible – especially when photographing practical work.

Assessment criterion 1a

Read through the specification topics for both AS and A2 and decide on two to four areas of interest. For each area, complete a mind map of the chosen topic areas. Select and reject the topic areas, leaving yourself with one area of interest. Give *full* reasons as to why you have selected the area of interest and rejected the others.

Activity 7.2

Review

Below are three examples of well-worded contexts and titles. Identify why you think they are well worded.

Example 1

- Current data suggests that 1 in 10 six-year-olds are obese.
- The total number of obese children has doubled since 1982.
- Should this trend continue then by 2020 half of all children in England could be obese.

Investigate the implications of this trend. What can we do to reduce this figure?

Example 2

The efficient management of resources is particularly important. Investigate how this can be achieved for *one* of the following scenarios:

- an elderly couple receiving a state pension
- a single parent with three children
- a family where both parents work full time
- a student.

Example 3

There are 125,000 diagnosed coeliacs in the UK today, although there are estimated to be over 500,000 that have not yet been diagnosed.

Investigate how easy it is to follow a diet which does not contain any wheat or products made from wheat.

Assessment criterion 1b

Conduct some initial research into your area of interest, using, for example, textbooks, magazines, newspapers and the internet. This will help you come up with ideas for contexts and task titles.

Select and reject, leaving yourself with one context and one task title and reject the others, again giving full reasons for your choice.

Correctly word the task into a context to set the scene and a question that you will investigate. Your teacher will be able to help you with this if necessary.

Assessment criterion 1c

Identify and explain all the possible opportunities for:

- practical work
- investigative work
- research from secondary sources that you could carry out as part of your study.

Figure 7.02

This could be done in the form of a table with the following headings:

What could I do	What information would I expect to find out?	Why would it be appropriate for my study	Select or reject with reasons

The most appropriate investigative techniques will depend upon the approach used for coursework. Here is a suggested list of techniques that could be used:

- shop survey
- market research
- packaging comparison
- interview
- **case study**
- questionnaire of target group
- practical food activity
- sensory analysis
- costing
- nutritional analysis
- comparison practical, for example, bought/homemade, low fat/higher fat, value range/luxury range
- study of relevant information on TV/magazines
- visits
- food diaries
- PowerPoint presentation
- leaflet design
- secondary research from a variety of sources – textbooks, recipe books, internet, magazines and newspapers.

Figure 7.03

Assessment criterion 1d

Now that you have decided upon the investigative techniques you are going to use, you are ready to write specific, detailed, and realistic aims and objectives for your study. Aims and objectives should be written using appropriate language.

An aim is *what you need to find out* in order to answer the question set as part of your title. Each aim should start with a trigger word, for example:

- Establish
- Find out
- Investigate
- Research into
- Examine
- Explore
- Consider.

Activity 7.3

Review

Draft your aims and share them with the rest of your group and your teacher. Are they specific, detailed and realistic? Do they make sense? Will they help you answer your question?

For each of your aims there must be an objective that explains *how* you will achieve your aim, for example:

Aim: Establish whether there is a difference in the quality and taste of foods made with gluten free flour and normal flour.

Objective: Make a batch of biscuits and cakes using gluten free flour and ordinary flour. Carry out some taste tests and evaluate the results to establish whether there is a difference in quality and taste.

Activity 7.4

Review

Draft your objectives and share them with the rest of your group and your teacher. Are they specific, detailed and realistic? Do they make sense? Will they help you achieve your aims?

Activity 7.5

Investigative study work

Present the work completed for assessment criteria I in four separate appendices labelled:

1 Exploration of area of interest
2 Selection of context and title to be investigated
3 Opportunities for practical and investigative work
4 Aims and objectives.

Hand your work in to your teacher to be checked.

Writing the report

The format in which the study is presented will depend upon the chosen approach, but is most likely to be a report on the findings, with labelled appendices to support and justify statements made in the report.

Once you have completed the work necessary for assessment criterion 1 you should start your report.

The report is a **summary** of your findings as you work through the investigative process. It is *not* an account or a diary of what you have done (therefore, avoid using sentences such as 'I did ...', etc.).

Your report must link to the appendices. It is therefore crucial that you cross reference to the relevant appendix because this will provide the evidence to back up statements made in the main body of the report. Use the phrase 'see appendix ...'

The report also draws conclusions from results and shows how your work moves forward in a logical way.

The report must be *no more than 3000 words* and a word count must be provided.

The statements you make in the report must be linked together; avoid jumping from one paragraph to another by using linking statements such as:

From this I can conclude that ...

- I found out that ...
- It is evident then ...
- This led me to ...
- I have decided to ...
- In order to ...
- I am going to ...

Activity 7.6

Review

This is an extract from a report. Highlight the linking statements.

'To begin I looked at the AS and A2 specifications. I noted down all the areas that interested me and mind mapped possible areas of interest (see appendix 1). I decided to choose health problems as I felt I didn't know much about this topic, I would have access to plenty of information and it would allow me to carry out lots of practical work.

'In order to check this was an appropriate topic I carried out some initial research and decided that I would complete my study on the modifications of diet suitable for people with osteoporosis. I established a range of contexts and task titles and selected the most appropriate one (see appendix 2). I chose this title because I felt it would give me a wide area to research into and I found the topic particularly interesting as I now realise how important it is for someone my age to have sufficient calcium and vitamin D in the diet in order to prevent osteoporosis in later life.'

You may find it useful to include the following subheadings in your report:

- Analysis, aims and initial research
- Planning and development
- Implementation (this should be further sub-divided into questionnaire, survey, practical, etc.)
- Evaluation.

Understanding assessment criterion 2

Planning and development

In this section you are required to **hypothesise**, plan and make informed decisions that direct the progress of the study. This section is marked out of 20.

Assessment criteria

Planning and development

Criteria	0–6 marks	7–13 marks	14–20 marks
2a	Establishes a simple prediction of what they aim to find out	Establishes a general prediction of what they aim to find out	Establishes a relevant prediction of what they aim to find out
2b	Determines outline for design	Determines design specification	Determines clear design specification
2c	Indicates some of the resource materials and methods to be used, with little detail	Indicates specific resource materials and methods to be used, with some detail	Indicates clearly specific resource materials and methods to be used, with all relevant details
2d	Takes evidence gained from the research and uses it in a limited manner to make simple judgements and justification for choice of investigative methods	Takes evidence gained from research and uses it as a basis for making judgements and justification for choice of investigative methods	Takes evidence gained from research and uses it as a basis for making valid judgements and relevant justification for choice of investigative methods
2e	Produces a plan of action for the entire piece of work.	Produces an effective plan of action for the entire piece of work with an appropriate time scale, indicating work to be completed	Produces a well ordered and effective plan of action for the entire piece of work with a detailed time scale, indicating work to be completed and problems that arise

Completing assessment criterion 2

Assessment criterion 2a

For this criterion you need to look at your task title and make a prediction of what you think you will find out – in other words, an answer to the task title.

Assessment criterion 2b

Your design specification can be detailed if the approach is food technology, or it can appear as a bulleted list for a food practical activity. Make sure you approach it by using the heading 'Design specification' when you write up your practical activities. You could write a series of bullet points describing what you hope your product

Figure 7.04

will be like. For example, if you are making a dish suitable for an obese person to lose weight, the design specification could include the following statements:

My product will:

- appeal to an obese person

- contain starchy carbohydrate

- be low in saturated fat.

> **ASSESSMENT HINT!**
>
> **Do not leave any of the assessment criteria out as you will not achieve high bracket marks even if the remainder of a section is excellent.**

Assessment criterion 2c

You are expected to plan and carry out a series of practical activities as part of your investigative study. Each practical must indicate clearly specific resource materials and methods to be used, with all relevant details. This is not a separate section and nor does it appear in the report. It will appear as part of the practical write up. When writing up the investigative methods used, including practical activities, the following information must be included:

- Recipe and methods

- List of equipment for practicals

- List of questions prepared beforehand for an interview

Figure 7.05

- Rationale and chosen target group for questionnaire

- List of what preparation and resources are needed to carry out a survey.

> **ASSESSMENT HINT!**
>
> **When planning practical activities use these headings to address criterion 2b:**
> - **Recipe title**
> - **Aim**
> - **Design specification**
> - **Oven temperature**
> - **Cooking time**
> - **Resources – ingredients and quantities**
> - **Resources – equipment needed**
> - **Method**
>   1
>   2
>   3
>   4
>   5
>   6

Assessment criterion 2d

As your work moves forward you must decide how your work will progress. You must clearly justify your chosen investigative methods, and there are three ways in which this can be achieved:

1 At the end of each piece of investigative research use the heading 'future developments' and make sure that each piece of investigative research progresses to the next. Explain what you have found out and how you can use that information to move your work forward.

2 Use statements in your report such as 'from this I found out that ...' 'I can conclude therefore ...' 'This led me to ...' as these ensure your work is moving forward.

3 Make sure you fully justify making specific choices, for example:

    a Why you chose to make the dishes you did for practical sessions.

    b Why you chose that person to interview.

    c Why you chose that target group for your questionnaire.

Assessment criterion 2e

A plan of action must be developed for the *entire* piece of work, with a detailed timescale and an indication of work to complete and any problems that may occur.

Figure 7.06

Activity 7.9

Investigative study work

Present the work completed for assessment criteria 2 in one separate appendix labelled:

5 – Plan of action

Update your report to include a prediction and reference to the plan of action.

Update your plan of action every week.

Hand it in to your teacher to be checked.

ASSESSMENT HINT!

Fill in your plan of action at the beginning of every week so it is up to date and work is planned in advance of being carried out. No marks are available for retrospective plans. A useful way is to do a plan of action in the form of a table:

Week	Date	Work to do	Completed? Any problems?
1			
2			
3			
4			

Understanding assessment criterion 3

Implementation process and realisation

In this section you are required to carry out a range of appropriate skills and resources to achieve the realisation of your objectives using a variety of primary and secondary investigative methods. It is necessary that you include some relevant investigative food practical work. The implementation section is marked out of 25 and the realisation is marked out of 20.

Assessment criteria

Process

Criteria	0–8 marks	9–16 marks	17–25 marks
3a	Researches from a limited number of sources and select suitable background information	Researches from a variety of sources and select appropriate background information	Researches from a wide variety of sources and selects particularly appropriate and relevant background information
3b	Demonstrates limited awareness of aspects of economy, safety and available technology when carrying out food related activities	Demonstrates awareness of relevant aspects of economy, safety and available technology when carrying out food related activities	Demonstrates a clear awareness of relevant aspects of economy, safety and available technology when carrying out food related activities
3c	Implements time scales when carrying out practical activities	Implements appropriate time scales when carrying out practical activities	Implements effectively appropriate time scales as planned when carrying out practical activities
3d	Carries out a limited range of investigative methods to a satisfactory standard	Carries out a range of investigative methods to a good standard	Carries out a wide range of investigative methods to a high standard
3e	Demonstrates a satisfactory level of competence in psychomotor skills	Demonstrates a good level of competence in psychomotor skills	Demonstrates a high level of competence in psychomotor skills
3f	Demonstrates a sound level of competence in the research methodology chosen	Demonstrates a good level of competence in research methodology chosen	Demonstrates a high level of competence in research methodology chosen

Realisation

Criteria	0–6 marks	7–13 marks	14–20 marks
3g	Achieves a limited piece of coursework which meets the original objectives	Achieves an effective piece of coursework which meets the original objectives	Achieves an effective piece of coursework which accurately meets the original objectives
3h	Demonstrates some originality, creativity and aesthetic awareness in an appropriate form	Demonstrates originality, creativity and aesthetic awareness of a good order in an appropriate form	Demonstrates originality, creativity and aesthetic awareness of a high order in an appropriate form
3i	Demonstrates basic technical competences to communicate the outcomes of the process	Demonstrates clear technical competences to communicate the outcomes of the process effectively	Demonstrates outstanding technical competences to communicate fully the outcomes of the process effectively

Activity 7.10

Discussion

Check you understand the assessment criteria by discussing them with your group. Looking at the high band only, explain in your own words what you think is expected of you.

Completing assessment criterion 3

Process

This criterion is concerned with carrying out the investigative part of the study. A variety of secondary and primary investigative methods should be used. It is necessary that relevant food practical work is carried out to address the **psychomotor** skills.

If the approach to coursework is of a 'design and make' type then the student would be expected to consider the possibilities and implications of quantity manufacture, including large-scale equipment, scaling up of ingredients, final costing to take into account overheads, etc., commercial production methods, additives, storage requirements, and technical and creative feasibility.

If a 'design and make' approach is followed, students will need to trial three initial ideas for practical products in order to demonstrate a wide range of skills. To show effective product development, they will need to carry out two developments before producing their final product. In this case, the written methods are only required for the three products that are trialled first; it is not necessary to write up methods during product development, as this would create repetition.

Realisation

The objectives stated in section 1 should be carried out. Originality, creativity and aesthetic awareness need to be considered by the candidate. These factors should also be apparent during the development of the products in practical work. Technical competences need to be clearly demonstrated in the presentation of the work, for example, use of ICT, digital images, scanning and colour printing.

A suggested list of investigative techniques can be found on page 188; the most appropriate ones chosen will depend upon the approach used for coursework.

Carrying out the investigative methods chosen

You will have chosen which methods you are going to use in assessment criterion 1c. This section explains what you need to do to carry out each method.

Figure 7.07

Shop survey

It is essential to establish an aim when carrying out a survey of what products are available, for example, 'The aim of this survey is to find out the range, cost and availability of gluten free products.'

Results need to be recorded, and a good way of doing this is to use a table. Once you have collated your results you will need to interpret them – in other words, what do the results tell you? Make sure that you stick to the facts only, and draw relevant conclusions.

Once you have interpreted your results you need to evaluate them – make sure you include your own thoughts and ideas about what you have found out.

Finally you need to consider future developments – what have you found out that you can use to move your work forward?

Market research

Market research involves obtaining, organising, analysing and presenting information. This information is usually from secondary sources. It can be used to address an aim that involves analysing trends, habits or patterns.

Before you start looking at market research, it is important to first consider the aim of the research; otherwise, irrelevant information may be collected, wasting valuable time. You must consider the kind of information you require to complete the aim. For example, to investigate the success of the 5-a-day campaign it may be necessary to look at household consumption of fruit and vegetables in the UK. The Office of National Statistics provides this type of information and is a reliable source.

There are many other sources of secondary information that can be consulted. Consider websites and paper-based sources such as journals, magazines, newspapers. However, care must be taken that relevant UK sources are consulted and that information is reliable and not biased to highlight a specific issue.

Presentation of results is very important. Always summarise concisely the information you have collected and present it in an appropriate style. Avoid including information without any explanation or link to the original aim.

Packaging comparison

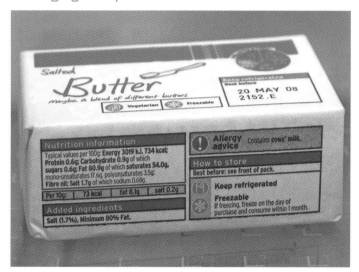

Figure 7.08

A packaging comparison is a useful research method if the focus of the investigation has an emphasis on the development of a new food product or meeting the needs of a specific individual. An investigation on children's diets may be useful in examining the fat content of a specific product and drawing relevant conclusions. This information could also be used as part of the decision making process for the selection of appropriate practical work later on in the investigation.

A packaging comparison can be achieved by examining carefully the food labels of similar products from the same or different food retailers. The types of information which can be compared include:

1 List of ingredients to assess the main ingredients in different products.

2 Shelf life – a product with an extended shelf life may be more cost effective than one with a shorter shelf life.

3 Weight or size of the product. Portion size is important as variations can occur between manufacturers. This information will help to support conclusions drawn about the cost and nutritional profile.

4 Nutritional information may be present on a food label and comparisons between the 'big four' nutrients – energy, fat, carbohydrate and protein – could be made.

5 Cost of the food product is also important, particularly if the investigation requires an element of sensitivity to this issue when planning dishes to prepare.

The packaging could be scanned and pasted electronically into a document for analysis. This would demonstrate technical skill. The results must be commented upon and possibly linked to the next stage in the investigation.

Interview

The interview is an effective method for collecting research evidence but must be organised properly. An interview typically involves a face-to-face meeting with an individual who can provide valuable information in addressing an **aim**. The interviewer (you) asks the individual or interviewee a series of questions.

To ensure you achieve your aim it is advisable to use a **structured interview**. This means that the interview questions are carefully prepared before the interview. There may be a definitive list of questions including a few sub questions. A structured format should be followed in the presentation of the questions to the interviewee. This type of interview is useful when interviewing more than one person as comparisons between the interviews can be made. Some interviews are more open, with the interviewer asking questions in a more unplanned way. These are called **unstructured interviews**. The interviewer needs great skill to handle this type of unstructured interview to ensure the aim of the interview is achieved.

Before you begin the interview decide which type of interview you wish to use. The interview must have an aim, for example, 'The aim of the interview is to find out about the choice of food available for coeliacs in a local supermarket.'

It is important to interview someone who is able to help you address your aim. For the example above, ideally you would interview someone who has coeliac disease, but you could interview someone who worked in a supermarket. It is also important that the individual has the right to remain confidential. They may be more willing to give honest responses if confidentiality is maintained.

Prepare your interview questions in advance and if possible share them with the interviewee. You are more likely to get fuller and more detailed responses to achieve your aim. The questions can be a variety of open and closed questions. Open questions are useful in finding people's views, for example, 'What is your opinion of... ?' You can also ask closed questions, for example, 'Would you agree with the following statement... ?'

ASSESSMENT HINT!

Be careful with closed questions as the interviewee can simply answer yes or no. A questionnaire may be more appropriate for a large number of closed questions.

Tape record, or visually record the interview if possible as this will help you to analyse the results. If this is not possible, try to transcribe (copy) exactly what was said during the interview. Share a written copy of the interview with the interviewee to make sure that they agree with the contents of the interview.

Write a summary report of the findings from the interview. This should be the factual information you found and could be a list of questions and responses. To evaluate the success of the interviews consider:

● *Accuracy and completeness*: Did you miss anything? Did you record all the information in written form exactly as it was said by the interviewee?

● *Bias*: Did you add any information by assuming something that was not stated directly by the interviewee?

● *Reliability*: Would someone else who had not interviewed the interviewee be able to get a clear, concise picture of what was discussed by reading your summary?

Case study

A case study is an intensive study of one individual; it focuses on a short, self-contained episode or segment of a person's life. The evidence can be collect from interview and observations and this evidence then becomes the basis of analysis and discussion.

It is only appropriate to choose a case study if you are able to collect detailed information on a specific situation. A good case study requires access to a reliable and valid source of information, usually a relevant individual. For example, if you were investigating the elderly and needed to investigate the issues faced by the elderly when shopping for food, it may be appropriate to use this method but you would need to interview an elderly person to produce the case study.

Guidelines for producing a case study:

1 Use short story-writing techniques. A case study has 'flesh and blood' characters that should be intriguing. Each story element should move the narrative forward.

2 Present situations without any attempt at analysis. Do not make any judgements in the case study.

3 Follow a logical order. Use sub headings if necessary. Use photographs, if relevant to support the information.

4 Provide relevant details. After an opening that sets up the situation, provide important details. Include issues that relate to the problems that you want to analyse later in the conclusion.

5 Use as much dialogue as possible to make the characters come alive. Straight narrative is boring. Include colloquialisms in the dialogue, if necessary.

6 Keep your audience in mind. Keep jargon to a minimum.

7 Endings are crucial. Leave the reader with a clear picture of the major problems, either ask or imply 'what is to be done now?'

Once you have written the case study it is important to demonstrate you can extract relevant information from the evidence you have collected. This evidence can then be linked to other findings or support the background research. The ability to make these links to earlier research demonstrates very good investigative skills.

An evaluation of the method used for the case study will allow the opportunity to discuss the constraints you have managed during its implementation.

Questionnaire

Figure 7.09

Before you begin, the questionnaire must have a **rationale**. A rationale is an aim, for example, 'The aim of this questionnaire is to find out ...' Choose your target group carefully to ensure the information you obtain will be useful to your study. Think about how you are going to select your sample. It could be:

● Cluster – whole area, e.g. street, form group

● Opportunity – anyone who passes

● Random – lottery, out of a hat

● Systematic – every sixth person on a register

● Self selected – volunteers.

You must then devise your questions. Questions can be closed or open; closed questions are easier to analyse and display. Open questions can result in a wide variety of answers. For example, 'What do you think of baked beans?' – imagine the different responses you might get! Another way to elicit the information that would be easier to analyse is to ask a closed question: 'Do you eat baked beans – yes/no/sometimes/never?'

Now plan your questionnaire. This will be called the pilot questionnaire.

Your questionnaire may now need altering, so give *full details* of the changes to the pilot and the reasons why.

ASSESSMENT HINT!

A pilot questionnaire is crucial because you can see any errors or confusing questions and find out whether you will gain the information that you want. You must include this pilot in your study.

Activity 7.11

Review

When you have devised your questions print them out with your method of recording results.

This will be your pilot questionnaire. Give each member of your class a copy and ask them to critically review it.

Once your questionnaire is in an appropriate format, ask 20 people to fill in the questionnaire in order that you can make some valid assumptions. Record the results accurately. In your study you need to include one clean copy of your questionnaire, and one filled in version.

The results must be displayed and some results may lend themselves to being displayed pictorially in the form of graphs or pie charts. No more than four graphs should be displayed and they must be all on one sheet. The title of each question must be clearly displayed.

Once you have collated your results you need to interpret them: What do the results tell you? – make sure that you stick to the facts only.

When you have interpreted your results, you need to evaluate them – make sure you include your own thoughts and ideas about what you have found out.

Finally, future developments – what have you found out that you can use to move your work forward?

Figure 7.10 shows an example of how to produce a pie chart from a question. Beneath the pie chart is some analysis explaining what the chart represents.

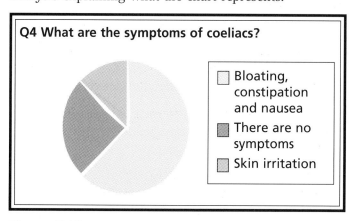

Q4 What are the symptoms of coeliacs?

- Bloating, constipation and nausea
- There are no symptoms
- Skin irritation

Figure 7.10

'From looking at these results, I can see that the majority of people answered Q4 correctly, this being 60 per cent answering 'bloating, constipation and nausea'. The number of people who believed there are no symptoms was 25 per cent, while 15 per cent thought a symptom was skin irritation.'

Practical food activity

Figure 7.11

Practical food work is a crucial part of the investigative study because it enables you to address the following criteria: 3b, 3c, 3d, 3e, 3f, 3h and 3i.

Choosing the right dish to make is very important. It must be both skilful and relevant to your study.

Activity 7.12

Discussion

As a group, compile a list of what you consider to be high order practical skills. Discuss your results.

Activity 7.13

Review

Mind map a range of recipes (minimum of eight) that would be suitable to make for your investigative study.

Identify in each recipe the skills needed to make it and why the recipe is a suitable choice.

Use this information to help you decide what you will make, and include it in your study.

ASSESSMENT HINT!

When planning practical activities use the headings shown below to address criterion 2b and 3b, 3c, 3e, 3f, 3h and 3i.

- Recipe title
- Aim
- Justification/reasons for choice of recipe
- Design specification
- Oven temperature
- Cooking time
- Resources – ingredients and quantities
- Resources – equipment needed
- Method
  1
  2
  3
  4
  5
  6
- Order of work
- Sensory analysis – carry out the most appropriate test (if applicable to the study)
- Evaluation of sensory analysis – describe what the results tell you about your product (if applicable to the study)
- Nutritional analysis – this need only be completed if applicable to the coursework
- Evaluation of the practical activity, referring back to the Aim
- Photographic evidence – try to include photographic evidence of the processes involved in making your dish as well as the finished results
- Further developments.

Completing assessment criterion 3c

Implementing time scales

Effective time scales need to be implemented when carrying out practical work and some reference should be made to safety. In the case of Food Technology, a detailed HACCP should show reference to safety but need only be carried out for the final product.

Here is an example of an order of work that would address criterion 3c.

Flapjack – Order of work

Time	Action	HACCP
1.00–1.05 pm	Wipe down table with antibacterial cleaner. Wash hands and tie back hair. Put apron on. Grease and line a tin. Put oven on to 180°C.	Avoid spread of bacteria by using antibacterial cleaner and washing hands with warm soapy water.
1.05–1.15 pm	Melt butter in a saucepan. Remove from heat. Mix the sugar and oats into the melted butter and stir together.	Be careful of hot hob and hot melted butter as it can scald.
1.20–1.25 pm	Cook in oven for 20 minutes until golden.	Use oven gloves to place flapjack in oven.
1.25–1.45 pm	Wash up using antibacterial washing up liquid. Dry up and put clean equipment away.	Avoid spread of bacteria by using antibacterial cleaner and washing hands with warm soapy water.
1.45–2.00 pm	Take flapjack out of the oven when cooked.	When removing from the oven use oven gloves and a surface protector when placing on the work surface. Photograph finished result. Finished dish should be cooled quickly and stored in the refrigerator to inhibit bacterial growth.

Sensory analysis

Sensory analysis is the scientific measurement of the qualities of a product. You can use sensory analysis in your investigative study to:

- describe the sensory characteristics of a food product

- determine the strengths and weaknesses of your food product

- compare product with product (for example, bought versus homemade; high fat versus low fat)

- match a product with a need (for example, high protein for a child).

Carrying out sensory analysis

The following conditions should be employed as far as possible when carrying out sensory analysis in order to gain the high bracket marks in 3f.

1 The area must be clear of everything except samples of food and response sheets.

2 Samples of food should be in identical plain containers and should be equal in size and quantity.

3 They should be coded so that the sampler knows as little about them as possible – for example, A, B.

4 Water should be sipped between each tasting to clear the palate.

5 There should be clear instructions for the tester and a simple response sheet to fill in.

A variety of tests that may be suitable for your study are as follows:

Difference test

This is used to determine whether there are any differences between two or more products. It is used if there has been a change of ingredient or process, or to compare your product with a manufacturer's product. It could be set out like this:

Sample	1st choice	2nd choice	3rd choice	Score	Order
A					
B					
C					

Ratings test

This is where the taster makes comments and gives a mark for a particular food product. It could be set out like this:

Tasting words or comments	Votes by tasting panel				Total	Average

Descriptive test or profiling (star profile)

This is where a food product is given a profile of suitable descriptors covering its flavour, texture and appearance. The taster gives each of the descriptors a mark from 1 to 5. A spider web diagram is produced and it is easy to pinpoint the areas where the product may need to be modified. A spider web can be produced using an Excel spreadsheet or a nutritional analysis program.

Costing

Costing a recipe is important and can be used to compare a homemade product with a shop bought product, which may be useful when investigating budgeting. Costing can be used to prove a hypothesis, for example, that a healthy meal can be prepared on a particular budget. For a costing to be useful in drawing conclusions, it is important to calculate the cost of the dish or the portions.

Below is an example of a costing, with a brief comment about the findings.

Home made fruity muffins

Ingredients	Amount in packet	Cost of packet of ingredients	Amount used	Cost of quantity used
Self raising wholemeal flour	1000 g	79p	225 g	18p
Dried apricots	250 g	£1.39	100 g	56p
Banana	6 bananas	£1.39	1 banana	23p
Skimmed milk	1 litre	58p	250 ml	15p
Egg	6 eggs	89p	1 egg	15p
Porridge oats	500 g	38p	2 tablespoons	2p
			Cost for muffins	£1.11
		Six muffins produced	Cost of individual muffin	18.5p

Comment: *A leading supermarket offers a 'healthy' fruit style muffin for 27p each, so this product costing 18.5p provides exceptional value for money, which is important for individuals on a low income.*

The discussion of the costing could also include suggestions on how to reduce costs further and could make reference to the time taken to produce the muffins and the amount of fuel used.

Nutritional analysis

Different software packages are available that can be used to produce a nutritional analysis of practical work. Calculations using the nutritional information from food labels or textbooks (for example, *McCance and Widdowson's The Composition of Foods*, published by the Royal Society of Chemistry, 2002) can also be used. Nutritional analysis is an excellent investigative method which is essential when planning and preparing meals for groups with special dietary needs.

The table below shows the nutritional analysis of spinach and chicken lasagne prepared for an elderly couple. Not all the nutrients present in the dish are included in the nutritional analysis; only those relevant to individuals being investigated and the aims of the investigation are included. (The RNIs for different groups can be found in Topic 1.) The appropriate RNI is divided by a third as this dish is a main meal and should provide a third of the daily nutritional requirements.

It is crucial to calculate a nutritional profile of a portion of the dish so this can be compared to an RNI. A discussion of the outcome can then include the data you have produced. An evaluative comment could be added on how to improve the nutritive value of the dish, perhaps by suggesting an accompaniment, for example 'serve with a salad'. When analysing the nutritional profile of practical work you can also demonstrate knowledge and understanding of the role of nutrients in the body and make references to earlier research.

Comparison practicals

Comparison practicals are very useful to investigate the similarities and differences between food products. They are most effective when linked to a packaging comparison, costing, sensory testing or nutritional analysis. They can be used in an investigation with either a research or a 'design and make' approach.

Before beginning the practical, consider which factors will be compared. Time to complete the comparisons should be built into the order of work for the practical. The outcome should also be evaluated and results could be recorded with photographic images.

Study of relevant information on TV/magazines

See the section on background research on page 203.

Figure 7.12

Nutrient	Third of requirement (male 65 years)	Third of daily requirement (female 65 years)	Total nutritional value of dish	Per portion
Energy (kcal)	776.7	633.3	2141	535 kcal
Protein (g)	17.7	15.5	215	53.7 g
Vitamin D (µg)	3.0	3.0	0.3	0.07 mg
Calcium (mg)	233.3	233.3	3274	818.5 mg
Iron (mg)	2.9	2.9	15.2	3.8 mg
Vitamin C (mg)	13.3	13.3	84	21 mg

Activity 7.14

Discussion

What comments can you make about the nutritional content of this lasagne?

Visits

Visits can provide valuable primary information. Evidence from a visit can be recorded with photographs and/or a written report. There are many places to visit, such as farms, luncheon clubs, food retailers, primary schools and food manufacturers.

Make sure any visit is relevant to the investigation and achievement of an aim. The visit should be organised and have a clear purpose, so making a list of points to observe on the visit in advance would be useful. The visit could also be linked to another research method, for example, the distribution of a question or interview.

Food diaries

Food diaries can be used to monitor the food intake of an individual or group. They are particularly useful when looking at eating patterns over a fixed timescale. The evidence collected in a food diary can be used to draw conclusions and make decisions about practical activities.

Figure 7.14 shows an example of a food diary that includes the quantity of food eaten. This may be relevant if, for example, you are investigating the 5-a-day campaign, as the portions of fruit and vegetables eaten each day would be very important.

The structure and purpose of the food diary needs to be explained to the individuals involved. Confidentiality of individuals may be required to ensure the information collected is reliable. A summary of the findings will be required, with suggestions on how to develop the technique further or take the next steps within the investigation.

PowerPoint presentations

Developing a PowerPoint presentation is a good way of achieving an aim to raise awareness about an issue or topic. The target audience for the PowerPoint should be considered and the type of information to be included. The written style may differ for particular groups, for example, a PowerPoint presentation aimed at young children should contain images and language that are appropriate to their needs.

Guidelines for producing a PowerPoint presentation:

- Slide layout should be simple and uncluttered.
- A dark background with light text is recommended.
- Include only one main point on each slide. Six lines of text and a headline on each slide is the general rule.
- Keep animations and movements on the screen simple.
- Use your own images of practical work or graphs if possible.
- Too many slides are boring!

Include a copy of your PowerPoint in your realisation (see Completing assessment criterion 3 on page 194). A handout version of the slides is adequate. It is important to evaluate the presentation and comment upon its success; this could be achieved by talking to the audience afterwards.

Leaflet design

Similar to a PowerPoint presentation, this method can be used to raise awareness of an issue to a group of individuals. It also allows you to demonstrate technical skill and aesthetic ability.

The leaflet must have a clear aim and the style and content should be appropriate for the audience. The leaflet could include your own images and recipes if appropriate. Feedback on the leaflet from the target audience can help you to make evaluative comments and develop the method further.

Food diary

Food/drink	How much	Time	Where	Alone or with company
apple	1	11.00am	school	alone

Figure 7.14

Completing assessment criterion 3a

Background research

You now need to research from a wide variety of secondary sources and select appropriate and relevant background information. The following sources could be used:

- newspaper – look for any relevant articles

- magazines – look for any relevant articles

- internet – visit at least four websites

- at least two textbooks

- at least two recipe books

- leaflets.

It is important to recognise that you get marks for using a *variety* of sources of information. You need to provide references for any information you decide to use, for example (website address, name of textbook and author) and a summary and analysis of what you find out. You will not gain marks for downloading excessive amounts from the internet; neither will you gain marks for photocopying chunks from textbooks. It may, however, be appropriate to select sections of text and cut and paste (or scan for extra technological marks). In the case of an article you find in a magazine, you may wish to cut and paste (or scan) this in.

How you present the research section is vital. Any research you carry out must have an aim. For example, if you intend to use the internet as a source of information, the aim should state what you want to find out.

Activity 7.15

Investigative study work

Present the work completed for assessment criteria 3 in labelled appendices:

6 – Background research

7 – Practical activities

8 onwards – will depend upon the investigative techniques you have chosen to carry out.

Update your report to include what you have found out from your chosen investigative techniques.

Hand in your work to your teacher to be checked.

Understanding assessment criterion 4

Evaluation

In this section you are required to conclude and evaluate the findings and results achieved during your study. You will also need to critically analyse and review your study as a whole. This section is marked out of 20.

Assessment criteria

Evaluation

Criteria	0–6 marks	7–13 marks	14–20 marks
4a	Summarises and interprets the outcomes of some of the individual investigative methods carried out and draws limited conclusions	Summarises and interprets the outcomes of most of the individual investigative methods carried out and draws appropriate conclusions	Summarises and interprets the outcomes of all of the individual investigative methods carried out and draws informed conclusions
4b	Recognises how some of the aims have been met	Recognises the degree to which the aims have been met	Recognises fully the degree to which the aims have been met
4c	Analyses to a limited extent strengths and weaknesses in the results/outcomes achieved	Analyses specific strengths and weaknesses in the results/outcomes achieved	Analyses and substantiates specific strengths and weaknesses in the results/outcomes achieved
4d	Produces a limited evaluation of the task	Produces a general evaluation of the task	Produces a critical evaluation of the task

Activity 7.16

Discussion

Check you understand the assessment criteria by discussing them with your group.

Explain in your own words what each one means.

Completing assessment criterion 4

> **ASSESSMENT HINT!**
>
> The evaluation should appear as the last section of the report. If, however, you find that you are exceeding the word count of 3000 words, then part of you evaluation could go in a labelled appendix.

Assessment criterion 4a

The results of each investigative process carried out must be analysed and evaluated, so this section will appear throughout the investigative study.

Assessment criterion 4b

You will need to document fully the degree to which the aims have been met. Each aim must be word processed separately and emboldened or underlined. You should then evaluate the outcome of each aim and the extent to which you feel the aim was met. However, simply stating 'Yes, I met that aim' or 'No, I did not meet that aim' is unacceptable; each statement made must be justified.

Assessment criterion 4c

The work as a whole needs to be analysed, and specific strengths and weaknesses should be identified and evaluated in terms of results obtained. What were your strengths and weaknesses in the work you carried out – how could you have improved on this?

Assessment criterion 4d

A critical evaluation should be produced, giving full consideration to the prediction and the context and question in your title. Everything you state must be backed up by reference to the relevant results achieved and also by referring to the relevant appendix. You must be critical of your findings – remember you have carried out a limited study looking at only a snapshot of society. You must also critically review your prediction – was it correct? Why do think it was correct? If your prediction was incorrect, why was this so? Once you have answered these questions you will be in a position to sum up by looking back at your task title and answering it critically.

Activity 7.17

Investigative study work

Present the work completed for assessment criteria 4 at the end of your report.

The study should now be completed.

Hand your work in to your teacher to be checked.

CHECK YOUR UNDERSTANDING

Check you understand the meaning of the following key terms. Write a sentence using each word.

investigative	context	assessment
analysis	aim	objective
hypothesise	criterion/criteria	specification
psychomotor	rationale	case study
summary	structured interview	unstructured interview

ASSESSMENT ADVICE

Learning objectives

By the end of this chapter you will be able to:

- explain the definitions of trigger or key words used in examination questions
- explain the importance of subject specific terminology – key words
- recognise some factors which can affect exam performance
- describe ways of overcoming the common errors that candidates may make in examinations.

How the A2 is examined

Answering examination questions is a skill, and as such, it is something that you can learn to do well. For your final external examinations, the techniques you use to answer questions are just as important as the information you have revised and retained. The structure of the exam at A2 is different from AS and so you need to prepare yourself for this.

Assessment objectives

At A2 you are expected to:

- demonstrate your knowledge and understanding of the Nutrition and Food Production unit – Assessment objective A01

- demonstrate your ability to apply knowledge, understanding and skills in a variety of situations and to analyse problems, issues and situations using appropriate skills – Assessment objective A02

- demonstrate your ability to gather, organise and select information, evaluate acquired knowledge and understanding, and present and justify an argument.

AO weightings in Advanced GCE

Unit	% of Advanced GCE			Total
	AO1	AO2	AO3	
A2 Unit G003: *Coursework Study*	7	13	5	25%
A2 Unit G004: *Nutrition and Food Production*	7	11	7	25%

Structure of the A2 paper

A2 Unit G004: Nutrition and Food Production

25% of the total Advanced GCE marks 1.5 hrs written paper 75 marks	The paper has **two** sections:
	Section A: consists of structured questions linked by a common theme. Some questions require a very short response and others require a longer response in continuous prose. Section A is mandatory.
	Section B: consists of essay questions that are worth 25 marks each. These essay questions all require answers in continuous prose. Candidates answer **two** out of **three**. This unit is synoptic.

Key words used in examinations

Throughout the course, you will have answered examination-style questions as part of your preparation for the final exam. A crucial skill is to understand what the question is asking. A question will begin with a trigger or key word, which will give an indication of the expected response. The trigger words in the A2 essay questions are designed to be more demanding.

Key/trigger words and their meanings

Assess – to make a judgement about something; to put a value on something or estimate its worth. For example, 'Assess the value of different packaging materials.'

Critically assess – as for assess, but to make a judgement of something backed by a discussion of the evidence. For example, 'Critically assess current nutritional labelling.'

Describe – to write out the main feature; put a picture into words.

Discuss – investigate or examine by argument, from more than one viewpoint, setting out factors that support, and those that cast doubt on the proposition. It is not always necessary to write a conclusion.

Evaluate – to judge the worth of something by means of stated criteria. For example, 'Evaluate the usefulness of a microwave.' (See also assess.)

Explain – set out the facts and the reasons behind them; make known in detail; make plain or clear. For example, 'Explain the choice and use of alternative protein sources.'

High order knowledge

To achieve the higher grades at A2 it is essential that wherever possible you use subject specific terminology. This will demonstrate high order knowledge and enable you to access higher marks and ultimately higher grades. For example, let's look at Topic 4, Section 2 – Performance ccharacteristics of eggs and flour.

Below are some of the key words associated with this section, which, when used correctly in an exam, can demonstrate high order knowledge. As part of your revision, write an explanation of each of these key words.

	Explanation
Amylopectin	
Amylose	
Blending method	
Coagulation	
Denature	
Dextrin	
Foam formation	
Gelatinisation	
Gliadin	
Globular proteins	
Gluten	
Glutenin	
Non enzymic browning	
Starch granules	
Syneresis	

Getting ready for your exams

When you start to prepare for your examinations it is important to recognise some of the factors which can affect your examination performance. These factors are summarised below:

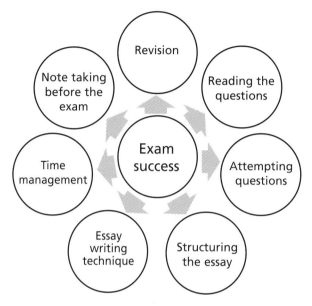

Figure A.01

We will now explore in a little more detail how these factors can improve your exam performance.

Note taking

Taking notes and writing information down helps to improve your ability to remember things and develops your writing style. The organisation of your class notes is very important to your examination success. Use dividers, clear headings for new topics and number pages to help you organise your work. If you have missed lessons, you need to ensure that you have copies of the associated notes. Good notes should sum up the key points in a topic. Try using abbreviations, bullet lists and numbered points and include diagrams, arrows and help boxes to make the key information more visible and to aid memory and revision. The use of mind maps and web diagrams to summarise information is a well-respected *aide-mémoire* or revision aid. Using coloured pens and highlighter pens to embolden text can help to emphasise key points or words. Leaving white space in between chunks of important information will allow you to add more detail at a later date or emphasise a key point.

Some of the information gathered during the course may have been completed by independent research. At Advanced GCE, students are expected to take more responsibility for their own learning. There may be aspects of the course that you have researched as part of your coursework investigation and so have more in-depth knowledge. It will be valuable to use this information if appropriate, but never write anything down that you don't understand, as it will be impossible to revise.

Revision

There is a considerable amount of knowledge that you must revise in preparation for your examination. The knowledge is organised into sections in the specification, so use the specification to organise your revision and identify the areas you need to focus on. Remember that the exam questions will link directly to the specification.

Underpinning knowledge is always examined in this subject. A knowledge and understanding of nutrition is very important as it permeates many different aspects of the specification. You should always revise nutrition so that you can apply it to a range of exam questions.

There are a variety of methods you can use to revise for your examinations. The key point to remember is that revision is an active process and you cannot revise just by sitting and reading information. Below are some suggestions for active revision.

● Make mind maps to summarise notes. Mapping your notes by radiating key words out from a central point will make best use of your memory. Use colour and images on your maps to stimulate both the creative and logical sides of your brain.

● Make revision cards that contain questions and answers to key topics. Test yourself or ask others to test you by writing the questions on one side of the card and answers on the other. By creating the cards and writing out the responses, you will be more likely to absorb information. The cards are also useful when travelling and during other times when you are unable to use other revision methods.

● Talking to friends about topics takes less time than making notes. Discussing topics will help to clarify issues and check your understanding. Having the confidence to contribute to a discussion means you are demonstrating knowledge and understanding.

- Use memory triggers to help you retain crucial knowledge. Distil your notes into key points or one or two words. Then devise mnemonics, or use visual associations, humour or repetition to help you remember the information.

Good revision involves:

- careful organisation of notes alongside the specification

- reducing and summarising notes or topics by making maps or cards

- checking your understanding by self test, discussion or practice questions.

Reading the questions

Careful reading of the exam question is very important. Read the questions at least twice and use a highlighter pen to underline key words in the question. All exam questions go through a very extensive process to make sure they are clear and straightforward. However, this does not mean a simple response is required; the question is a platform for you to demonstrate your knowledge to the examiner.

Attempting the questions

In Section B of the Nutrition and Food Production examination paper, there are two essay questions to answer from a choice of three. Before you begin to write, you should consider 'Which question can I answer best?'

When attempting your first question, always select the question with which you feel most comfortable. This will help build your confidence and put you in a more positive state of mind to attempt the remaining questions.

Once you have decided which essay question to attempt, don't spend too much time answering it. Earning the first 10 marks in an essay question is much easier than earning the last ten. Waffling and padding out a response does not necessarily gain any extra credit.

Time your answer; even with your strongest response you must have a cut off time and start the next question. If you manage to spend 30 minutes writing sensibly about a topic, it is likely you will demonstrate your knowledge and understanding to the examiner.

However, you must then move on, otherwise you may jeopardise your chances of doing well on the whole paper.

Structure your response

Section A questions are presented to you with a structure to guide your response. One line usually indicates that a very brief response is required. Use the amount of space presented on the paper as a guide to the depth of response required.

Essay questions require more consideration before you begin writing. A simple plan in the form of a list or diagram will help to organise your thoughts before writing and avoid repetition. Write in paragraphs, and group points together, otherwise your response will be confused. Candidates that do not plan usually end up using annotations and asterisks to link points together. Occasionally, this is acceptable when you have genuinely forgotten a key point, but the over-use of annotation could demonstrate you have not given sufficient thought to the structure of the essay. Begin with an introduction that provides the background to the essay. Each point should be clearly explained and contained in a separate paragraph. One way of remembering this is to use PEGEX for each paragraph.

PEGEX stands for point, example and explanation.

- Point: make sure the paragraph is directed at answering the question.

- Example: now use some facts to prove the point.

- Explanation: now explain how the point contributes to the question.

Use every opportunity to demonstrate your knowledge and understanding when answering exam questions. The use of evidence from coursework research, subject specific terminology, relevant statistics, and making connections between areas of the specification can all show this.

Essay writing technique

Practise writing essay questions – use the specimen exam questions and mark schemes to help you as you need to be aware of what a good response looks like. Your paper will be scrutinised for evidence of your knowledge and understanding, but your communication must be clear, organised and the legible. This means your handwriting, grammar and spelling will also be considered in the awarding of a final mark. Remember that it is not just the *content* of your written response that is assessed, but also the *quality* of your written response.

The response you write must be relevant. Make sure you fully understand the trigger words such as discuss, analyse and explain, etc.

Remember too that you may need to practise timed essays to build up your speed in producing a written response; this is especially relevant nowadays as many students word process their coursework and homework, and do not therefore have a rapid handwriting style.

Time management

During the revision period before the exam, time management is very important. You need to make sure you allocate sufficient time to revise all aspects of the specification and that your revision programme is punctuated by breaks. Striking a balance between revision and relaxation time is essential. A lack of revision and too much relaxation probably means you will not achieve your potential, similarly too much revision and no relaxation can cause stress and underachievement too. Organise your day to include both revision and relaxation periods.

Time management during the exam is also very important. The A2 examination is one hour 30 minutes. Section A carries one-third of the potential marks but this does not mean it should be allocated one-third of the examination time, as the questions are shorter and you can 'jump in' with less planning than Section B. If necessary, move on to the Section B essays and return to Section A later.

Practise a timed essay question in a 30-minute slot under exam conditions. Keep reading the question while writing your response as it will help you remain focused. Avoid writing down everything you know about a topic. You must attempt two essays, so finish the first with a shorter conclusion, if necessary, to provide sufficient time for the second essay.

Activity 1

Discussion

The table below shows the common errors made by candidates.

Discuss these errors with your class and make suggestions on how to avoid them.

Common errors	How to avoid them
Candidate fails to read the question properly and makes irrelevant points	
Candidate makes mistakes when using key terminology	
The essay response is repetitive	
There are annotations everywhere linking different paragraphs together	
Candidates writes everything they know about a subject for a Section B question	
Candidate has knowledge but does not demonstrate it in their response	
Candidate fails to answer two essay questions in sufficient detail due to lack of time	
Candidate writes an essay in bullet points instead of paragraphs	

Summary of assessment advice

- Avoid writing everything you know about a topic regardless of its relevance.

- Never ignore the question posed and instead answer your own question.

- Follow the instructions contained in the question. There will be one or more trigger words giving exact instructions, and these *must* be followed.

- Read the question carefully and note *exactly* what you are asked to do – the context and question will set the scene.

- Plan essay questions. List the content or mind map – do *not* rewrite this but use it effectively.

- Decide how to order your content after you have planned – use numbers if this helps.

- Maintain an awareness of time. Be strict on yourself and allow half an hour for section A, and half an hour each for the two essays in section B. You can always return to a question if you have time at the end.

- Try to read your answers when you have completed the paper.

- As a very general guide, for a 10 mark question you need 5–7 well explained points, and for a 15 mark question 7–9 well explained points.

- Each point you make in an essay must be well explained – remember PEGEX – make the point, explain it and give an example.

- Stick to the point – for example, if the question asks you to describe the nutritional significance of meat, do not expand to cover other commodities.

Answers to exam-style questions

Topic 1 Introduction to nutrition

1 Describe the concept of a balanced diet. (2 marks)

A balanced diet provides the correct amounts of each nutrient that an individual needs. This is a combination of proteins, fats, carbohydrates, vitamins and minerals. A balanced diet can be achieved by eating the correct amount of food from the different food groups.

2 Describe the concept of malnutrition in the UK. (2 marks)

Malnutrition is a deficiency, excess or imbalance of nutrients that causes adverse effects on health. Malnutrition can include wasting and obesity but is usually associated with undernutrition. The symptoms of malnutrition may include tiredness, slow growth, brittle nails, dry and scaly skin, slow wound healing and increased susceptibility to infections.

3 Explain why the elderly have a greater risk of malnutrition. (6 marks)

High 5–6
Candidates are able to explain clearly why the elderly have a greater risk of malnutrition. There will be few, if any, errors of grammar, punctuation or spelling.

Middle 3–4
Candidates are able to explain why the elderly have a greater risk of malnutrition. There may be occasional errors of grammar, punctuation or spelling.

Low 0–2
Candidates are able to explain briefly why the elderly have a greater risk of malnutrition. The information may be poorly expressed and errors of grammar, punctuation and spelling will be intrusive.

Answers may include the following points:

- Mobility problems can prevent travel to food shops.
- Dexterity may be poor and preparation of food will be affected by this problem.
- Loneliness and depression can result in apathy towards food and individuals may not feel like eating.
- Poor memory can cause individuals to forget to eat.
- An elderly person may eat poorly due to dental problems; they may find it difficult to chew food due to ill-fitting dentures and may have difficulty swallowing food.
- Certain medication can affect the appetite, reducing the desire to eat.
- Concerns about spending money can decrease the motivation to go shopping.
- Those in care homes or hospitals may not like the food offered.

Topic 2 Nutrients and energy

Proteins

1 Explain the term high biological value protein. (2 marks)

Answer may include any TWO of the following:

- The quality of protein (its biological value) depends upon whether it can supply all of the essential amino acids in the quantities needed.

- If a protein contains the essential amino acids in the approximate amount needed, it is said to have a high biological value.

- If it is low in one or more of the essential amino acids, it is said to have a low biological value. The amino acid that is in shortest supply in relation to need is called the limiting amino acid.

2 Discuss the implications of excess protein and a deficiency of protein in the diet. (10 marks)

High 7–10
Candidates are able to discuss clearly the implications of excess protein and a deficiency of protein in the diet. The explanation is well developed and supported by the use of subject specific examples. Ideas are expressed clearly and fluently. There are few, if any, errors of grammar, punctuation or spelling.

Middle 4–6
Candidates are able to discuss satisfactorily the implications of excess protein and a deficiency of protein in the diet. The explanation may not be fully developed and may lack specific examples. There may be occasional errors of grammar, punctuation or spelling.

Low 0–3
Candidates are able to discuss superficially the implications of excess protein and a deficiency of protein in the diet. The information may be poorly expressed and errors of grammar, punctuation and spelling will be intrusive

- A deficiency of protein is extremely rare in the UK.

- In developing countries protein deficiency can occur. Protein energy malnutrition (PEM) describes a range of disorders.

- The two most common forms of PEM are Marasmus and Kwashiorkor.

- Excess protein consumed which is not required for growth and repair is used as energy, and therefore can contribute towards a surplus of energy.

- Marasmus occurs in infants under one year of age who have been weaned off breast milk onto a diet containing too little energy and protein. As a result, the child becomes severely underweight and very weak and lethargic.

- Kwashiorkor occurs in children who, after breast feeding, are weaned onto a diet high in starchy foods which are low in energy and protein. Kwashiorkor often follows an acute infection. The body swells with oedema (water retention), the hair is thin and discoloured, and the skin may show patches of scaliness and pigmentation

- High protein intake may be harmful and may contribute to demineralisation of bone and to a deterioration of kidney function in patients with kidney disease.

Fats

1a Describe four functions of fat in the diet. (4 marks)

Answer may include any FOUR of the following:

- Supplies more energy than the same weight of protein or carbohydrate.

- Provides the body with a long-term energy store.

- Helps to protects organs such as the kidneys.

- Component of all cell membranes in the body.

- Source for the fat-soluble vitamins A, D, E, K.

- Contains the essential fatty acids.

1b Explain the term saturated fatty acid. (2 marks)

TWO marks for a detailed explanation.

- Saturated fatty acids have no double bonds between any of the carbon atoms in the carbon chain.

- All of the bonds are saturated with single carbon bonds.

- Saturated fats are usually from animal sources.

1c Name an essential fatty acid and its food source. (2 marks)

One mark for identifying a fatty acid and one mark for a correct source.

- Alpha linolenic acid (Omega 3 fatty acid).

- Rapeseed oil (canola), mustard seeds, pumpkin seeds, soya bean, walnuts, green leafy vegetables and grains.

- Linoleic acid (Omega 6 fatty acid).

- Oils made from sunflower, corn, soya, pumpkin and wheat germ.
- Coldwater and oily ocean fish including tuna, salmon and sardines.

Carbohydrates

I Explain the benefits of dietary fibre in the diet. (6 marks)

Answer may include:

High 5–6
Candidates are able to explain clearly the benefits of dietary fibre in the diet. There will be few, if any, errors of grammar, punctuation or spelling.

Middle 3–4
Candidates are able to explain benefits of dietary fibre in the diet. There may be occasional errors of grammar, punctuation or spelling.

Low 0–2
Candidates are able to explain briefly the benefits of dietary fibre in the diet. The information may be poorly expressed and errors of grammar, punctuation and spelling are intrusive.

- Cellulose adds bulk to the faeces. Because of its water binding capacity, it greatly assists the passage of waste products and indigestible material through the intestines thus preventing constipation. It is thought therefore that a high intake of fibre-rich foods may protect against bowel cancer.
- Polysaccharides such as pectin in fruit and beta glucan in oats may slightly reduce the level of cholesterol in blood.
- Diets high in dietary fibre are of use to diabetics because the dietary fibre slows down the release of glucose to the bloodstream.

Vitamins

I Describe two good sources of vitamin A. (4 marks)

Answer may include any TWO of the following foods:

- Retinol is found in eggs, oily fish, liver, full fat milk, butter and cheese.
- β-Carotene is found in carrots, sweet potatoes, apricots, cantaloupe melon, broccoli, spinach, pumpkin and all other green and orange fruits and vegetables.

2 Explain the value of vitamin supplements in the diet. (10 marks)

High 7–10
Candidates are able to explain clearly the value of vitamin supplements in the diet to groups with special dietary needs. The explanation is well developed and supported by the use of subject specific examples. Ideas are expressed clearly and fluently. There are few, if any, errors of grammar, punctuation or spelling.

Middle 4–6
Candidates are able to explain satisfactorily the value of vitamin supplements in the diet to groups with special dietary needs. The explanation may not be fully developed and may lack specific examples. There may be occasional errors of grammar, punctuation or spelling.

Low 0–3
Candidates are able to explain superficially the value of vitamin supplements in the diet to groups with special dietary needs. The information may be poorly expressed and errors of grammar, punctuation and spelling are intrusive.

Answers may include:

Some groups will benefit from increasing their intake of specified nutrients. Experts suggest only those with special dietary needs should increase their intake.

- **Women who are planning to get pregnant.** The Government advises women who are planning to get pregnant to consume folic acid supplements daily 0.4 mg/400 microgram. Those who have conceived should continue taking the supplement for the first 12 weeks of pregnancy. Folic acid is believed to prevent the development of spina bifida.
- **People with limited exposure to sunlight.** Some groups, including Asian women (who may be required to keep their skin covered for cultural reasons) and housebound elderly people, may have limited exposure to sunlight and lack vitamin D. This could be taken in supplement form to avoid deficiency.
- **Vegans.** They may need to take vitamin B12 in tablet form to reduce the risk of pernicious anaemia.
- **People who are malnourished due to illness.** Illness or surgery can cause some people to have difficulty eating or swallowing.
- **Elderly people.** Supplements are necessary if the individual has problems eating due to loss of appetite or problems with chewing, swallowing or digestion.

- People who are following an intense training regime or sporting activity.

Some people for training purposes may need to take extra vitamins (B1 thiamine) to support their increased energy requirements.

Minerals

1 Minerals are essential micronutrients. Identify four minerals necessary for good health. (4 marks)

Answer may include any FOUR of the following:

- Iron
- Calcium
- Phosphorus
- Potassium
- Zinc.

2 Describe the functions of the minerals identified in question 1. (8 marks)

High 6–8
Candidates are able to describe clearly the functions of the minerals. The description is well developed and supported by the use of subject specific examples. Ideas are expressed clearly and fluently. There are few, if any, errors of grammar, punctuation or spelling.

Middle 3–5
Candidates are able to describe satisfactorily the functions of the minerals. The description may not be fully developed and may lack specific examples. There may be occasional errors of grammar, punctuation or spelling.

Low 0–2
Candidates are able to describe superficially the functions of the minerals. The description is vague. The information may be poorly expressed and errors of grammar, punctuation and spelling are intrusive.

Iron
- Needed for the formation of haemoglobin in red blood cells, which transports oxygen from the lungs to body tissues.
- Required for energy metabolism, and for metabolism of drugs and foreign substances that need to be removed from the body.
- The immune system also requires iron for normal function.

Calcium
- Calcium is the main constituent of hydroxyapatite, the principal mineral in bones and teeth. It is essential for building and maintaining healthy bones and teeth.

- Required for the contraction of the muscles, including the maintenance of a regular heart beat, and for nerve function.
- Required for blood clotting.
- The activity of several enzymes depends on calcium.

Phosphorus
- Essential for bone and tooth structure. Calcium phosphate provides the strength of bones and teeth.
- It is needed for the release of energy from cells. When glucose is oxidized, the energy produced is stored in phosphate compounds which break down to give energy when required.

Potassium
- Potassium works with sodium in the functioning of cells, including nerves.
- It is essential for water and electrolyte balance.
- Potassium has a beneficial blood pressure-lowering effect in people with raised blood pressure because it can counter the effects of sodium.

Zinc
- Zinc is essential constituent of over 100 enzymes, and it plays a part in protein and carbohydrate metabolism.
- It is needed for the functioning of the immune system and in the structure and function of the skin and, therefore, in wound healing.

Energy

1a Identify four good sources of energy in the UK diet. (4 marks)

One mark available for each correctly identified source.

Answers may include:

- Fats including butter, margarine, suet and lard
- Oils (vegetable, nut and animal)
- Fatty foods including cheese, cream, red meats, chocolate
- Sugar and sugar rich foods, e.g. biscuits
- Nuts and seeds
- Cereals and cereal products
- Starchy vegetables
- Fried or roasted foods
- Processed foods, e.g. pizzas, pies, dried fruits or in syrup.

Credit to be given for all valid points.

1b Explain the term energy imbalance. (6 marks)

High 5–6
Candidates are able to explain clearly the term energy imbalance. There are few, if any, errors of grammar, punctuation or spelling.

Middle 3–4
Candidates are able to explain the term energy imbalance. There are occasional errors of grammar, punctuation or spelling.

Low 0–2
Candidates are able to explain briefly the term energy imbalance. The information may be poorly expressed and errors of grammar, punctuation and spelling are intrusive.

Answers may include:

- Body weight is influenced by energy intake and energy expenditure. Extra energy is stored in the body as fat.
- Energy from fat is more likely to be stored as fat in the body than energy from carbohydrates. Fat is energy dense.
- The conversion of excess dietary fat to body fat is a much more efficient process than converting carbohydrates and protein to body fat.
- Most dietary carbohydrate is stored as glycogen or used directly as energy.
- An imbalance in energy intake arising from a diet high in fat coupled with a decrease in physical activity has contributed to the growth of obesity.
- If a person regularly consumes less energy than they use up, they will lose weight. An inadequate energy intake over a period of time can result in malnutrition.

Credit to be given for all valid points.

1c Explain four factors that affect energy requirements. (8 marks)

High 6–8
Candidates are able to explain clearly four factors that can affect energy requirements. The description is well developed and supported by the use of subject specific examples. Ideas are expressed clearly and fluently. There are few, if any, errors of grammar, punctuation or spelling.

Middle 3–5
Candidates are able to explain satisfactorily two or three factors that can affect energy requirements. The description may not be fully developed and may lack specific examples. There may be occasional errors of grammar, punctuation or spelling.

Low 0–2
Candidates are able to explain superficially one factor that can affect energy requirements. The description will be vague. The information may be poorly expressed and errors of grammar, punctuation and spelling are intrusive.

Answers may include:

Rate of growth/Age
- Young children have higher relative metabolic rates than adults. They require more energy in relation to their size than adults. This is because they are generally more active and are growing rapidly.
- With increasing age, energy requirements decrease. This is partly due to a reduction in physical activity and a reduction in lean body mass.

Size/Gender
- In general the larger the body mass the greater the energy expenditure.
- Men require more energy than women because they tend to have a larger overall body size and higher lean to fat ratio than women.
- Men's metabolic rate is higher and they tend to use more energy.

Activity level
- Sedentary occupations including office workers, drivers, shop workers and those following a sedentary lifestyle require less energy.
- Moderately active occupations including light industrial workers require more energy.
- Very active occupations, e.g. builders' labourers and steel workers, require the greatest physical exertion and therefore have the largest energy requirement.
- Athletes who train for long periods will require a greater energy intake.

State of body
- Pregnancy: Extra energy is required for the healthy growth and development of the baby.
- Lactation: the production of breast milk requires extra energy.

- Illness: the metabolic rate rises during a fever and may decrease due to reduction of physical activity.

- Weight reduction: to lose weight a person must reduce their energy consumption from food.

- Body composition: lean body tissue is metabolically more active and uses more energy than adipose tissue.

- Hormonal imbalance: an overactive thyroid gland can increase the metabolic rate and individuals may need to consume more energy to address the imbalance.

Environmental conditions

- Food plays a role in prevention of hypothermia since it is the primary source of fuel for body heat production. A high-energy intake is required when working or living in extremely cold environments.

Credit to be given for all valid points

Topic 3 Nutritional and dietary needs of different groups

1 Discuss the nutritional and dietary needs of children aged 4 to 12 years. (25 marks)

High 16–25
Candidates are able to discuss fully the dietary needs of children aged 4 to 12 years and show a detailed level of understanding. Information is presented in a fluent and well-structured manner. Subject-specific terminology is used accurately. There are few, if any, errors of grammar, punctuation and spelling.

Middle 9–16
Candidates are able to discuss the dietary needs of children aged 4 to 12 years. They show a reasonable level of understanding. The information is well presented and some subject-specific terminology is used. There are occasional errors of grammar, punctuation and spelling.

Low 0–8
Candidates are able to demonstrate a superficial discussion of the dietary needs of children aged 4 to 12 years. The discussion is generalised. The information is poorly expressed and limited subject-specific terminology is used. Errors of grammar, punctuation and spelling may be intrusive.

Answers may include the following points:

- Schoolchildren are growing fast and are also very active. They have high energy and nutrient needs, particularly during periods of rapid growth and development.

- **4–6 years:** Energy requirements increase and there is a greater need for protein, all the vitamins apart from Vitamin C and D, and all the minerals apart from iron. The requirement for vitamin C remains the same as for younger children. The action of sunlight on the child's skin is the major source of vitamin D. Asian children may be at risk of vitamin D deficiency because of low vitamin D intake from food and/or inadequate exposure of skin to sunshine.

- **7–10 years**
  There is a marked increase in requirements for energy and protein. There is no change in the requirement for thiamine, vitamin C or vitamin A; however, the requirements for the other vitamins and minerals are increased.

- It is again crucial that schoolchildren have a healthy, balanced diet, which is rich in fruit, vegetables and starchy foods.

- Schoolchildren should be eating at least five portions of fruit and vegetables each day.

- The family continues to influence eating habits early in life. It is difficult to change habits once they are established. It is therefore important that the whole family adopts a healthy lifestyle and avoids salty, sugary and fatty foods.

- If children do eat foods and drinks containing sugar it is best to have them only at meal times.

- Eating sugary foods frequently between meals can cause dental decay. Snack foods such as cakes, biscuits, crisps, chocolate and sweets are often high in sugar and saturated fat, and low in certain vitamins and minerals, so intake should be reduced.

- To achieve a high-energy intake, energy-rich foods should be eaten as part of small and frequent meals. This may be necessary for younger children (4–6-year-olds), who do not have large enough stomachs to cope with big meals.

- Weight gain should be gradual and in line with height increases, so that a child grows to be an acceptable weight for his height.

- Milk and dairy products remain essential for tooth development and with vitamin D, helps make bones stronger. For schoolchildren, this is an important time for tooth and bone development.

- Iron deficiency anaemia is associated with frequent infections, poor weight gain and delay in development. If iron-rich foods, such as liver and red meat, are not popular with children, other sources such as dark green leafy vegetables, pulses, nuts, bread and some fortified breakfast cereals should be included in the diet.

2 Discuss the issues involved in meeting the dietary needs of elderly people. (25 marks)

High 16–25
Candidates are able to fully discuss the issues involved in meeting the dietary needs of the elderly and show a detailed level of understanding. The information is presented in a fluent and well-structured manner.

Subject-specific terminology is used accurately. There are few, if any, errors of grammar, punctuation and spelling.

Middle 9–16
Candidates are able to discuss the issues involved in meeting the dietary needs of the elderly. They show a reasonable level of understanding. The information is well presented and some subject-specific terminology is used. There may be occasional errors of grammar, punctuation and spelling.

Low 0–8
Candidates are able to demonstrate a superficial discussion of the issues involved in meeting the dietary needs of the elderly. The discussion is generalised. The information is poorly expressed and limited subject-specific terminology is used. Errors of grammar, punctuation and spelling may be intrusive.

Answers may include:

I There is very little difference between the nutritional requirements of most adults and the elderly. However, as we get older we tend to become less active so the main difference is that energy expenditure decreases.

- The elderly age group is the fastest growing sector in society, so ensuring they receive an adequate diet is of increasing relevance.

- An elderly person's personal circumstances such as living alone, being lonely, or on a limited income should be taken into consideration, because this may affect what they eat.

- Their state of health such as reduced mobility, recovering from illness, being in hospital or dependent on others for meals also needs to be taken into consideration, because, again, this can affect what they are able to eat.

- The elderly should aim to eat meals based upon starchy foods – pasta, potatoes, rice and bread. These are filling sources of carbohydrate.

- A useful source of protein is oily fish; consumption of oily fish may help reduce the risk of thrombosis.

- There are huge benefits from eating fruit and vegetables. Fruit and vegetables provide valuable vitamins, minerals and fibre. They also contain antioxidants, which mop up damaging 'free radicals'.

- Some degenerative diseases that are common in later life may be exacerbated or even caused by free radical damage, including cancer, vascular diseases, degenerative eye diseases and possibly neuro-degenerative diseases like Parkinson's disease.

- The crucial antioxidant vitamins (A, C and E) and minerals (zinc, copper, manganese and selenium) found in fruit and vegetables can halt the damage caused by free radicals.

- Fruit and vegetables have many other important jobs to do, including lowering blood pressure, because the potassium they contain increases sodium (salt) excretion. Potassium is found in many fruits and vegetables including bananas, citrus fruits, raisins and other dried fruits, potatoes and avocados.

- An intake of iron is very important and should come from both haem (meat, offal) and non-haem sources (fortified cereals, dried fruit, pulses and green leafy vegetables) every day. Absorption of iron is increased by consuming vitamin C at the same time, for example, by drinking a glass of fruit juice with meals.

- An intake of zinc is important and sources can be found in meat and meat products, seafood, milk and dairy products, wholemeal bread, lentils, eggs, nuts, sweetcorn and rice.

- Calcium-rich foods such as milk, cheese and other dairy products, green leafy vegetables, sesame seeds, bony fish, dried fruit and baked beans are needed for good bone health.

- Elderly people who live alone should have at least one well-balanced meal a day, although this does not necessarily have to be a hot meal.

- It is also useful for the elderly to have a well stocked store cupboard full of essential items such as long life milk, cereals, canned foods, pulses, pasta, and a freezer with some readymade meals and bread in case they become ill or housebound.

Topic 4 Properties of food

I Discuss the choice and use of fats and oils in the UK diet. (25 marks)

High 17–25
The candidate is able to discuss clearly the choice and use of fats and oils in the UK diet. The information is presented in a fluent and well-structured manner. Subject-specific terminology is used accurately. There are few, if any, errors of grammar, punctuation and spelling.

Middle 19–16
The candidate is able to discuss satisfactorily the choice and use of fats and oils in the UK diet. The information is well presented and some subject-specific terminology is used. There may be occasional errors of grammar, punctuation and spelling.

Low 0–8
The candidate is able to discuss superficially the choice and use of fats and oils in the UK diet. The information is poorly expressed and limited subject-specific terminology is used. Errors of grammar, punctuation and spelling may be intrusive.

Answers may include:

Choice of fats:
- Butter is not pure fat, but an emulsion of water in oil. It provides about 80 g fat/100 g.
- Ghee is made by heating and clarifying butter.
- Lard comes from pigs' fat and provides about 99 g of fat/100 g.
- Dripping is the fat which 'drips' from meat being roasted and it also contains 99 g fat/100 g. It has a meaty flavour.
- Suet is obtained from the shredded fat of cattle or sheep. It is solid at room temperature.
- Fish oils contain a high proportion of unsaturated fatty acids. Fish oils are rich in n-3 fatty acids and vitamins A and D, and are used for vitamin supplements.
- Types of oil most commonly used in food production are palm oil, olive oil, hazelnut oil, walnut oil, sunflower oil, corn oil and herbal oils.
- Oils such as olive oil are suitable for adding flavour to a salad dressing. The temperature at which the oil breaks down is an important consideration if the oil is being used to deep fat fry. Some oils such as sunflower oil are rich in polyunsaturates.

- Margarine is made from a mixture of highly unsaturated oils such as rapeseed and sunflower oils. It contains less saturated fatty acids and more polyunsaturated fatty acids than butter.
- Margarine is a popular alternative to butter because it can be used in cooking in the same way as butter. Margarine is made by the process of hydrogenation where hydrogen is added to unsaturated fatty acid molecules. This changes the liquid oil into a solid fat. However, during this process trans fatty acids may be produced. Trans fatty acids can accumulate in our body and high intakes of trans fatty acids have been associated with raised blood cholesterol levels, one of the risk factors associated with coronary heart disease.
- Margarine can be bought in two main formats – block and soft.
- There are many types of buttery blends and spreads on the market and they vary considerably in terms of fat content, the type of oil from which they have been made and whether butter fat or milk solids have been added.
- Cholesterol-lowering spreads such as Benecol contain plant sterols or plant stanol esters, which have a similar structure to cholesterol and so can inhibit the absorption of cholesterol.
- Low fat spreads have a very high water content and have a similar composition to margarine but are usually lower in fat. Low fat spreads are spreads with 40 g fat/100 g. Spreads may also be fortified with vitamin A and D at levels similar to margarine, and although this is not required by law, it is often carried out voluntarily.
- Butter, margarine and spreads should be stored in a refrigerator. They should be covered to prevent oxidation and kept away from foods with strong odours. Oils should be stored at room temperature, preferably in their original container, e.g. a glass or plastic bottle. When deep fat frying, the oil needs to be strained to remove any impurities that could lead to the oil going rancid. Oils that have been used frequently for deep fat frying should be thrown away.

Uses of fats and oils:
- Aeration: Creamed cakes such as a sandwich cake need air incorporated into the mixture in order to give a well risen texture. This is achieved by

creaming the fat with caster sugar using a wooden spoon or an electric mixer. A fat that has been creamed contains tiny bubbles of air and forms a stable foam. The end result is a well risen product with a light texture. Both butter and margarine are used to aerate products.

- Flavour: Margarine contributes to the flavour of many foods. However, it can easily absorb strong odours from other ingredients. Butter is often used in cakes, biscuits and sauces because it gives a richer and more distinctive flavour. Butter can help retain a bakery product's moisture; this in turn can increase its shelf-life.

- Flakiness: Flaky and puff pastry use fat to help form separate layers of gluten and starch in the dough. The fat melts during cooking, leaving minute air pockets. The liquid present produces steam, which evaporates and causes the layers to rise and prevents them from joining. Margarine and butter are used in flaky and puff pastry although butter gives a richer flavour; low fat spreads contain too much water to make successful flaky or puff pastry.

- Retention of moisture: In bakery items, margarine can help retain a product's moisture and therefore increase its shelf life. It can also be used to baste foods that are cooked using dry heat. Fats such as dripping, butter and oil can also be used to baste food being cooked by dry heat, for example, barbecuing meat can be brushed with oil, or the basting of a roast joint of meat.

- Shortening: Fats give food such as shortcrust pastry, biscuits and shortbread their characteristic short crumbly texture. The fat acts as a shortening agent which coats the flour particles and prevents them from absorbing water. This prevents gluten formation and therefore stops the mixture from being chewy or tough.

- Margarine can be used for shortening. Margarine produces a distinctive golden colour, while lard produces a pale yellow colour. A mixture of margarine and lard may be used to produce the desired flavour and texture combination because lard adds shortness in baked products and a crumbly texture.

- Flavour: All fats and oils have unique flavours and odours. Some are more suited for particular purposes than others, for example, olive oil is used for salad dressings. Sesame seed oil is used to make tahini, ghee is used in curries and butter is used in shortbread.

- Plasticity: Fats do not melt immediately, but soften over a range of temperatures, which is determined by the nature of the individual fat. This property is called plasticity, and gives each fat its unique character. The plasticity is due to the mixture of triglycerides, each with its own melting point. Some fats have been formulated so that their melting points are low and they can be spread straight from the fridge, for example, soft margarine, 'spreadable butter'.

- Cooking: Block margarine can be used for cooking and is recommended for making pastry. Soft margarine is useful for making cakes made by the all-in-one method. Fats with a high smoke point that are free from water, salt and non-fat solids are recommended for frying.

- Spreading: Low and reduced fat spreads are not suitable for frying or baking because of their high water content. Their main use is for spreading to reduce the fat content of the diet. Butter substitutes are formulated so that their melting point is low so they can be spread straight from the fridge.

- Sauce making: Fat is used in the preparation of roux- or all-in-one-based sauces. The fat prevents the flour particles from clumping together.

- Colour: The colour of some foods depends upon the fat used. Margarine and butter provide a rich golden brown colour.

- Glazing: Butter is sometimes used to glaze foods, particularly vegetables such as carrots, peas and potatoes, to make them shiny in appearance.

2 Explain the uses of sugar in the production of food products. (8 marks)

High 6–8
Candidates are able to explain in detail the uses of sugar in the production of food products. The explanation is well developed and supported by the use of subject specific examples. Ideas are expressed clearly and fluently. There are few, if any, errors of grammar, punctuation and spelling.

Middle 3–5
The candidate is able to explain satisfactorily the uses of sugar in the production of food products. The explanation may not be fully developed and may lack specific examples. There may be occasional errors of grammar, punctuation and spelling.

Low 0–2

The candidate is able to explain superficially the uses of sugar in the production of food products. The explanation is poorly expressed and errors of grammar, punctuation and spelling are intrusive.

Answers may include:

- Sugar is not just a sweetener; it is used in baking, food processing, preservation and cooking because it has a variety of specific characteristics.

- Aeration: When fat and sugar are beaten together during the creaming stage of cake production, air is incorporated into the mix. Caster sugar is most suitable for this due to its fine structure. It also inhibits gluten development in flour, giving the cake a lighter texture.

- Bulking: Sugar may be used to increase a product's size, volume or weight, giving the characteristic texture to foods such as ice cream, jam and cakes.

- Coating: Sugar can be used to make a fondant icing which can be used to cover or decorate cake products.

- Colour: Sugar has a browning effect on the surface of many bakery products.

- Gelling: Sugar plays a crucial role in jam making. The setting of jam depends on having pectin, acid and sugar in the correct amounts to form a gel.

- Moisture retention: Sugar has water-attracting properties so the addition of sugar improves shelf life and maintains texture and mouth feel.

- Preservation: High concentrations of sugar help stop microorganisms growing and so prevents food spoilage. Jam is a good example of this.

- Stabilising: Sugar stabilises egg white foam without destroying its structure. It also lowers the freezing temperature so prevents ice crystals forming in ice cream production.

- Storage: Sugar, honey and syrup should be stored in airtight containers to prevent moisture entering, or moisture loss and caking in the case of brown sugars.

3 List three sugar substitutes. (3 marks)

One mark for each sugar substitute named:

Splenda, Canderel, saccharin, aspartame, sucralose, Sorbitol.

4 Describe the performance characteristics of eggs. (25 marks)

High 17–25

The candidate is able to describe clearly the performance characteristics of eggs. The information is presented in a fluent and well-structured manner. Subject-specific terminology is used accurately. There are few, if any, errors of grammar, punctuation and spelling.

Middle 19–16

The candidate is able to describe satisfactorily the performance characteristics of eggs. The information is well presented and some subject-specific terminology is used. There are occasional errors of grammar, punctuation and spelling.

Low 0–8

The candidate is able to describe superficially the performance characteristics of eggs. The information is poorly expressed and limited subject-specific terminology is used. Errors of grammar, punctuation and spelling are intrusive.

Answers may include:

Egg protein produces three main performance characteristics

- Coagulation, which includes setting, binding, coating, thickening, enriching and glazing.

- Whisking air into liquid to create a foam.

- Emulsification.

Coagulation

- Baked products containing eggs will form a smooth, non-porous gel.

- The egg products used in the manufacture of baked products are pasteurised and then dried, frozen or liquid chilled.

- The proteins in an egg coagulate during the cooking process.

- The egg white will coagulate at temperatures between 60°C and 65°C. This results in the egg white losing its transparency; when the egg reaches 70°C it becomes firm.

- The egg yolk proteins coagulate at a slightly higher temperature than egg white proteins. Coagulation begins at 65°C and finishes at 70°C.

- In the preparation of baked dishes containing eggs, it is important to avoid overcooking as the protein will denature.

- If egg is over cooked the process of syneresis may occur. The texture will become porous and as the protein shrinks pockets of water are left in the baked product.

- Other ingredients in the mixture can affect the coagulation process. A firmer set can be achieved at a lower temperature if there is an increased concentration of egg proteins or an acid is added.

- A looser set is achieved and higher coagulation temperature by the addition of sugar to the mixture.

Foam formation

- A foam is formed when gases are dispersed through the liquid. Egg white foams very easily.

- Egg white can be used for aeration due to the ability of the ovalbumin to stretch and hold air, for example, in meringues and mousses.

- When egg white is whisked the proteins are denatured and uncoil. This forms a 3D air/liquid matrix. This can hold air when folded into food mixtures. The foam is unstable but the properties can be manipulated with the use of additional ingredients:

  - Salt will decrease the pH of the egg white and this increases the resistance so the foaming time is increased. This makes the foam more stable and gives a better flavour.

  - Sugar will interfere with the bonds that form as the whites uncoil. Therefore, the whisking time is increased and the resulting foam is denser. However, the foam is much more stable. The property is used in the production of meringues.

  - Fat including egg yolk interferes with the development of the foam structure. It prevents new bonds being formed in the 3D matrix. Often full foam will not develop.

  - Alkalis will increase the pH of the foam, decreasing the foaming time but making the foam more unstable.

  - Acids like tartaric and acetic (vinegar) will soften the foam.

- The ability of the whole egg to trap air can also be used in cake making by creaming and whisking methods, for example, Swiss roll, sponge cakes.

- If an egg mixture is under whisked the baked product will have poor volume.

- The fat in the yolk exerts a shortening effect on the flour and can enhance the texture of the baked product.

- Eggs act as emulsifiers to assist the formation of a stable emulsion in a creamed cake mixture containing fat and sugar.

- Sponge batters must be baked shortly after preparation. During baking the steam produced from the liquid in the egg expands.

- The coagulated egg will also contribute to the structure of a baked product and the egg yolk to the golden colour.

Emulsification

- An emulsion is formed when one liquid is dispersed in small droplets into a second liquid with which it will not normally mix, for example, milk, salad dressings or egg yolks.

- Emulsions usually cannot exist without an emulsifying agent.

- Egg yolk has emulsification properties, which means it has the ability to hold large quantities of fat in emulsion.

- The yolk contains lecithin, which has a hydrophobic (water hating) end and hydrophilic (water loving) end. When fat is whisked into the yolk, the lecithin can hold the oil in suspension and prevent it separating out, for example, mayonnaise and other salad dressings.

5 Describe the behaviour changes in shortcrust pastry. (8 marks)

High 6–8
Candidates are able to describe in detail the behaviour changes in shortcrust pastry. The explanation is well developed and is supported by the use of subject specific examples. Ideas are expressed clearly and fluently. There are few, if any, errors of grammar, punctuation or spelling.

Middle 3–5
Candidates are able to describe satisfactorily the behaviour changes in shortcrust pastry. The explanation is not fully developed and may lack specific examples. There are occasional errors of grammar, punctuation or spelling.

Low 0–2
Candidates are able to describe superficially the behaviour changes in shortcrust pastry. The explanation is poorly expressed and errors of grammar, punctuation and spelling are intrusive.

Answers may include:

- The ingredients in shortcrust pastry include flour, fat, water and salt.
- The flour and solid fat are rubbed together to produce a mixture which resembles breadcrumbs.
- During the rubbing in stage many of the flour particles are coated with fat. This forms a waterproof barrier.
- Cold water is added and uncoated flour particles absorb the water. The water allows the dough to stick together.
- Water produces vapour (steam) when the pastry is cooked.
- Rolling the pastry out causes the gluten strands to stretch and allows the pastry to be rolled very thinly. Rerolling can cause an excess of gluten and lead to tough pastry.
- On heating, the fat will melt and will be absorbed by the starch granules, causing them to gelatinise.
- The air and steam will expand and create crumbly layers, which will give the cooked pastry its distinctive flakiness.
- The layers set due to the coagulation of the gluten in the flour.
- The surface of the pastry browns due to non enzymic browning and the formation of dextrin.

6 Explain the benefits to the consumer of food additives. (6 marks)

High 5–6
Candidates are able to explain in detail the benefits to the consumer of food additives. The explanation is well developed and is supported by the use of subject specific examples. Ideas are expressed clearly and fluently. There are few, if any, errors of grammar, punctuation or spelling.

Middle 3–4
Candidates are able to explain satisfactorily the benefits to the consumer of food additives. The explanation is not fully developed and may lack specific examples. There are occasional errors of grammar, punctuation or spelling.

Low 0–2
Candidates are able to explain superficially the benefits to the consumer of food additives. The explanation is poorly expressed and errors of grammar, punctuation and spelling are intrusive.

Answers may include:

- Additives enable a wide range of food products to be made to meet consumer demands, for example, margarine, ice cream, chilled ready meals.
- To prevent food spoilage and preserve food products, for example, sulphur dioxide is added to many processed foods.
- To improve a specific characteristic of a food product, for example, strawberry flavour added to strawberry yoghurt.
- To meet consumer expectations about a product, for example, tinned salmon should be pink or red; tinned peas should be green.
- To promote the qualities and advantages of the product to the consumer, for example, micronutrients are added to baby foods and sugar free drinks.
- To help maintain the consistency in large scale production, for example, anti foaming agents are used to reduce foaming in jams.
- To develop a product range, for example, new flavours of potato crisps.
- Emulsifiers and stabilisers allow fat and water to be mixed together to create low fat spreads. They also give food products a smooth, creamy texture.
- Antioxidants slow down enzyme activity in fruit and vegetables, extending shelf life and delaying the process of rancidity in fats.
- Anti-caking agents ensure that dried food products or food crystals remain free flowing, for example, calcium silicate is added to salt.
- Thickening agents are used to provide a product with desirable consistency, for example, powdered custards.
- Flour improvers are added to the bread-making process to produce a stronger and more elastic dough.
- Raising agents such as bicarbonate of soda provide a lighter texture to a baked product.

Topic 5 Design, development and production of new products

1 Explain *one* benefit to a manufacturer of the following stages in product development. (4 marks)

i Market research

ii testing a prototype

iii quality control

iv risk assessment

One mark only for a correct statement such as:

- Provides food manufacturers with information to help them identify new ideas.
- Reduces uncertainty when launching a new food product.
- Helps identify refinements or developments in a product.
- Can be used to monitor the performance of a product.

ii Testing a prototype

One mark only for a correct statement.

- Designers can evaluate in more detail the characteristics of the product.
- Many aspects can be tested and refined.
- Can be used to attract investment in the product.

iii Quality control

One mark only for a correct statement.

- Used to ensure maintenance of a good quality end product.
- Uniformity of the end product will be monitored and controlled during the manufacturing process.
- Reduces wastage.
- Gives consumer confidence in the product.

iv Risk assessment

One mark only for a correct statement.

- Ensure the food we eat is safe.
- Meets statutory requirements.
- Demonstrates the manufacturer has exercised diligence to prevent an offence being committed.

2 Discuss the costs involved in the design, development and production of a new food product. (25 marks)

High 19–25

Candidates can explain in detail the costs involved in the design, development and production of a new food product. Information is presented in a fluent and well-structured manner. Subject-specific terminology is used accurately. There are few, if any, errors of grammar, punctuation and spelling.

Middle 11–18

Candidate can explain satisfactorily the costs involved in the design, development and production of a new food product. Information is well presented and some subject-specific terminology is used. There may be occasional errors of grammar, punctuation and spelling.

Low 0–10

Candidates can identify briefly some costs involved in the design, development and production of a new food product. Information is poorly expressed and limited subject-specific terminology is used. Errors of grammar, punctuation and spelling may be intrusive.

Answers may include:

- Market research includes the use of qualitative research, e.g. interviews. Quantitative research is analysis of factual data, e.g. consumption patterns. Both will incur costs. Statisticians may be employed.
- Disassembly of existing products.
- Design possibilities explored with the development of a product specification and product prototypes for the new product. The use of CAD will be employed to model ideas. Equipment and software will incur costs.
- Costing of raw materials and the reliability of supplies will be examined. Importing ingredients will be expensive. Bulk purchase of ingredients may enable negotiation of a discount.
- Development of prototypes using sensory tests.
- Nutritional analysis and profile of the product will increase costs.
- Small-scale factory trials and consumer trials are expensive to manage.
- Ideas for packaging will be explored and the legal requirements implemented. There will need to be consideration of the target market, storage and cost of packaging designs.
- If production of the food product is large scale, it will be controlled by a Computer Aided Manufacturing (CAM) system, which may be expensive to create.

- A new factory may need to be constructed, which means land will need to be purchased or rented.
- Fixed costs and variable costs must be considered.
- New machinery may be rented/purchased or existing machinery may need calibrating for a new production system.
- A food manufacturing system controlled by HACCP schedules will add to production costs.
- Surveillance during production, for example, microbiological checks and quality control systems, will ensure maintenance of the end product.
- Labour costs including training may be required for production. Staff may be required to work shifts, so labour costs may increase.
- Legal advice will be sought to ensure compliance with legislation relating to the manufacture and sale of food.
- A distribution system must be established. Refrigerated warehouse storage and transportation may be required, generating further costs.
- A marketing team will be required to manage advertising campaigns via television, the internet and magazines.
- Advertising and merchandising of the product will incur costs.
- Participation in exhibitions and trade shows can be expensive for manufacturers.

Credit will be given for all valid points.

3 Describe the different sensory analysis tests that may be completed on a new food product. (12 marks)

High 9–12

Candidates are able to describe clearly the different sensory analysis tests that may be completed. They show a detailed level of understanding. Information is presented in a fluent and well-structured manner. Subject-specific terminology is used accurately. There are few, if any, errors of grammar, punctuation and spelling.

Middle 5–8

Candidates are able to describe satisfactorily different sensory analysis tests that may be completed. They show a reasonable level of understanding. Information is well presented and some subject-specific terminology is used. There may be occasional errors of grammar, punctuation and spelling.

Low 0–4

Candidates are able to demonstrate a superficial understanding of the different sensory analysis tests

that may be completed. The description is generalised. Information is poorly expressed and limited subject-specific terminology is used. Errors of grammar, punctuation and spelling may be intrusive.

Answers may include:

- **Preference or acceptance tests** are used to evaluate the acceptability of a product by finding out opinions. The information gathered is subjective and large numbers of consumers are required to complete the testing.
- **Paired preference tests.** A tester is presented with two samples and asked which they prefer.
- **Hedonic ranking or descriptors** allow the consumer to rank the product in order of preference. These tests are used to screen the best samples from a group.
- **Differences tests** can also be conducted to highlight specific change to a product, e.g. reduced sugar. They are objective tests. Difference testing can include the following.
  - **Paired comparisons** help a product developer confirm what they can predict about a particular product, e.g. reduced fat may make a biscuit harder.
  - **Triangle test** is used to demonstrate small differences between products. Three coded samples are presented together; one is the odd one out. This is used to detect small differences between products.
  - **Duo-trio test** is used when a smaller sample is required. Used with strong flavours, the tester is presented with a control sample and two further samples are given, one of which is identical to the control. The tester must identify the sample that is different from the control.
  - **Two Out of Five test** is used to see if differences can be detected between two products. Three samples are identical and two are the same.
  - **Taste threshold test** is occasionally used to find out the lowest minimum quality of an ingredient or substance which can be added to a product before a noticeable change occurs to its flavour or colour, for example.
- **Grading tests** are used to produce a ranking, rating and profiling of a product. Trained testers can also assess the flavour or texture of a product to provide a sensory profile. These tests assess the intensity of specific sensory qualities. A set of sensory descriptors may be represented as a star profile, which may help the product developer modify the product characteristics.

– **Ranking test** is used to sort a variety of foods into order (e.g. different flavoured crisps made by one manufacturer).

– **Ranking test with descriptor** is used to place a variety of one type of food into order, for example, flavour of tomato soups processed by different methods.

– **Rating test** allows people to show how much they either like or dislike a variety of products, for example, tasting the flavour of different biscuit bases in a cheesecake.

– **Rating test with descriptor** is used to show how much tasters like or dislike several aspects of one product, for example, flavour, colour, nutrition of a cold dessert or an aspect of several products.

– **Star diagram** is used to describe the appearance, taste and texture of a food product. It is used to record the suitability of other products, for example, packaging.

4 Describe three advantages and three disadvantages of each of the following packaging materials:

i glass (6 marks)

ii paper (6 marks)

iii plastics (6 marks)

iv metals (6 marks)

A maximum of 3 marks for advantages and 3 marks for disadvantages for each material.

	Advantages	**Disadvantages**
Glass	<ul><li>Contents can be seen</li><li>Can be recycled</li><li>Gives an impervious barrier to protect food</li><li>Variety of shapes, sizes and colours</li><li>Coloured glass protects against light damage</li><li>Cheap to produce</li><li>Non-toxic, no reaction with food substances</li></ul>	<ul><li>Breaks easily</li><li>Glass is heavy and gives additional weight for the consumer to carry</li><li>Dark and mixed coloured glass is difficult to recycle</li><li>Can be difficult to open</li><li>Tamper proof seals may be required on some products</li></ul>
Paper	<ul><li>Can be printed on easily</li><li>Cheap to produce</li><li>Easily to open</li><li>Can be laminated/waxed to resist fat/oils</li><li>Can be recycled</li><li>Lightweight, easy to carry</li><li>Ovenable boards available</li><li>Versatile variety of thicknesses, colours shapes and sizes</li></ul>	<ul><li>Damaged by moisture</li><li>Card/board recycling not yet widespread</li><li>Virgin pulp still required in recycling process</li><li>Food-contaminated paper unable to be recycled</li></ul>
Plastic	<ul><li>Variety of shapes and sizes to hold liquids and solid foods</li><li>Polystyrene is a good insulator used for hot drinks/takeaway foods</li><li>Pouches are easy to store and display</li><li>Modified atmospheric packaging/vacuum packaging can extend shelf life</li><li>Lightweight</li></ul>	<ul><li>Consumer confusion over recycling of types of plastic</li><li>Food-contaminated plastics difficult to recycle</li><li>Biodegradable plastics are expensive</li><li>Some melt at high temperatures</li><li>rPET not widespread and expensive process to produce</li></ul>
Metal	<ul><li>Expensive to produce</li><li>Long shelf life</li><li>Coating the inside of a can with lacquers protects the product from discolouration</li><li>Metals can be used for screw tops, bottle tops, trays and foil wrappings</li><li>Strong and retains shape</li><li>Can be recycled</li></ul>	<ul><li>Unsuitable for microwave cookery</li><li>Heavy to carry</li><li>Difficult to open</li></ul>

Topic 6 Developments in the food industry

1 Describe the environmental and moral concerns that affect food production. (10 marks)

High 7–10
Candidates are able to describe clearly the environmental and moral concerns that affect food production. The explanation is well developed and supported by the use of subject specific examples. Ideas are expressed clearly and fluently. There will be few, if any, errors of grammar, punctuation or spelling.

Middle 4–6
Candidates are able to describe satisfactorily the environmental and moral concerns that affect food production. The explanation may not be fully developed and may lack specific examples. There may be occasional errors of grammar, punctuation or spelling.

Low 0–3
Candidates are able to discuss superficially the environmental and moral concerns that affect food production. The information may be poorly expressed and errors of grammar, punctuation and spelling will be intrusive.

Answers may include the following points:

- Food miles are of increasing concern to consumers. Food retailers are sourcing more local products and ingredients.
- Consumer concern about the distance food travels has resulted in the emergence of more regional brands and the promotion of regional products in supermarkets.
- Some supermarkets and food manufacturers have made commitments to source fish from sustainable sources that are carefully managed.
- Organic farming has severe restrictions on the use of pesticides and avoids the use of artificial chemical fertilisers. Consumer expenditure has increased on these products.
- Animal welfare is an area of growing public concern. TV programmes highlight instances of poor animal welfare and have contributed towards development of RSPCA Freedom logo.
- Ethical consumerism means buying products that are made with minimal harm to or exploitation of people, animals and/or the natural environment. Research suggests that more consumers are choosing ethical products as a conscious decision to improve standards of welfare in food producing animals.

- Fairtrade products are concerned with fairer prices, decent working conditions, and sustainability for farmers and workers in the developing world. Fairtrade products attempt to address the injustices of conventional trade, which usually discriminates against the poorest, weakest producers. UK consumers have the biggest choice of Fairtrade products.
- Food waste is an important moral concern in the UK and retailers and manufacturers are taking steps to reduce food waste.
- Food processing generates large quantities of waste food and packaging materials. It has been suggested that 18 million tonnes of carbon dioxide is unnecessarily emitted each year because of food waste.

2 Explain the term food security. (2 marks)

Award two marks for a detailed explanation.

- Food security occurs when all people, at all times, have physical and economic access to sufficient, safe and nutritious food to meet their dietary needs and food preferences for an active and healthy life.
- Food security is linked to issues of availability, access and affordability of food.
  - Availability is about how much food is produced and the reliability of the supply.
  - Access is concerned with the distribution of food.
  - Affordability is about food being available at prices that people can afford to pay.

3 The range and types of food available is constantly changing. Explain how food manufacturers have responded to consumer need for healthier foods. (25 marks)

Answers may include the following points:

- The growth of ready meals and ready prepared products has increased significantly in the last decade due to social change.
- The food industry has responded with an increasing range of convenience products.
- Foods which are ready to heat, for example, cook–chill meals that can be microwaved, canned foods and ready to cook pastry products.
- Foods which are ready to eat, for example, sandwiches, salad pots.

- Foods which are part or ready prepared, for example, cooking sauces.

- There are many ranges within the ready meal sector, including healthy eating, organic, gourmet products, vegetarian and value for money.

- Growth in the need for convenience is reflected in the growing demand for part prepared and 'value added' products such as ready rolled pastry.

- The frozen ready meal market has seen a higher than average level of new product development. Changes in the population to smaller households, more families with busy lifestyles and an increase in single person households have led to the development of many frozen ready meal products.

- Supermarket own brand groceries account for large amounts of supermarket sales.

- Retailers own brand range includes many sub brands, for example, value ranges, premium ranges, healthy eating ranges and children's ranges of food products.

- Indulgence products have increased and are often described as premium, gourmet, fine and speciality foods. This development is due to time-poor, stressed and tired consumers finding relaxation and reward through luxury food and drink products.

- The range of products has also been expanded to include healthy, free range and organic indulgence products.

- There is growing consumer demand for local products. Consumers have become more interested in food production and provenance.

- The market for food products that are specially designed for consumers with food intolerance has increased. The range of products is expanding but sometimes supplies are restricted to major food retailers or specialist shops.

- A wider range of healthier food products is available and many different food products have been introduced or modified to meet growing consumer need for healthier foods.

- Concern about fibre intake has lead to the introduction of many more varieties of high fibre and wholegrain crackers, cereals and breads.

- Functional foods have become popular.

- Healthier snack products include dried fruits and nuts.

- Consumer concern about health issues and food has led to the introduction of fat substitutes, artificial sweeteners and a range of cholesterol lowering products.

- The low salt market and salt free market is growing. Many products now exist in a low sodium format, including soups, crisps, bacon and ham.

Credit to be given for all valid points.

4 Describe four reasons for changes in the supply and availability of food. (8 marks)

High 6–8
Candidates are able to describe clearly four reasons for changes in the supply and availability of food. The description is well developed and supported by the use of subject specific examples. Ideas are expressed clearly and fluently. There are few, if any, errors of grammar, punctuation or spelling.

Middle 3–5
Candidates are able to describe satisfactorily two or three reasons for changes in the supply and availability of food. The description may not be fully developed and may lack specific examples. There may be occasional errors of grammar, punctuation or spelling.

Low 0–2
Candidates are able to describe superficially one reason for changes in the supply and availability of food. The information may be poorly expressed and errors of grammar, punctuation and spelling will be intrusive.

Answers may include the following points:

- Climate change – small changes in global temperatures may adversely affect areas of the world where agriculture depends upon rainfall. Many developing countries would be affected and their yields reduced.

- Poor weather affects the supply of food. In recent years successive poor harvests in countries that are major exporters of cereals has affected the amount of food for sale on the world market.

- Water shortage – in some parts of the world food production is based on extensive water use.

- The growing demand for biofuels has meant use of agricultural land has changed. Land that was previously used for growing cereals and staples is now used for growing crops that can be converted into biofuels.

- Increase in oil prices. The production, processing and distribution of food all require the use of energy from oil and petrol. Increases in the price of oil result in high fuel, fertiliser, transport, packaging and storage costs.

- Fish stocks continue to decline due to over fishing. This may affect the choice available to both the consumer and the manufacturer when developing products containing fish or purchasing fish.

- European legislation affects the supply and availability of food. European laws restricting the use of some artificial food colourings has already resulted in the removal of some products from the market.

- Emerging economies are those areas of the world that are experiencing industrialisation and rapid growth. High income growth of emerging economies is increasing consumer demand for meat and dairy products. This reduces the affordability of cereals and staples to the poorest consumers across the globe and can cause shortages in the UK.

Glossary

Actin the protein in muscle fibres

Above the line advertising uses the media, including television, cinema, radio, advertising hoardings and search engines

Additives substances that are deliberately added to food during processing to achieve a specific technological function, e.g. to preserve, colour or improve the texture of a food product

Aeration where air is introduced into a mixture

Alpha linolenic acid the Omega 3 fatty acid; sometimes expressed as α-linolenic acid; found in rapeseed oil (canola), mustard seeds, walnuts and green leafy vegetables

Amino acids form the building blocks of protein. Amino acids are joined together in chains by peptide links

Amylopectin a component of starch, it consists of branched chains of glucose molecules

Amylose one of the components of starch; it is a smaller molecule than amylopectin and consists of straight chains of glucose molecules

Anaemia a deficiency of red blood cells

Analysis separation of a whole into its parts for study or interpretation

Anorexia nervosa deliberate loss of weight, usually by avoiding foods containing energy. Individuals deliberately vomit, take laxatives or appetite suppressing drugs, or do excessive amounts of exercise to lose weight

Anthocyanins the purple colour pigment in fruit and vegetables

Anti-caking agents added to allow powders to flow and mix evenly

Antioxidants block some of the damage caused by free radicals to body cells. They include vitamins A and E. Antioxidants also make food last longer by stopping chemical reactions with oxygen in the air

Artificial additives these do not occur in nature and are made synthetically. They are not carbohydrates but have the ability to give the sensation of sweetness. Some artificial sweeteners, including saccharin, are artificial food additives

Ascorbic acid Vitamin C

Ascorbic acid oxidase an enzyme that destroys vitamin C

Aseptic packaging involves filling a sterilised pouch with a sterile food in a hygienic environment. Gives a product an extended shelf life without the use of preservatives or refrigeration. Aseptic packaging uses paper, plastic and aluminum foil. The materials are laminated together to produce a material that is excellent for packaging oxygen- or moisture-sensitive foods

Assessment the act of judging or assessing a person

Balanced diet provides the correct amounts of each nutrient that an individual needs

Basal Metabolic Rate (BMR) the energy required to support the basic processes required for life, e.g. heart beat and maintaining body temperature

Batch production when small numbers of identical products are produced

Beating a method used to incorporate air into a mixture

Below the line advertising more personal form of advertising; uses brand-building strategies, such as direct mail, price promotions and printed media

Beri beri a deficiency disease associated with severe thiamin deficiency

ß-carotene form of vitamin A found in carrots, sweet potatoes, apricots and cantaloupe melon

Beta glucan present in the bran of barley, oats, rye and wheat. It may be beneficial in lowering blood cholesterol

Biodegradable packaging can be broken down by microorganisms into carbon dioxide, water and inorganic compounds in the right circumstances

Biotechnology includes the process of genetic modification of food products

Blanching immersing prepared vegetables in boiling water or steam for a specific amount of time and then cooling rapidly. It inactivates some enzymes and is used before freezing

Body Mass Index (BMI) a statistical measurement which uses a person's weight and height to establish whether they are underweight, overweight or the correct weight

Bran accounts for 13 per cent of the grain and is a tough outer skin

Bulk sweeteners sugar substitutes that are about the same sweetness as sucrose and so are used in similar quantities to replace sugar

Caramelisation the oxidation of sugar produced by the effect of dry heat on sugar

Carotenoids orange colour pigment in fruit and vegetables

Casein curd milk solid produced when rennet is added to milk protein to produce cheese

Caseinogen the protein in milk

Case study an intensive study of one individual, it focuses on a short, self-contained episode or segment of a person's life

Cellulose consists of many thousands of glucose units. It is the main structural carbohydrate of plants and is found in the outer wall of the cell. It is found in all foods that are vegetable in origin

Cephalopod fish such as octopus and squid

Cereals cultivated grasses, where the grains are used as the food source

Chalaza holds the yolk in position within the egg

Chlorophyll green colour pigment in fruit and vegetables

Cholecalciferol form of vitamin D; can be produced by the action of sunlight on the skin

Cholesterol lipid fat made by the liver from fat-rich foods. It is a vital part of cell membranes, required for hormone production and enables the body to produce bile salts

Cis fatty acids have the hydrogen atoms both on the same side of the molecule

Coagulation to solidify; the process in which proteins change from their natural liquid state into a gel or solid

Cobalamin Vitamin B12 (see also **Cyanocobalamin**)

Collagen the main component of tendons which attach muscles to bones. Separates the fibres of fish

Conalbumin a protein in egg white

Competition based pricing a manufacturer examines its competitors' prices and selects a price broadly in line with them

Complementary action of proteins when a protein food deficient in a particular amino acid is eaten with another protein food containing the amino acid, the one protein compensates for the other and the mixture becomes of a high biological value as the proteins complement each other

Compostable packaging may require specialist treatment to break down

Computer Aided Design the use of a computer to support the design process

Computer Aided Manufacturing (CAM) the use of a computer to assist the manufacturing process

Concept generation involves developing ideas for new food products

Concept screening involves developing ideas for new food products

Connective tissue a thin network of tissue which holds together the bundles of fibres in muscle

Constipation difficult, incomplete, or infrequent evacuation of dry, hardened faeces from the bowels

Context a setting

Continuous flow production often used in the mass production of food products. Usually involves the production of one product 24 hours a day, 7 days a week

Control measure or point where hazards are likely to occur in the process

Control point in HACCP, any point that can be used to prevent or eliminate a food safety hazard or reduce to an acceptable level

Corrective action required when monitoring suggests that critical limits have not been met

Cost based pricing based on the costs involved in production. The price is by set by calculating the average cost of producing the product and adding a mark up for profit

Creaming can be completed by hand or electric mixer. Air is beaten into the mixture of fat and sugar to form an air in fat foam. The abrasive action of the sugar crystals will separate the fat, and air will become trapped in the mixture

Criterion a standard by which someone or something can be judged

Critical Control Point in HACCP, a point in a stage of food handling at which control can be used to eliminate a hazard or reduce to a safe level.

Critical limit the maximum or minimum tolerance to which a physical, biological or chemical hazard must be controlled at each critical control point. Used to distinguish between safe and unsafe operating conditions at a Critical Control Point

Crustaceans shellfish which have legs and a partially jointed shell

Cullet broken or waste glass returned for recycling

Cyanocobalamin Vitamin B12

Cytoplasm jelly-like substance inside the cells of fruit and vegetables, which contains fat droplets and fat soluble pigments

Deficiency disease caused by a lack or poor absorption of a nutrient

Denaturation a permanent change to the protein structure caused by heat, mechanical action or acids

Design brief a statement identifying a problem to be addressed

Design specification general list of criteria that initial design ideas are evaluated against

Dextrin a type of sugar that gives a crust a golden brown colour

Diastase an enzyme in flour that changes the starch in it to maltose, a type of sugar

Diet used to describe the actual food a person eats every day

Dietary fibre a polysaccharide found in the cell walls of vegetables, fruits, pulses and cereal grains

Dietary Reference Values (DRVs) estimates of the amount of energy and nutrients needed by different groups of healthy people in the UK population

Disaccharides made up of two monosaccharide molecules

Disassembly involves taking apart a product to find out more information about it

Dispensable (non essential) amino acids made by the human body

Durum wheat flour a special type of wheat flour used to make pasta. Sometimes called dopio zero flour (double 00)

Elastin the main component of ligaments which are attached to bones or cartilage

Emergency issues relating to how changes in production or supplier affect the quality of a product

Emerging economies those areas of the world that are experiencing industrialisation and rapid growth

Emulsification the process of using an emulsifier to stabilise an insoluble mixture

Emulsifiers help to improve the consistency of food during storage and processing

Emulsion tiny drops of one liquid spread evenly through a second liquid

Endosperm the starchy part consisting of mainly carbohydrate and protein. The largest part of the wheat grain – accounts for 85 per cent of the grain

Energy balance a concept concerned with having an energy intake that matches energy expenditure so there is no weight gain or loss

Energy expenditure the rate at which kilocalories or kilojoules are burned

Enzymic browning browning of fruit and vegetables that are cut and left exposed to the air; caused by oxidation

Essential fatty acids must be consumed in the diet as the body cannot manufacture them, e.g. linoleic acid (Omega 6) and alpha-linolenic acid (Omega 3)

Estimated Average Requirement (EAR) estimate of the requirement of energy or a nutrient needed by a group of people. Approximately 50 per cent of a group of people will require less, and 50 per cent will require more. For a group of people receiving adequate amounts, the range of intakes will vary around the EAR

Ethical consumerism buying products that are made with minimal harm to or exploitation of people, animals and/or the natural environment

Extraction rate the percentage of wheat grain found in flour

Fairtrade products produced by manufacturers concerned with fairer prices, decent working conditions, and sustainability for farmers and workers in the developing world

Fat soluble vitamins vitamins A, D, E, and K

Fatty acids chains of carbon and hydrogen atoms

Fermentation the process in which starch is broken down by yeast to produce alcohol and carbon dioxide, or where milk is curdled by bacteria. Used in brewing, baking and yoghurt making

Fixed costs maintenance, staff salaries, fuel and insurance costs

Flavour enhancers improve the taste of food

Foam the dispersal of a gas in a liquid, e.g. whisked egg white

Foaming addition of air to a liquid by agitation, e.g. whisking

Food allergy reaction by the immune system to a particular food

Food colouring added to make food look more attractive to the consumer. May be used to replace natural colour lost during food processing or storage, or to make food products a consistent colour between different batches of the same food product

Food desert an area where access to food shops and healthy food is relatively limited

Food intolerance not an allergic reaction and is usually not life-threatening but can make the individual feel unwell

Food miles the distance food travels to reach the retailer

Food provenance origin or source of product

Food security occurs when all people, at all times, have physical and economic access to sufficient, safe and nutritious food to meet their dietary needs and food preferences for an active and healthy life

Fortified or fortification vitamins or minerals added to food irrespective of whether they were there originally

Free radicals by-products that result when the body converts food into energy

Fructose occurs naturally in some fruit and vegetables

Frutarian foods of animal origin as well as pulses and cereals are excluded from the diet. The diet mainly consists of raw and dried fruits, nuts, honey and olive oil

Functional food defined as a food which has health promoting benefits beyond the usual nutritional value

Galactose found with glucose as lactose, the sugar that is present in milk

Gelatine connective tissue (collagen) which, on cooking, converts to gelatine

Gelatinisation occurs when starch granules are heated in a liquid. After further heating the granules move more rapidly and the molecule bonds weaken, enabling liquid to enter the granules and become trapped, causing the liquid to thicken

Gels systems where large volumes of liquids are held by a small amount of solid

Genetic modification (GM) when genetic material is altered (or a gene is transferred from another organism) in order to produce certain characteristics

Germ the seed part of the grain

Glazing agents used to create a protective coating or sheen on the surface of a food

Gliadin protein found in flour that converts to gluten

Globalisation the wider sourcing of food within the UK and overseas

Glucose occurs naturally in fruit and plant juices and in the blood of living animals

Gluten formed by gliadin and glutenin combining together

Glutenin protein found in flour that converts to gluten

Glycogen similar to starch but is made from glucose by animals not plants. Small amounts are stored in the liver and muscles as an energy reserve

Goitre swelling of the thyroid gland caused by a deficiency of iodine in the diet

Grading tests used to produce a ranking, rating and profiling of a product

Guideline Daily Amounts (GDAs) the approximate amount of calories, fat, saturated fat, carbohydrate, total sugars, protein, fibre, salt and sodium required for a balanced diet for healthy adults

Haem iron iron from animal sources

Hazard anything that can cause harm to the consumer

Hazard Analysis and Critical Control Point (HACCP) a risk assessment system that has been adopted by the food industry

Hidden sugar a product that contains added sugar or non-milk extrinsic sugars

High biological value when all essential amino acids are present

High density lipoprotein (HDL) often referred to as 'good cholesterol'; may prevent heart disease

High energy dense foods contain more than about 225 to 275 kcal per 100 g

Homogenised milk where milk is forced through a fine aperture to break up the fat globules to an even size so that they stay throughout the milk and don't form a cream layer on top of the milk

Hydrogenation process used to turn vegetable oil into a solid substance. It improves the shelf life of fat and reduces the likelihood of oxidation

Hydrophilic from the Latin: *hydro* = water; *philic* = loving; substances that are hydrophilic will dissolve in water

Hydrophobic from the Latin: *hydro* = water; *phobic* = hating; substances which are hydrophobic will not dissolve in water

Hydroxyapatite principal mineral in bones and teeth

Hypercalcaemia condition where deposits of calcium are found in the soft tissues, caused by an excess intake of vitamin D

Hypothesise to speculate

Indispensable (essential) amino acids cannot be made by the body in sufficient amounts for health

Intense sweeteners sugar substitutes that are many times sweeter than sucrose and need to be used in small quantities

Intrinsic sugars sugars that form a vital part of certain unprocessed foods

Investigative process of finding information or ascertaining certain facts

Invisible fat cannot be seen easily and is inside a food

Job production making a one-off food product for a specific customer

Kilocalorie (kcal) a unit of heat. One kilocalorie is required to raise the temperature of 1 g of water by 1°C

Kilojoules (kJ) used for measuring energy. One calorie is equal to 4.18 kilojoules

Kneading a process used to mix together ingredients and add strength to a dough; used in bread making

Knocking back re kneading dough to produce smaller bubbles, giving bread an even texture

Lactalbumin protein in milk

Lactation when a woman produces breast milk to feed her baby

Lactic butter pasteurised cream that is ripened before churning with a lactobacillus culture to improve its keeping qualities

Lactoglobulin protein in milk

Lacto vegetarian all meat, fish, poultry and eggs are excluded from the diet. Milk and milk products are still consumed

Lacto-ovo-vegetarian all meat, fish, poultry are excluded from the diet but milk, milk products and eggs are still consumed. Most UK vegetarians follow a lacto-ovo vegetarian diet

Lactose made up of one molecule of glucose and galactose

Lean body mass everything in the body except for fat, it includes bone, organs, skin, nails, all body tissue including muscles and water

Lecithin found in egg yolk

Limiting amino acid the amino acid that is in shortest supply in relation to need

Linoleic acid Omega 6 fatty acid. Converted into arachidonic acid, from which hormone-like chemicals prostaglandins are made

Local source product made within a 30-mile radius of where it is sold

Low biological value when some essential amino acids are missing

Low density lipoprotein (LDL) often known as bad cholesterol; thought to increase heart disease. Carries cholesterol from the liver to the cells and can be deposited in arteries

Lower Reference Nutrient Intake (LRNI) the amount of a nutrient that is enough for only the small number of people that have low requirements (2.5%)

Macronutrients required by the body in large amounts; includes proteins, fats, carbohydrates and the mineral elements

Maillard reaction a chemical reaction between proteins (amino acids) and starch (maltose) to produce a brown colour

Major minerals the eight minerals required in larger quantities by the body – iron, calcium, phosphorus, magnesium, sodium, potassium, zinc and chloride

Malnutrition a deficiency, excess or imbalance of nutrients that causes adverse effects on health and wellbeing

Maltase enzyme which changes maltose into the simplest form of sugar glucose

Maltose made up of two molecules of glucose. Maltose is formed when grain is germinated for the production of malt liquors such as beer

Manufacturing specification provides the manufacturer with accurate information on proportions, ratios and tolerances within a product

Marbling invisible fat found in the connective tissue of the muscles

Market based pricing based on an analysis of the conditions in the market at which the product is aimed and on consumer requirements

Market research to gather, organise and analyse information that will be used to identify the market for a product and anticipate customers' future needs and wants

Marketing mix focuses on the price, product, promotion and place when launching a product

Mass production used to make large quantities of identical food products

Meat analogue products that provide alternatives to meat protein. Designed to imitate the taste and texture of meat

Merchandising an attempt at the point of sale to influence the consumer to make a purchase

Menstruation the monthly flow of blood from the uterus beginning at puberty in girls

Metabolic rate speed at which the body uses energy

Micronutrients needed by the body in small amounts; includes vitamins, essential fatty acids, trace minerals

Modified atmosphere packaging (MAP) involves the use of three gases – carbon dioxide, nitrogen and oxygen. Food products are sealed inside packs with a single gas or a combination of all three gases, depending on the physical and chemical properties of the food

Molluscs shell fish which have a hard outer shell and no legs. They may also be bivalves – a shell in two hinged parts

Monitoring in HACCP, the act of carrying out a planned sequence of observations or measurements of control parameters to assess whether a critical control point (CCP) is under control

Mono-unsaturated fatty acids a type of unsaturated fat; two of the carbon atoms are joined by a double bond, meaning that there are two missing hydrogen atoms

Mycoprotein also known as Quorn. Produced by fermentation of the organism *Fusarium graminearum* to produce fine fibres, which are formed together to produce a meat alternative

Myoglobin pigment in muscles which gives meat its colour

Myomeres segments of short fibres that make up the structure of muscle in fish; they give fish its characteristic flaky texture

Myosin protein in muscle fibres

Natural additives obtained from natural sources

Nature identical additives synthetic copies of substances that occur naturally

Niacin Vitamin B3

Night blindness the inability to see well in dim light; associated with a deficiency of vitamin A

Non-enzymic browning occurs on the crust of a baked product. Maillard reaction and caramelisation are both types of non-enzymic browning

Non haem iron iron from plant sources

Non intrinsic sugars not located within the cellular structure of a food. Can occur naturally in milk and milk products

Non-milk extrinsic sugars includes fruit juices, honey, and 'added sugars', which comprise both recipe sugars and table sugars

Nutrients chemicals which have important roles in the body

Nutrition study of the nutrients in food, how the body uses nutrients and the relationship between diet, health and disease

Nutritional additives used to improve the nutrient content of certain foods

Obesity condition in which excessive fat accumulates in adipose tissue, thus impairing health

Oedema water retention

Omega 3 alpha linolenic acid; important in proper nerve and brain function

Omega 6 linoleic acid; converts into arachidonic acid from which hormone-like chemicals prostaglandins are produced

Omniverous eating both animal and vegetable foods

Organic farming imposes severe restrictions on the use of pesticides and avoids the use of artificial chemical fertilisers

Osteomalacia an adult version of rickets

Ovalbumin protein in egg white

Ovenable boards packaging that is coated with polypropene; can withstand microwave temperatures and is useful for ready prepared foods

Ovomucoid protein in egg white

Oxidation a chemical reaction that involves an increase in oxygen or the loss of hydrogen. Oxidation of fats in foods results in rancidity

Pasta the name for a wide variety of wheat flour products. It is a simple mixture of flour, salt and water; sometimes egg is added to make richer pasta

Pasteurised milk heat processing of milk that has been treated to a temperature of 71.7°C for 15 seconds and then cooled quickly to less than 10°C

Pectin present in apples and many soft fruits. Forms a stiff jelly and is important in the setting of jam. It is not fibrous but is thought to help reduce the amount of cholesterol in the blood

Pellagra very rare deficiency of niacin found in developing countries

Peripheral neuropathy nerve condition which develops if excessive amounts of vitamin B6 are consumed over a long period of time

Pernicious anaemia caused by vitamin B12 deficiency

Pesco-vegetarian all red meat and poultry are excluded from the diet but fish and other animal products are still consumed

Plasticity fats do not melt immediately, but soften over a range of temperatures, which is determined by the nature of the individual fat

Polythene terephthalate (PET) a rigid and tough plastic that makes it suitable for bottles to hold liquids. PET is one of the main plastics used in food packaging

Polyunsaturated fatty acids fatty acids in which there are more double bonds and therefore more than two missing hydrogen atoms. Can be subdivided unto n-3 (omega 3) and n-6 (omega 6) group

Polyunsaturates have two or more double bonds in the carbon chains

Preference (or acceptance) tests used to establish the acceptability of a product by finding out opinions

Preservatives help to keep food safe for longer by slowing down or preventing the reactions of decay

Product specification specific details that will allow the development of a prototype

Protein energy malnutrition (PEM) describes a range of disorders mainly affecting young children who have too little energy and protein in their diet

Proteolytic enzymes added to the surface of meat to digest muscle fibre and connective tissue

Prototype an example or model of what a food product will be like

Psychomotor of or relating to movement, or muscular activity associated with mental processes, e.g. preparing or cooking food uses psychomotor skills

Puberty the process during adolescence when there is a spurt of physical growth leading to an increase in height and weight, changes in body composition, and sexual development

Pyridoxine Vitamin B6

Qualitative research involves in-depth interviews or questionnaires with consumers

Quantitative research involves the study of factual data about consumption patterns and market size

Rancidity the process in which fats exposed to the air oxidise and deteriorate

Rationale principles or reasons

Recommended Daily Allowance (RDA) estimates of the average amount of vitamins and minerals needed to meet the needs of groups of adults rather than individuals

Record system details of each aspect of the food production process that must be retained

Reference Nutrient Intake (RNI) indicates the amount of a nutrient required to meet the dietary needs of about 97 per cent of a specified group of people

Rennet enzyme added to milk protein to form cheese

Retinol form of vitamin A found in meat, eggs, oily fish, liver, milk and cheese

Retrogradation when starch starts to shrink and loses moisture

Rhodopsin pigment located in the retina which helps vision; made by vitamin A

Riboflavin Vitamin B2

Rickets a weakening of bones caused by a deficiency of vitamin D in babies and toddlers

Risk assessment used by the food industry to ensure the food we eat is safe

Safe intake the amount of a nutrient thought to be needed by everyone

Saturated fatty acids where all of the carbon atoms are saturated with hydrogen atoms

Saturated fats fats that contain mainly saturated fatty acids. They have no double bonds between any of the carbon atoms in the carbon chain; usually found in red meat, butter, milk, cheese and eggs

Scientific Advisory Committee on Nutrition (SACN) advises the Department of Health and the Food Standards Agency (FSA) on issues related to nutrition and nutrient intake

Scurvy a deficiency disease of vitamin C

Shortening when fat is used in baked goods to produce a crumbly texture

Sodium chloride salt

Specification detailed description of features in the design of something

Spina bifida meaning 'split spine'; it is sometimes referred to as a neural tube defect

Stabilisers help to improve the consistency of food during storage and processing

Starch the main food reserve in plants. Made up of many molecules of glucose

Sterilised milk where milk is preheated to 50°C, separated and standardised to produce whole, semi skimmed or skimmed milk. The milk is then bottled and passed through a steam pressure chamber at temperatures between 110 and 130°C for 10 to 30 minutes and then cooled in a cold water tank.

Structured interview interview questions that are carefully prepared before the interview takes place

Sucrose made up of one molecule of glucose and fructose

Summary a brief account giving the main points of something

Surveillance issues used to monitor a process and complete microbacterial checks

Sustainable food aims to minimise the energy used in the food chain

Sustainable source a food system that can be maintained economically, socially and environmentally

Sweetcream butter cream that is not ripened before churning and therefore has a higher salt content in order to assist its keeping qualities

Syneresis the loss of water from a gel. Protein molecules shrink, releasing water which produces pockets of water in a baked product

Target market a group that a food product is aimed at, e.g. people following low fat diets

Textured Vegetable Protein (TVP) developed from the protein of a number of plants especially the soya bean

Thiamin Vitamin B1

Thrombosis development of a blood clot that may block narrowed arteries and result in a heart attack

Tinplate sheet steel covered with a thin layer of tin; used to manufacture cans

Tocopherols members of the vitamin E family; found in every cell membrane in the body

Toxoplasmosis an infectious disease that can be transmitted by infected humans and animals, especially cats, often by contact with faeces. Toxoplasmosis can be a mild illness with fever and swollen lymph nodes, or progress to severe damage to the liver, heart, lungs and brain. Foetuses that become infected during pregnancy may have congenital blindness and brain damage

Traceability the ability to track any food, animal feed, animal or substance that will be used for consumption, through all the stages of production, processing and distribution in order to protect public health

Trace elements those minerals required by the body in small quantities – manganese, chromium, cobalt, iodine, fluoride, selenium and copper

Traffic light labelling used by many supermarkets and food manufacturers on the labels of products to help consumers make the right choice of healthy foods

Trans fatty acids have the hydrogen atoms on opposite sides of the double bond. Artificially created trans fats are associated with coronary heart disease

Triglycerides made up of three fatty acid molecules or chains to one glycerol molecule

Unsaturated fats have some hydrogen atoms missing from the chain of carbon atoms. This creates an unsaturated molecule and results in a 'double-bond' between two of the carbon atoms in the chain

Unstructured interview an interview carried out where the questions are not planned beforehand

Value added food product one that has been processed to make it more appealing to the consumer

Variable costs are affected by output and include the cost of ingredients, packaging materials, running costs of machinery

Vegan all foods of animal origin are excluded from the diet. The diet mainly consists of grains, vegetables, vegetable oils, cereals, pulses such as beans and lentils, nuts, fruit and seeds. Non-food animal products, such as leather, may also be avoided

Verify the system a check on the food production process and including such activities as review of HACCP plans, CCP records, critical limits and microbial sampling and analysis

Visible fat can be clearly seen on food

Vitelline membrane separates the egg yolk from the egg white

Water soluble vitamins includes the B-vitamin complex and vitamin C

Weaning when babies are introduced to solid foods and a mixed diet

Whey liquid that forms when rennet is added to milk protein to produce cheese

Whisking used to add air to a mixture

Zymase turns glucose into carbon dioxide and a little alcohol

Index